A RECIPE FOR JOY

The elements of happiness are simple and accessible. In THIS WAY FOR HAPPINESS, CLYDE M. NARRAMORE examines the resources that are available to us and explains how you can dramatically change your life to one of contentment and pride.

HOW TO LEARN LOVE
HOW TO ACHIEVE SUCCESS
HOW TO HANDLE FEAR
KNOWLEDGE AND SATISFACTION
THE SECRET OF BELONGING

are among the absorbing and inspiring principles of joy explored in this highly readable, acclaimed, and satisfying bestseller.

THIS WAY TO HAPPINESS

Psychology for Living

Clyde M. Narramore, Ed.D.

ZONDERVAN BOOKS • Grand Rapids, Michigan

THIS WAY TO HAPPINESS

A ZONDERVAN BOOK
Published by Pyramid Publications for Zondervan Publishing House

Zondervan Publishing House edition published June, 1958
Eighteenth printing March, 1968

Zondervan Books edition published March, 1969
Fourth printing June, 1971

ZONDERVAN BOOKS are published by Zondervan Publishing House, 1415 Lake Drive, S.E., Grand Rapids, Michigan 49506,

ACKNOWLEDGMENTS

THIS WAY TO HAPPINESS has grown out of a desire of many people to consider the relationship of vital Christianity to psychology. I am indebted to many individuals and groups throughout America who have encouraged me to write and speak on this subject. Without their inspiration I am sure this book would never have been written.

Grateful appreciation is extended to Dr. Harvey C. Roys for his quotations from *God and the Emotions*. Dr. Gilbert L. Little and Moody Press have graciously given permission to use materials from Dr. Little's publication, *Nervous Christians*. Appreciation is also expressed to Dr. Richard Halverson for thoughts from his weekly publication, *Perspective*.

A special thanks is given to Sylvia Locke and Marion Ferguson for their splendid work on the manuscript, and to Mr. and Mrs. Edwin A. Elliott for their contribution in editing all material.

Loving appreciation is extended to my wife for her months of planning, research, writing and editing in connection with this project.

C. M. N.

SIGNS ALONG THE WAY

1

The Search for Happiness

EVERYONE wants to be happy. And people the world over are devising ingenious methods and going in every direction to find happiness. In fact, much of our amazing space age progress is the result of man's search for a happier life.

Men of the twentieth century hold several distinctions. One is their unusual understanding of the human mind and body. This knowledge outstrips that of all other generations. But strangely enough, the more they know about themselves, the less happy they seem to be.

Surely, something is lacking. Because the "things" that many people seek to bring them happiness do not seem to "do the job." With our modern means of earth and space travel, man has still not found his way to happiness. Millions of hospital beds are added each year, but people feel no better. Although an impressive array of clever labor-saving devices give him more leisure time, still he is not content. Today we have more and better foods on the market, yet people are starving for satisfaction. Insurance companies are issuing more policies with wider coverage, but people feel more insecure than ever. Millions are adding tranquilizers to their regular diets, yet they have no peace.

Why is this?

Obviously people are overlooking something important—the ingredients of happiness!

When skilled psychologists and psychiatrists probe into the innermost feelings of man, they find basic

9

psychological needs that demand fulfillment. Just as people have physical necessities—food, shelter and clothing, so they have definite psychological needs. "People," the specialists agree, "cannot possibly function at their best, or find *real happiness until these needs are met.*"

What are these needs? And how are they satisfied?

As you identify your psychological needs and take steps to meet them, you will say, "THIS IS THE WAY TO HAPPINESS."

2

Love and Affection

LITTLE JOHNNIE leaned into the whipping wind as he walked cautiously on the ice coated sidewalk. It was slippery. And it was cold—a biting, stinging cold. Johnnie gripped his jacket tightly around his neck and slid his tousled head low into the upturned collar. Every breath froze before him in the cold morning air. This was winter in Chicago, and Johnnie was on his way to Sunday school. Since carfare money was scarce, he walked the three miles. But rain or shine, hot or cold, Sunday after Sunday, Johnnie was always in his place at Sunday school.

This morning it was colder than usual. But the weather didn't stop Johnnie. He tramped on, block after block, passing by many churches and Sunday schools. Some were large, others small, but Johnnie kept on going.

As he rounded the corner of a large building, he dodged into the entry way to escape the wind and catch his breath for a moment. But someone else had beat him to it. For as he swung around the corner, he almost bumped into a tall man standing against the wall. The man held his hat on his head with one hand and a Bible in the other.

He smiled at Johnnie and said, "Hello, son. Where are you going on this cold morning?"

"To Sunday school," the boy replied.

"Fine," the man said, "I teach a Sunday school class myself. May I ask *where* you attend?"

"Oh, I go to Mr. Moody's Sunday school."

The man looked surprised. "That's a *long* way from here," he said. "Why don't you come to *my* Sunday school this morning. It's much closer and you won't have to walk so far. It's awfully cold, you know."

"No thanks, mister," Johnnie answered.

"Why not?" the teacher persisted.

"I'd rather not," the boy replied. "I wanna go to Mr. Moody's Sunday school."

When the teacher saw that he could not persuade the boy to go elsewhere, he asked him why he went so far through the cold just to be in Mr. Moody's Sunday school.

Johnnie looked up at the man with all his boyish sincerity. "Well, mister," he said, "it's 'cause they *love* a fella over there!"

And Johnnie's reason was a good one. People are willing to go to the ends of the earth to find *love*. To be loved and wanted is a basic psychological need that surges in the heart of every human being. It is the "sweet mystery of life"—and *all* the world is seeking it.

There is an old saying, "Love makes the world go 'round."

In a sense, this is true. It not only makes it go around—but it makes it go around *right*. One can never be his best if he is not loved and wanted. From the time he is a tiny baby in his mother's arms until he becomes an elderly man, one needs to feel that he is valued and loved. Love adds zest to living, and it keeps one at his best so that he does not yield to undue stress and strain.

Those who have given and accepted love and affection find it easy to love others. They are confident, relaxed and happy. They are more likely to have faith in people and get along well with them. In short, love draws the best out of a person. It is the foundation of a good personality. It makes a person joyful and optimistic, And when one feels that he is loved, he sees the world as a challenge—not as a threat. Yes, love is a basic ingredient in happy living. Little wonder then that people search for it the world over.

Yet there are many lonely and unloved people. Mrs. Landis, a teacher, was one of them. As a psychologist, I was asked on several occasions to visit her class for the mentally retarded. She was an outstanding teacher and I often complimented her for the fine work she did. I noticed, too, how much she appreciated it.

At the close of the school year Mrs. Landis came to my office.

"I want to thank you," she said, "for the encouragement you have given me this year." Then with tears filling her eyes she continued, "You may not believe it, Dr. Narramore, but as a child no one ever showed me much kindness. There was no one to love me. And I was grown before anyone ever told me that he or she cared for me. In fact, I often wondered whether I was worthy of notice or attention, and it has bothered me all my life. That's why your encouragement has meant so much to me."

And Mrs. Landis is only one of many. In fact, the key that unlocks most hearts is the one marked, "Love and affection."

WHEN LOVE IS NOT THERE

Have you ever unravelled an old, worn-out baseball to see how it was made? You pull the string, unravelling it until it is only half size, then you unravel some more until you come to the little rubber ball in the very center. There you can clearly see that the kind of ball you have depends upon what goes into it and how it is constructed.

When psychologists analyze people they do something similar. Through various tests, individual histories and discussions, they can follow the development of a person from early chldhood. They discover what has gone into a person to make him the way he is; they uncover the circumstances that have contributed to his personality. And as they unravel a person's past experiences, they take a careful look at the love and affection that has gone into his life. Have people shown him love and affection? Was it consistent? Who loved him? Was the love genuine and spontaneous? Did they love him for himself or was it for what he could do? How did people express their love to him?

The reason psychologists delve into such an analysis is to help them understand the "why" of behavior. It reveals the motives behind the actions. It is a way of learning the reasons people act the way they do.

And since love is so important, it cannot be overlooked. If the need for love is *not* met in a person's life, he may develop attitudes and tendencies which will affect his entire personality. And he may resort to behavior that will shape his whole life in a distorted pattern.

Consider, for example, people who are always *suspicious* of others. Many times it is because their lives have been robbed of love and affection. If they had known genuine, wholesome love, they would have little cause to be suspicious. But since they have tasted little or no love themselves, they distrust others. Naturally, they tend to look at the future through the same glasses with which they have seen the past. This makes it difficult to accept cordiality and friendliness on its own merit. So even when others do show an interest in them, they suspect that it is fostered by ulterior, selfish motives. This is an uncomfortable, unpleasant feeling. But there are many people who live with it every day. For example, a lady told me not long ago that whenever she saw two or more people talking, she always wondered if they were talking about her. This woman had been raised on a meager diet of love. And because of this undernourished facet of her life, she always imagined the worst. Why? Because her past experiences kept telling her, "They don't care for you."

Then there is *jealousy*. This does not just happen. There are reasons why people are jealous. Often a reason is lack of affection. A person who senses this lack often compares himself with others. Others have received love—but he was deprived of it. Since he wanted to be loved more than anything else in the world, he resents the fact that others were given what he was denied. And he becomes jealous. And what would happen to a group of children if some were given food while others stood by hungry? It would be inevitable: jealousy. Yet the same thing is taking place every day. Many are starved, not from lack of food— but from lack of love. Is it surprising then, that jealousy creeps in? Naturally, it is only a matter of time before these unloved people transfer their feelings of jealousy from one person to another.

Some people find it *difficult to love anyone*—even those dearest to them. This may stem from the fact that they have never been loved themselves. On the other hand, those who have been raised in an environment of warmth and affection find it easy to express their love to others.

Love is learned. The ability to give and recieve affection is something that is acquired. It grows and develops as a person lives with those who express their love to each other. A child who is raised in a family where there is a warm, cordial relationship soon learns to be a warm, cordial person. But when a youngster is brought up in a home where love is scarce, he looks upon affection as a strange, peculiar thing—something that makes him feel uncomfortable and ill at ease.

Not long ago a husband talked to me about this very thing. He could not see the necessity of expressing his love to his wife.

"She's always complaining," he said, "that I don't love her."

"But you *do*," I commented.

"Of course I do," he assured me, "but she seems to think that if I don't go into ecstacies about it, I don't love her.

"I don't know," the husband continued, "but maybe it's because she was raised in a family where they were all very close. In fact, even now when they see each other they still kiss and make a lot over each other. But my family was different. We never acted that way. Oh, we liked each other okay, but we didn't say anything about it. I don't ever remember my Dad hugging or kissing me. And Mom—well, she was a good woman and I know she loved us but she never said much about it. I guess that's the reason I don't make a fuss over my wife. I like her, but that's that. I don't go for this 'gushing' business."

There are many people like this husband. They don't show affection because it is something they have never *learned* to do. And to them it feels strange and unnecessary.

How unfortunate when people have never learned to love! Not only do they make poor marriage partners, inadequate parents and meager members of society—but they miss so much themselves.

Those who have never received much love and affection sometimes react in rather strange ways. Some people spend much of their time trying to *assure themselves that they are worthy of love*. They go to all extremes—make unusual overtures to get others to like them—perhaps even come right out and ask if people love them. Very often they turn the conversation so that the ones with whom they are talking can compliment them. If their friends don't take the hint, they compliment themselves. And then they ask their friends to join in the compliment.

A man once asked me about an acquaintance of his.

"I don't understand her at all," he said. "She's always bragging on herself—tells everyone how good she is. I always figured it was a superiority complex. But now I'm beginning to wonder. Maybe it's the opposite. Maybe she's starved for love and attention so she tries to get it this way. But I do know this, she's smart enough to know better."

I imagine the fellow had it "figured out" about right. When a person has missed out on love and affection he keeps trying to convince himself that he is worthy of it. When this happens, the I.Q. seems to take a back seat. His need may be so strong that he by-passes an intelligent approach.

I have known some prominent men and women whose lives have been void of any real love and affection. Even though they may have had recognition and respect, they have not had love. And it is not uncommon for these people to act in somewhat peculiar ways in an attempt to win the love and affection that they crave so deeply.

Life is a series of *decisions*. From the time we begin reaching for certain toys, we show our preferences. And since choices result in courses of action, our happiness depends upon them.

Have you ever wondered why some people make such poor choices? Oh, they may be intelligent enough. But they don't make intelligent decisions. There are a number of reasons for this. One may be the fact they are grasping for love and affection. Seem strange? It is strange. Nevertheless, it is often true.

When a person has never received much love, the void may be so strong that it colors all his thinking, even when he is making important decisions. He may weigh the facts, then completely disregard them in favor of something that promises some recognition and affection. His emotions are stronger than his reason.

Like a group of young children choosing sides for a ball game. If the chooser is a youngster who is starved for love, he is likely to by-pass the good ball players and choose someone whom he thinks will be a good friend to him. It short, his strong need for affection keeps him from choosing team members who can win the game. His decision is dictated by his inner needs.

And this trait carries over into adulthood. Grownups also let their maladjustments make poor decisions for them. Take Bill White, for example. He is a father, but he refuses to discipline his own children. Why? The basic reason is rather subtly hidden. But it is this: Bill has never been genuinely loved. And he feels that if he disciplines his children, he will lose their affection. And Bill can't afford to run such a risk. He feels that he must hold on to this one thread of love—at all costs.

I have seen similar examples in the classroom—teachers who could not maintain good classroom discipline simply because they were trying to "hold on" to the friendship of their students. These teachers' only love relationship was with their students—and they dared not sever it.

I'm sure you have seen certain couples, and wondered, "How did those two ever get together? Little in common, so completely different. And one has so much more ability than the other."

The answer often lies in the fact that one, or both, suffered from lack of love. This drive over-shadowed all other considerations. Anyone who offered some temporary love and affection was willingly accepted, even though it was a very poor match.

So it is that some people make unwise decisions. Their minds are controlled by a lack in their hearts.

When affection is withheld from people it sometimes shows up in the form of *aggressive behavior*. Since they have not been loved they feel that they have missed out on something which all human beings deserve. They resent this "discrimination." "Others are loved," they reason, "but I've been left out. I'll show them."

So they retaliate.

Feeling that they have a right to "get even" with

society, they devise many ways of "punishing" and "striking out" against people.

I was reminded of this one Monday morning when the head secretary of our staff of psychologists stepped into my office and introduced Miss Peters, the new filing clerk. As they left the room and were passing the filing cabinets in the hallway, I heard Miss Peters ask, "Which cases are filed here?"

"These," the secretary explained, "are all behavior problems—boys and girls who have not been able to adjust to the regular classroom."

"My," exclaimed the new clerk, "there are certainly a lot of them."

"Yes," said the secretary, "but these are just a few; we have them filed under twelve classifications, and these represent only one group."

Miss Peters sighed. "You never think about so many people being in trouble until you work in a place like this."

How true, I thought. And it would be serious enough if this were the only office where thousands of cases of unhappy people were filed. But actually it is only one of many in *every section of the nation*. Children's problems, marriage problems, court cases—an unending list. And at the heart of most of them smoulders a common cause, lack of love and affection.

Not everyone "strikes out" against society for depriving them of love and affection. Some react by *withdrawing*. They feel that they are probably not worthy of love—since they have never received it. So they belittle themselves and pull into their shells.

It is difficult for a person to build *self-confidence* and poise if he feels that he does not merit love. Love and affection are a dynamic impetus in spurring people on to greater self assurance.

Not long ago I counseled with a lady who was suffering from times of mental depression. After several sessions, it became apparent that among other things this lady had been robbed of her self-confidence. I found that her parents had left her when she was only a small child. This was bad enough, but then she was "boarded out" to another family who didn't genuinely care for her. From there she was shuttled from one foster home to another. No one spent time building up her confidence. Rather, they tore it down. No one really loved her.

Finally she withdrew into a make-believe world— one that was much more pleasant than the real world. Here she attempted to avoid the grim reality of being forsaken and unloved.

There are many people like this. Their lack of self-confidence can be traced to lack of love and affection. And whether it is merely an annoying factor or whether it leads to a serious maladjustment, the price of being unloved is too high.

People who have never experienced much love and affection may show this lack in a variety of ways. But after studying many cases, I am convinced of this: regardless of their behavior, they always accept *some* kind of substitute for love. Love is something humans cannot do without. So when it is not within their reach, they turn to something else—even though it is a counterfeit. It may be harmful, but they take it anyway because the basic need for love and affection keeps crying out for some kind of satisfaction.

"Bob" was an example of a fellow living on substitutes. I can still see him as he walked into my office. About twenty-one, he was tall, masculine and alert. His eyes shifted around the room, then settled on me.

Suspecting Bob of using and peddling dope, the police had planted a "girl friend" at a local drive-in. She played the game just right. On their second "date" in his car, he handed her the reefer she had been begging for. She "bumped" the horn, and suddenly, from out of nowhere two officers flashed their lights on the couple, arrested Bob and locked him up in the county jail.

After a preliminary hearing the courts ordered his family to find psychological help for him. So here he was in my office.

After a few sessions Bob began to see how his trouble started. He was starved for love and affection and felt that no one had a place for him. So he joined a gang. As time went on, he got a little of what he had always wanted—friendship and affection. But this "love-substitute" carried a terrible price tag—minor crimes, needles, arrest, shame and a possible prison term, plus a host of other vile things. But he was willing to take the chance just to have the recognition and love that his heart so badly craved.

Many cases are not as severe as this dope addict. But some are. It is not unusual for young men and women to sell their souls and bodies for some attention, even though the love and attention will only last for a few weeks or even a few hours.

People seeking love and affection get into organizations and groups that are very harmful to them, but they are willing to take a chance because they feel they will be loved and appreciated. In their desire for love and affection they search in every direction. If they can't get the real thing, *any substitute* will do.

Many people do not go to such precarious extremes. But they still feel the need to compensate for a lack of love in their lives. So they adopt other mild substitutes as their love objects. It may be a pet that bridges the gap. All their love and affection is showered upon a mere animal. Pets can be a real pleasure. But when people go "overboard" about them, the situation becomes unwholesome and unnatural. Animals are wonderful and they can be our friends—but they should never take the place of human beings.

When love is not there! The symptoms are many. They may include suspicion, jealousy, inability to love others, unwise decisions, aggressive behavior, lack of self-confidence and love substitutes. These and many more—when love is not there.

OTHERS

The story is told about a young lady who fancied herself to be a poetess. In an effort to have her poems accepted for publication, she made the rounds of the various publishing companies. Although she trekked from one editorial offce to another, she seldom got past the secretaries. At last she was granted an interview with the editor of a large, national magazine. Her heart pounded nervously as the receptionist ushered her into his office. She was confident in the excellence of her poetry but she knew that her big task was to "sell" the editor.

As soon as she was seated by his desk, the editor asked specifically what she had in mind. She told him that she had composed some poetry she would like to have published in his magazine.

"Poetry? About what?" asked the editor.

"All about *love,*" she replied.

"Hmmm," mumbled the editor. Then pointedly he asked, "Well, *what is love*? Tell me."

Now was the time to sell. The girl lifted her eyes in a rapturous gaze. "Love," she sighed, "Is filling one's soul with the beauties of the night, by the shimmering moonbeams on the lily pond when the fragrant lilies are in full bloom, and—"

"Stop, stop, stop!" cried the editor curtly. "You are all wrong—very, very wrong. I'll tell you what love is: It's getting up cheerfully out of a warm bed in the middle of the night to fill hot water bottles for sick children. That's real love. I'm sorry, but I don't think we can use your poems."

The editor was right. Love is more than fanciful dreams. When translated into everyday living, love means unselfishness, it means kind and thoughtful deeds. Love is a manner of life.

When I was a boy my mother used to say, "Talk is cheap." And she wasn't far wrong. It is much easier to *say* we love other people than it is to *show* it by the kind things we do. But if we are to help other people meet this basic psychological need—the need for love and affection—we must *do* something about it.

Missionaries from Africa brought back the story of a little native girl who had been sold as a slave. She had never known what love was. Even her name, Keodi, meant "Nobody loves me!"

Keodi's life was hard and bitter. Then when she was nearly ten years old, she contracted a skin disease which covered her body with repulsive sores. The natives turned her out of the village. They would have nothing to do with the poor, sick child.

Then the missionaries took the rejected girl in, bathed her, fed her, cared for her sores, and clothed her. At first she could not believe that anyone really loved her.

"Nobody loves me," she would say. "I am only Keodi."

The missionaries patiently explained over and over again that Jesus loved her. And they tried to *show* her that they loved her.

Then one day she looked down at her dress, her clean body, her bandaged sores. "Is this love?" she asked.

And Keodi had learned the meaning of love. Love is shown by kindness, by doing, and by giving. And as the song writer states it, "What we *do* speaks so loud that the world can't hear what we say!"

There is no better way to show others that we love them than to *give* of ourselves. Giving of *things*, as fine as that may be, is never a substitute for giving our time, our attention, our interest, our affection—*our-*

selves. And true giving has no strings attached: we give because we love.

What are the attributes of love? How can we show others that we love them? By following the simple, yet thorough guide in God's Word. "Love is very patient, very kind. Love knows no jealousy; loves makes no parade, gives itself no airs, is never rude, never selfish, never irritated, never resentful; love is never glad when others go wrong, love is gladdened by goodness, always slow to expose, always eager to believe the best, always hopeful, always patient" (I Cor. 13:4-8—Moffatt's translation). This is the ideal set before us: it is *living* our love for others.

But to love without saying so is not enough. People need to be *told* they are loved. Children and adults alike want to be constantly reassured that they are loved and appreciated. A wife may ask her husband, "Honey, do you love me?" She may know full well that he does, but it is reassuring to hear him say it again— and again.

It is unkind and thoughtless to leave our loved ones in doubt as to our affection for them. And it is unnecessary. Only recently I worked with a teenage boy who was having serious problems. As we talked I raised the question as to whether his parents loved him. He looked up and said, "I don't now, but if they do, they've never told me." How sad. They may have loved him—and perhaps they thought he should know. But it never pays to take love for granted.

Many people make this mistake. They excuse themselves from any display of affection by saying, "I'm good to him (or her). He *knows* I love him. Why say more?" So they never put their feelings into words. Naturally, the one on the receiving end wonders, "Does he love me, or not?"

Not long ago a letter came to my desk from a husband whose heart was crying for some love and affection. "I think my wife really loves me," the husband wrote, "but it's hard to tell. She seems to think that since she keeps the house clean, cooks good meals and sews on buttons—that is enough."

That isn't enough. There are many things more important in life than keeping house and cooking meals—there are things much more vital than earning a living and driving a fine car. King Solomon wisely said, "Better is a dinner of herbs where *love is*, than a stalled ox and hatred therewith." (Prov. 15:17).

True, actions *do* speak louder than words. And if there needed to be a choice, deeds would be the more virtuous of the two.

But a choice is *not* necessary. Showing a person that you love him and telling him so, are very compatible partners. Yes, love needs to be expressed in language—as well as in behavior.

> If you have a friend worth loving,
> Love him. Yes, and let him know
> That you love him, ere life's evening
> Tinge his brow with sunset glow.
> Why should good words ne'er be said.
> Of a friend—till he is dead? *Anonymous*

So if you love your "neighbor"—as yourself—you'll not only show him that you love him by the things you do, but you'll tell him too.

THE GREATEST LOVE

The story is told of a strange, yet true incident that occurred in Scotland some years ago. A quaint little Highland village lay nestled between the barren cliffs of the rugged Scottish mountains. Many of the villagers earned their living by working in the fields while the small children played nearby and the babies slept in baskets.

One morning a gigantic eagle swooped down upon the field and snatched away a sleeping infant. The whole village pursued it, but the eagle soon perched itself upon a lofty mountain crag and everyone despaired of the child's life.

A brave sailor tried to climb the ascent, but it was too steep and too dangerous and he was forced to give up. A robust Highlander who was a veteran climber also tried to scale the mountain, but neither could he make it.

At last a poor peasant woman tried to climb the dangerous ledge. Risking her life, she clutched the sheer rocks and bravely edged her way higher and higher until she finally climbed to the very top of the cliff. Then, while the tense onlookers below waited with abated breath, she slowly made her way down step by step until at last, amid the shouts and cheers of the villagers, she reached the bottom of the mountain, holding the baby in her arms.

Why did the woman succeed when the strong seaman and the experienced Highlander failed? Why? Because of *love*. That woman loved the baby with a strong love —she was his mother.

Yes, a mother's love is strong. A mother loves her children when the whole world turns against them. Many poems and songs have been written about the love of a mother. The world believes that mother-love is the greatest of all.

But there is a love that is greater. Yes, greater than *all* others. A love that caused the sinless Son of God to climb the hill of Calvary that He might die for our sins. Human love is nothing when compared to the greatness of God's love. It is beyond our limited comprehension. But this we know: when God loves, He loves a *world* —when He gives, He gives His *Son*. "For God so loved the world that He gave His only begotten son that whosoever believeth on Him shall not perish but have everlasting life" (John 3:16). Such is the boundless love of the eternal Father.

You can depend on the love of God. Nothing can deprive you of it. No evil, no transgression—nothing you can do (except to refuse His Son) is bad enough to shut you off from the love of God. You cannot escape His love. It reaches to the farthest corner of the universe —into every nook and cranny, every crack and crevice.

God's love is constantly, continually, eternally dependable for it is based upon God's character. God loves . . . because HE IS LOVE! (I John 4:8).

Human love is different. Man loves the lovely—has almost no capacity to love the unlovable. Man's love depends on the one being loved. God's love depends on the character of Himself. For God not to love is to be untrue to His own nature. If there were to be one man anywhere, any time in history whom God did not love for any reason whatsoever would mean that God is inconsistent. If it were possible for any man to commit a deed so terrible that God could not love him, God would not be *love*.

God's love is not conditional. He does not love us because we are lovable. He does not love us because we are good.

When Dr. Harry Ironside was a small boy he attended a missionary rally where he learned this great truth. The speaker, a missionary from Africa, turned to where Ironside sat with a group of boys and said, "Now boys, I want to tell you the kind of Gospel we preach to the people in Africa. How many good boys have we here?"

"A lot of us thought we were good," Dr. Ironside said, "but since our mothers were there, not one of us dared hold up our hands."

"Well," said the missionary, "not one good boy here; then I have the same message for you that we have for the heathen in Africa; God loves *naughty* boys."

Mr. Ironside thought, *he is all mixed up*, for you see he had heard people say, "If you are *good*, God will love you." Then as the speaker continued, Dr. Ironside found out that those people were wrong. God does not love us only when we are good. And He is not waiting for us to be good so that He can love us; *God loves sinners.* "God commendeth his love toward us, in that, while we were yet sinners, Christ died for us" (Rom. 5:8).

Yes, God's love is constant and consistent. And it is available—now and for eternity. Yet you may miss it simply because you ignore it. And worse yet, refuse it. There is only one thing that a man can do to deprive himself of God's love: He can *reject* it. For love cannot coerce, it cannot force, otherwise it would not be love. Love woos—and waits. And it is up to the beloved to receive it.

God's love is persistent, passionately pure, impartial, inexhaustible and everlasting. It is for every man. It is for YOU—for me. But it is up to us to accept His gift of love, His Son, Jesus Christ. When we do, we are safe in His love—*forever.*

Do you have difficulty believing that God loves you so greatly? Then it is probably because you have never experienced His love. Those who have tasted nothing greater than human love can not understand the love of God.

This was true of Tom. We were shipmates in the U.S. Navy. He was a clean-cut fellow, in his twenties, highly intelligent, married, and the father of a four-year-old girl.

One night as we were standing watch together, chatting about one thing or another, the conversation turned to God.

"I don't understand what God is all about," he said.

"What do you mean?" I asked.

"Well," he said, "I don't see how God could pay attention to individual people. And even if He did, I don't see how He could *love* them."

"Tom," I said, "God is *not* like we are. His nature is such that He knows *each* of us, and He is interested in us *individually.*"

"But how can He *love* us?" Tom inquired.

"Well, Tom," I explained, "there is really nothing with which we can compare God's love. About the best love we know is that of a parent for his child. For example, you've told me about your little girl, Joy."

Tom's eyes lighted up. If there was anyone who was especially dear to his heart, it was his little Joy. Several times he had shown me her picture and I knew he loved her dearly.

"Tom, you love Joy, don't you?"

"Oh," he said, "I love her more than I can tell you." Then with a look of real sincerity, Tom said, "I'd gladly die for that little tyke."

"All right," I continued. "You love her so much that you would do *anything* for her. Now let me ask you something: Where does all love come from? Who invented love? Who is the source of all love?"

"I don't know," Tom said, "I've never thought about that."

"All love comes from God," I explained. "He is the One who created love. God *is* love. And He is the One who makes it possible for us, His creatures, to love.

"Tom," I continued, "the love you have in your heart for your wife and your little girl is nothing compared to God's love for you! Human love is only a thimble full. But God's love is like a great, inexhaustible ocean. He can love us a million times more than we can love each other. He is the *source* of all love!"

Tom sat quietly for a minute, mulling it over in his mind. Then he spoke, "Now I see it . . . But how do we *know* He loves us so much?"

"God's love is manifested to us in a thousand ways," I said, "But the only *real* way to know, is to *experience* it."

"How do you do that?" he asked.

"Just let Him love you." Then I turned to some verses in the Bible that showed us how much God loves us: "In this was manifested the love of God toward us, because that God sent His only begotten Son into the world, that we might live through Him" (I John 4:9). "Herein is love, not that we loved God, but that He loved us and sent His Son to be the propitiation [mercy seat] for our sins" (I John 4:10). "Hereby perceive we the love of God, because He laid down His life for us" (I John 3:16).

God was speaking to Tom. And he was beginning to understand.

"Now, Tom," I continued, "through the Bible you can *learn* that God loves you. But through accepting Christ as your personal Saviour, you can *experience* His love. Some years ago I did this very thing. I saw that God loved me. Then I asked Christ to come into my heart and save me. I asked Him to forgive my sins, and I placed my trust in Him. Immediately, like a miracle, He quietly took up His abode in my heart. And through the years God's love has become more and more real to me.

"Wouldn't you like to experience His love?" I asked.

With tender heart he looked up and said, "Yes, I would." So we knelt and prayed—and Tom asked Christ to come into his heart and save him. And he thanked God for loving him enough to die for him.

The next day Tom began reading the Bible. And every day he talked to God in prayer. And of course, he began to *know* the *love* of God. Tom grew to be a strong Christian, telling others about God's love. Tom *knew*—he had *experienced* it!

But even after we experience the love of God, it is something that we cannot fully grasp. It is so great—so completely inexhaustible. "That Christ may dwell in your hearts by faith; that ye, being rooted and grounded in love, May be able to comprehend with all saints what is the breadth, and length, and depth, and height; And to know the love of Christ, which passeth knowledge that ye might be filled with all the fulness of God" (Eph. 3:17-19).

When Nansen, the great explorer, tried to measure

the depth of the ocean in the far north, he used a long measuring line. When he discovered that he had not touched bottom, he wrote in his record, "Deeper than that." The next day he tried a longer line, only to write again, "Deeper than that." Several times more he tried but he did not reach the bottom. Finally he fastened all his lines together and let them down. But his last record was still like the first, "Deeper than that." He left without ever knowing the depth of the ocean at that particular point—except that it was deeper than so many thousands of feet.

It is much the same with God's love—the love that transcends all knowing. We may know how much a young child loves, or a growing son or daughter, or a brother or sister, or a husband or wife. We may understand the love of a parent for his children, or a patriot for his country, or a Christian for his Saviour. But in each case, the measuring line will be too short to measure God's love. And even if we were to add all these measurements together, we still could not begin to measure the love of Christ. At best, our knowledge is only partial. We can only say it is "Deeper than that."

The beloved Christian poetess, Annie Johnson Flint, has beautifully expressed the magnitude of God's love in the following lines:

How *broad* is His love? Oh, as broad as man's trespass,
As wide as the need of the world can be;
And yet to the need of one soul it can narrow,
He came to the world and He came to me.

How *long* is His love? Without end or beginning,
Eternal as Christ and His life it must be,
For to everlasting as from everlasting
He loveth the world and He loveth me.

How *deep* is His love? Oh, as deep as man's sinning,
As low as the uttermost vileness can be;
In the fathomless gulf of the Father's forsaking,
He died for the world and He died for me.

How *high* is His love? It is high as the heavens,
As high as the throne of His glory must be;
And yet from that height He has stooped to
     redeem us,
He "so" loved the world and He "so" loved me.

How *great* is His love? Oh, it passes all knowledge,
No man's comprehension, its measure can be;
It filleth the world, yet each heart may contain it,
He "so" loved the world and He "so" loved me.

The greatness of God's love overwhelms us. Yet,
there are some who dare to question His love.

"How can you believe in a God of love when there
is so much suffering in the world?" You have heard
people ask this. For some strange reason they blame
God for everything that goes wrong in this sin-cursed
world.

Dr. Richard Halverson, prominent Christian leader,
tells of an incident that deals with this very thing. A
godly pastor, recuperating from a siege of illness, sat in
a wheel chair on the patio of the hospital. Another
patient also in a wheelchair pointedly questioned him
as to why God, if He loved people, would allow suffering. This woman had endured much pain and suffering,
and her heart was bitter toward God.

"Do you believe in suffering?" asked the pastor.

"What do you mean by that?" the woman replied.

"Is suffering real?" continued the man. "Is suffering
a fact?"

"Is It a Fact!" she exclaimed angrily. "You don't
spend three months in a hospital listening to the
screams of women and children—seeing a woman

brought into your ward one day, carried out under a sheet the next. You don't stay in a hospital as I have these past three months and have any doubt that suffering is real. Of course suffering is a fact!"

For thirty minutes the woman poured out the bitterness and cynicism that had soured in her spirit. True, her body had suffered much. And now her soul was suffering more.

"Very well, suffering is a fact. On this we agree," said the pastor. "Now try to explain this suffering without God. Does suffering make any more sense without believing in a God of love? Is suffering more bearable when you don't believe in Him?"

The woman was quiet for a long time. Slowly it dawned upon her that either consciously or unconsciously, the only thing that kept her sane through her intense physical suffering was the feeling that somehow, somewhere there was a God who cared, who loved, who understood. But overcome by self pity she had allowed bitterness to distort her reason and make her angry with God.

It may be difficult for finite human beings to explain how a God of love can allow the terrible agony and suffering and tragedy in the world. But it is infinitely more difficult to explain these tragic events by leaving God out of the picture. If there is no God that loves, then Shakespeare was right when he pessimistically described life as a "tale told by an idiot—full of sound and fury—signifying nothing . . ."

Suffering and tragedy remain. And there is no hope, no reason, no sense to life if man cannot count on a God who loves—and who can somehow in His providence turn tragedy into triumph! "Who shall separate us from the love of Christ? Shall tribulation, or distress, or persecution, or famine, or nakedness, or peril, or sword? . . . Nay, in all these things we are more than conquerors through Him that loved us (Rom. 8:35, 37).

God never leaves His redeemed in doubt as to His

love for them. He writes it on nearly every page of His
Holy Word.

As we read the Bible He tells us that we are the
object of His affection. On one page He says that He
loves us. Then on the next He tells us again. Then
again, and again. A wonderful story of love! He says,
". . . He that loveth me shall be loved of my Father,
and I will love him and will manifest myself to him"
(John 14:21).

This is in contrast to human love. People love in their
limited way, and for a limited time. You can't always
depend on human love, but you *can depend* on God's
love. People may change their minds and turn against
you—even forget you.

Dr. George Matheson was one of Scotland's ablest
preachers and one of the world's greatest writers of
devotional literature.

As a young man he was a student at the University
of Glasgow. And it was then that he fell in love and
was engaged to be married to a beautiful young Christian woman.

But before their wedding date, George Matheson
became ill and the doctors told him that in time he
would lose his eyesight. Immediately his mind turned to
his sweetheart and his forthcoming marriage. He felt
that it was his duty to write her and to tell her about
the blindness which was coming over him. Hoping, of
course, that she would not let him go, he offered to
release her from the engagement.

When his sweetheart read the shocking news, she
agreed that she would *not* want to go through life with
a blind man. So she wrote him, stating that she would
like to be released from the engagement.

This was a great blow to George Matheson. And
after several years of severe mental suffering, he wrote
the words to the immortal hymn, O LOVE THAT WILT
NOT LET ME GO:

O Love that wilt not let me go,
I rest my weary soul in thee:
I give thee back the life I owe,
That in thine ocean depths its flow
May richer, fuller be.
O joy that seekest me through pain,
I cannot close my heart to thee;
I trace the rainbow through the rain,
And feel the promise is not vain
That morn shall tearless be.

On his way to happiness, George Matheson learned that human love is fragile, but that the love of God is endless and Divine!

The Guilt Complex

WITH ROGUISH grin and tongue in cheek, Sir Arthur Conan Doyle used to tell of a practical joke he played on his friends.

The story goes that he sent a telegram to twelve famous people, all of whom were men of great virtue and reputation and of considerable position in society. The message was worded, "Fly at once, all is discovered."

Within twenty-four hours all twelve of the so-called virtuous men had left the country!

Guilty conscience? Evidently! However, feelings of guilt are not limited to the famous. We *all* have them.

But the majority of us try to camouflage or rationalize our guilt. We excuse ourselves on the basis of being "better" than someone else. We "make up" for our guilt by doing kind and helpful deeds. Yet, mixed with these mental mechanisms are some troubled thoughts. Somehow we sense that such reasoning is flimsy and unsound. We strongly suspect that the guilt is still there.

RIGHT AND WRONG

This is a strange world—one filled with contrasts and incredible paradoxes. Light and dark, joy and sorrow, beauty and ugliness, love and hate, life and death —they are all here together and we accept them as a part of living. Conflict? Yes, constantly.

Looming up before us as one of the greatest of these conflicts stands *right* against *wrong*. Ever since the beginning of civilization when Adam and Eve used their free will to choose evil, it has always been *good* vs. *evil, innocence* vs. *guilt*. And because of man's nature, he has a bent toward sinning. Try as he might to do right, there is always *conscience*—condemning, pointing an accusing finger at every misdeed and inconsistency. And this insistent shadow haunts him day and night. The situation seems hopeless.

Yes, the situation *is* hopeless. And moreover, it is harmful. It is damaging to the human mind and body. Psychologists and psychiatrists know that a person cannot develop as he should if he harbors the feeling that he is guilty and sinful. It restricts and distorts his growth both emotionally and mentally. Since this is true, a sense of guilt is not a matter to be taken lightly.

Probably no one realizes better than those of us engaged in professional counseling, how really unique each person is. No two clients are alike. And yet, with all their differences they are much alike—especially in one way: at the core of most of their problems are feelings of guilt and sin.

Is it any wonder then, that in psychological circles, the "guilt complex" is a much *talked* about and much *written* about subject? Bookshelves and magazine racks are bulging with treatises and articles about the "guilt complex" and its detrimental effect on people. Naturally there are many solutions offered for resolving one's feelings of guilt. Because as psychologists and psychiatrists work with people they can see the trail of damage caused by guilt. They know it is a real menace.

A Universal Problem

It really doesn't matter on what part of the globe a person may live: if he is old enough to understand right and wrong, he realizes that he is guilty of sin. No, he may not want to admit it to you or anyone else. But deep down inside, if he's honest, he knows that all is not well.

Sin is a problem—a *real* problem—one that confronts the savage tribesman in Africa as well as the society belle in Hollywood. Here is a problem that must be dealt with by both the beggar in the alley and the millionaire on Wealthy Street. The guilt complex is "standard equipment" for all human beings. God says that "*all* have sinned and come short of the glory of God" (Rom. 3:23). And truly, man's conscience re-echoes the condemnation—"all have sinned."

I think of an experience in our own family. One evening not long ago, we sat listening to the radio as a mighty servant of God brought a challenging gospel message over the air. This particular night the subject was "The Fact of Sin." Evidently our little five year old daughter, Melodie, was impressed.

"Mommie," she said, looking up at my wife, "am *I* a sinner?"

"Yes, honey," my wife replied. "We are *all* sinners.

"You see," she continued to explain. "It is very easy for us to do naughty things. That's our nature. But we really have to *try* to be good."

Little Melodie sat quietly for a moment. Then she repeated thoughtfully, "Yes, that's right. It's *easy* to be naughty but it's *hard* to be good."

How true! There's not a person in the world who, if he is honest at all, cannot say the same thing.

THE CONSEQUENCES

What happens when we continually feel guilty? How does it affect our health and personality?

In the first place, a sense of guilt robs us of our happiness because it is a nagging reminder that we have not done the right thing. Happiness stems from inner satisfaction—a quality that disappears when guilt casts its dark shadow across our lives.

A guilt complex also shatters our confidence. When we look into our own lives, we see our imperfections. We know only too well what we are made of—what our inclinations are. The hope we once held for ourselves is gone. We are weak and we *know* it.

Guilt feelings remind us of the *past* and dim our *future*. Neither looks bright. Our past is marred by sin. And the future is but an extension of the past. When we look ahead our experience reminds us of what has happened before.

As it was with Adam and Eve in the garden of Eden, we, too, want to run away and hide from God— or to compensate for our wrongs. Sin never seeks the light. Sin is discouraging. It constantly reminds us that we are not worthy of love and respect.

The result?—we feel insecure. Our enthusiasm is dulled, and we become preoccupied with self rather than the challenging jobs at hand. We are not sure of ourselves because our conscience keeps hammering away—"guilty."

But that's not the only consequence of sin. Because we do not like to admit that we are sinners, we set up an emotional block against facing the facts—the facts that each of us is accountable to God and that God condemns us! We go through life trying to "prove" that we are all right when we know we are not.

It is little wonder then that people spend much time dodging serious thought about themselves and their sin. Some drink, some keep on the go, some occupy their minds with reading or viewing. Others search out entertainment—anything to avoid quiet times of serious reflection.

Humanity is *restless*. Searching—always searching but never finding that "something" which brings inner satisfaction and peace. People are troubled and uneasy. God Himself, knowing the nature of man, declares: "But the wicked are like the troubled sea, when it cannot rest, whose waters cast up mire and dirt. There is no peace, saith my God, to the wicked" (Isa. 57:20, 21).

WHERE SHALL WE HIDE IT?

"We must *do* something about this," insist psychologists and psychiatrists. "We must find ways to erase the guilt complex from people's minds."

So they devise various methods to assist people in "resolving" their guilt feelings. They have developed many ways to *rationalize* wrong doings and to discount sins as mere human "mistakes." They also lead their clients to think of sin as a behavior pattern which has not yet been incorporated into our society—frowned upon "here" but acceptable "there."

Sounds nice? Yes. The only trouble is that IT DOESN'T WORK. Why? Because man does not have the power to remove sin. And the stark, grim reality is that no one is exempt: everyone *is* guilty.

But people do not like to admit guilt. That is why the world is filled with many methods of human justification. From the centers of advanced civilization to the most remote tribes of the world, people are busy with pseudo attempts to do away with guilt feelings. Some try to atone for their sins by inflicting bodily torture on themselves while others ease their conscience by donating to charity. But the principle is the same.

True, people can learn to *overlook* and *minimize* their guilt feelings. But they cannot eliminate sin. Oh yes, it may be possible to drive guilt feelings from a place of constant awareness, rationalize them to the point where they are not always confronting us. But in so doing, we drive them to a more damaging and subtle place—the subconscious. They are not eliminated at all: they are just planted a *little deeper*. And they will be sure to crop up again—more vigorous than ever. So it is that by merely painting over our sins, we do not eradicate them. In time, the paint will wear off.

Every man, woman and child who is honest with himself knows that he is not perfect. By nature and by choice he is a sinner. And it is the same the world over.

Deep down inside the heart of man, he realizes that he has missed the mark and is unfit to stand in the presence of perfection—a Holy God! And that, of course, is why he feels guilty.

A complex? Yes. But much more than that. People *feel guilty* because they *are guilty*.

FACING REALITY

All children like to play "hide and seek." And our little daughter is no exception.

She does fairly well at it now—too well at times. But when she was younger, the game was quite amusing to us. For when it was her turn to hide, it made little difference to her if she were completely hidden or not. She seemed to think that as long as her face was hidden so that she could not see us, neither could we see *her*. Just like the proverbial ostrich burying his head in the sand.

Adults smile at this childish reasoning. But many times, we do no better in our reasoning about sin. How immature and childish we are to believe that just because we close our eyes and hide our faces from our sins, no one else sees them either. But even if we should camouflage our sins from the eyes of other people, God sees them all. We cannot hide from Him.

Think of it this way. Suppose we refuse to accept the fact that we have a serious illness. This does not make us well. To say we have no hideous malignancy when we know that it is viciously eating away at our very life is not to face the facts. And so it is with sin— ignoring it will by no means lessen its deadly consequences.

In the Bible God speaks simply and plainly of guilt and sin. He declares it to be a fact. In the Old Testament we read, "All we like sheep have gone astray; we have turned everyone to his own way, and the Lord hath laid on Him [Christ] the iniquity of us all" (Isa. 53:6). And in the New Testament God says, "For all have sinned and come short of the glory of God" (Rom. 3:23). "If we say that we have no sin, we deceive ourselves, and the truth is not in us" (I John 1:8).

Like others, I have read the writings of many men, but I have yet to find any scientific data that would even suggest that man has a perfect nature and is without sin. It is true that every person has innate ability—no doubt much more than he realizes. Yet, with all of his talents, he does have a sin problem that must be solved. To ignore this fact is pure folly—no matter how great our human potential may be.

But why do professional counselors such as psychologists and psychiatrists spend so much of the time trying to "resolve," "cover up," and "spell away" the guilt complex? Since sin is a reality, one wonders why they dodge the issue. Why don't they deal directly and practically with guilt and sin?

For years I have associated and worked with other professional counselors. The reason why my colleagues who are non-Christians will not look squarely at sin and deal with it directly is not difficult to understand. *Since they are not believers themselves, they have no spiritual insight.* People have spiritual understanding *only* when the Holy Spirit indwells them and guides their thinking. The Bible says, "But the natural man receiveth not the things of the spirit of God; for they are foolishness unto him; neither can he know them, because they are spiritually discerned" (I Cor. 2:14). This means the man in his natural (unsaved) condition can neither accept nor understand spiritual things because they are spiritually detected and understood. So naturally we cannot expect a professional counselor (regardless of his intellect or specialized training) to give godly advice if he does not have spiritual perception.

Not long ago I counseled with a man who had committed nearly every sin in the book. After paying out hundreds of dollars to unregenerate, professional counselors, he came to see me.

"I'm no better than I was when I first started receiving psychological help," he said.

And he was right. You see, he needed forgiveness—a clear conscience. And only God could give him that. So we settled it that day. He accepted Christ as his personal Saviour! Did he get relief? He surely did. Immediately his problem started clearing up.

Like this man, everyone needs to face facts. Sin is a *reality* and it must be dealt with in a *real* way.

The Real Remedy

Guilt and sin are too big for man to cope with. But he doesn't need to. Christ has already paid the penalty for sin. With His great heart of love God opens His arms to us and says, "If we confess our sins, He is faithful and just to forgive us our sins, and to cleanse us from all unrighteousness" (I John 1:9).

Confess! This is the key.

Some time ago I talked with a well-educated man about his relationship to God. He was honest with himself and soon admitted that his own righteousness did not measure up to the standards of a holy God. For several weeks he read various portions of Scripture. And as he read, his heart and mind were touched by such verses as these: "Come now, and let us reason together, saith the Lord: though your sins be as scarlet, they shall be as white as snow; though they be red like crimson, they shall be as wool" (Isa. 1:18). "This is a faithful saying, and worthy of all acceptation, that Christ Jesus came into the world to save sinners; of whom I am chief" (I Tim. 1:15). "For God so loved the world, that he gave his only begotten Son, that whosoever believeth in him should not perish, but have everlasting life" (John 3:16).

A few weeks later this man told me that he wanted to accept Christ. We knelt quietly together and he opened his heart to Him and was truly saved. During the months that followed, he eagerly read God's Word and took part in Christian activities. My heart rejoiced as I saw him develop into a fine, mature Christian.

A few weeks later I had luncheon with a different man, also well educated. We discussed the Bible's concept of man and God's remedy for sin. When I had presented the thrilling story of God's plan of salvation, he looked at me and said, "I like the *love* part, Narramore, but the *damnation* part leaves me as cold as a clam. If I as a parent would not harm my child, why should God *harm* me? He's got us in a corner—He says 'Do what I say or I'll fry you in hell.' " Then with a look of arrogancy he added, "If I couldn't do a better job than God in making arrangements for love and rewards, I'd quit." This man, bitterly refusing the facts, rejected Christ and continued in his own, willful way.

Several years have passed. But I still see both of these men occasionally. They made their choices—and what a contrast! The first man is thrilled with life. The second is existing. One is realistically shaping the present and anticipating the future. The other is still betting on the human race, hoping that things will turn out all right sometime, somehow.

The first man, an outstanding educator, is leading others to Christ, while the second squirms any time God or death are discussed. The first man's family is following in his footsteps. The second man is leading his children into the dark with him.

The first man's basic psychological need—to be FREE FROM GUILT—has been met! As a child of God, he not only possesses eternal life, but he has forgiveness from sin. The second man is still attempting to rationalize his sin. He is struggling daily with a guilt complex—and fighting a losing battle.

The contrast between these two men started the day when each faced his accountability to God. One accepted it; the other rejected it. But whether we wish to acknowledge it or not, man is responsible to God not only after death, but during his life on earth.

It is evident that man is dependent upon God. Man did not create the world or the universe. God did. Man did not make himself. Neither did he give himself life. Man does not even provide the air which he breathes. Man is completely dependent on God and His creation. *Absolutely everything a person has is lent to him by God.* Man can lay claim to nothing. He is a user, an enjoyer of God's creation. But man himself cannot create anything independently. The songs he composes, the pictures he paints, the children he bears, even the steps he takes are the result of God having given him the necessary ability.

"But," you may say, "if man is accountable to God, doesn't this take away his free choice? Doesn't this make him a mechanical robot?"

No, because God *does* give man a mind, furnishing him with free choice. But *only in God's framework*. This is because God is infinite, but man is finite. Man must decide which road he will take. He must choose God or Satan—Heaven or Hell. He may think, "Why must I choose? I'll serve neither. I'll refuse both Heaven and Hell." But there is no neutral ground. Man can refuse God, but when he does, he is responsible for his own sin. He has made his choice. This means eternal separation from God.

Man's desire to set up his own terms is a clear revelation that he does not want to submit himself to God. And this rebellion is sin.

Can we trust and admire a God who controls the future? Yes! God is love. He is more concerned about our welfare than we are about our own. It was this divine concern that brought Christ to Calvary to make provision for our sin.

Freedom from guilt? Yes, God provides it be *removing our sin* from us. "As far as the east is from the west, so far hath he *removed* our transgressions from us" (Ps. 103:12).

A NEW NATURE

An interesting story is told about a traveler in Italy who spent the night at a little wayside inn. The floor in his room was dreadfully dirty. He thought to himself, "I'll ask the landlady to scrub it." But when he saw that the floor was made of mud he gave it a second thought. *That won't do,* he mused. *The more she scrubs, the worse it will be.*

The same is true of man's nature. No amount of "fixing up" will change it. Trying to scrub away a person's guilt only shows up his sin to be blacker and muddier than ever. What he needs is a *new* nature. As God says, "You must be born again" (John 3:7). Then, and *only* then, can he have a new nature.

"How can a man be born when he is old?"

This is a legitimate question. Nicodemus asked the same thing. But Jesus had the answer!

First He made it clear that the new birth is a mystery. The wind blows where it wills, and you hear the sound, but you do not know whence it comes or whither it goes; so it is with every one who is born of the Spirit" (John 3:8).

This does not mean it is irrational . . . it is supra-rational. It is the WORK OF GOD and therefore outside man's intellectual comprehension. And even though the new birth cannot be explained, it can be experienced! You may not know where the wind comes from or where it's going—but you know it's blowing. So it is that a man can be born again without knowing how it works.

What does a person do to be born of God? Jesus said simply, "Come unto Me . . ." And anyone who responds to His simple invitation will be met by God. The new birth is not something one can do for himself. It is not a human invention. It is the work of God alone! God will do this for any man who desires it. The only requirement for the new birth is *willingness.*

So when a person admits his guilt, asks forgiveness for his sins, and invites Christ into his heart, God meets him with the gift of a new spiritual life—a nature that is God-like rather than sinful. "But as many as received Him, to them gave He power to become the sons of God, even to them that believe on His name. Which were born, not . . . of the flesh, nor of the will of man, but of God" (John 1:12, 13).

With sins forgiven and with a new nature, the guilt complex doesn't stand a chance. It goes out when the guilt is removed. "Therefore if any man be in Christ, he is a new creature: old things are passed away; behold, all things are become new" (II Cor. 5:17).

GONE FOREVER

Life offers no joy that compares with the realization of sins forgiven. The past and present are as white as snow. This is our condition when we accept Christ.

Satan doesn't give up that easily, however. Although he has lost the battle for an eternal soul, he continually tempts the Christian with, "Are your sins *really* forgiven—*all* of them?"

These questions remind me of Joe. We were graduate students together at Columbia University; he in the field of science and I in education and psychology. Then one day I had the privilege of leading Joe to the Lord. Immediately we set up a program of study and memorization of the Word.

A couple of weeks passed. Then one day when we saw each other in the library he said, "Narramore, are you sure *all* my sins are forgiven?"

"Why do you ask?"

"Don't get me wrong. I'm saved, and I know it. But last night I got to thinking about some of the things I had done in the past. As I thought about them I wondered, 'Can it be that God has forgiven me of *all* those sins?' "

"Yes, Joe," I said. "There's nothing you can think

of that He hasn't forgiven. But come, sit down. Let's get God's own assurance."

As we sat there together we turned to Isaiah 1:18, "Come now, and let us reason together, saith the Lord: though your sins be as scarlet, they shall be as white as snow; though they be red like crimson, they shall be as wool." Next we looked at I John 1:9, "If we confess our sins, He is faithful and just to forgive us our sins, and to cleanse us from all unrighteousness."

"How much sin is He able to cleanse us from, Joe?"

"*All* unrighteousness."

"Who says so?"

"God."

"Can God lie?"

"No, never!"

"Then, on the basis of the fact that you have accepted Christ as your own personal Saviour, and have asked Him to forgive your sins, has He forgiven you of *all* your past sin?"

Joe looked up from The Book and with tears in his eyes said, "Praise God! They're *all* forgiven!"

Satan never tempted Joe again about his past sins. Joe had God's Word for it and he knew it was settled —*forever*.

How about you? Has Satan been tempting you with the thought that perhaps not all your sins were forgiven the day you gave your heart to Christ? That is a trick he often pulls. You see, if he can get you to believe that lie, he will rob you of your joy and he will cripple your testimony.

If you are a believer, your sins are forgiven! It makes no difference whether you feel it or not—it does not change the facts. You may *think* your sins are not forgiven, but God says they are forgiven. So they are.

Not long ago a lady from the midwest wrote me a letter saying that although she was born-again and daily asked forgiveness of sin, a wrong she had done many years ago was still tormenting her. I wrote this dear lady, giving her the same Scriptures I had given Joe several years before. I also suggested that she read the Fifty-first Psalm several times. Then I pointed out that no matter what she *thought* about her past sins, she couldn't possibly change the fact that they *were* forgiven.

"It's your feelings over against God's Word," I added. "Wouldn't you prefer to believe God?"

When the lady really believed God, she soon had victory over this concern and ceased her doubting.

You see, if human beings did the "forgiving" we couldn't be so sure that they would "stay" forgiven. But because of the life and death and resurrection of Christ, we are assured of God's complete forgiveness for *all* our sin. We are free from all guilt. Past, present and future! But to experience God's *daily forgiveness* we need only to confess our daily sins, then we have complete forgiveness. Naturally, we must do this as soon as we are aware of any sin in our lives. "And if any man sin, we have an advocate with the Father, Jesus Christ the righteous" (I John 2:1).

As children of God we are not to be satisfied with sin in our lives. If we find that we are doing things which are contrary to the Bible and the will of God, we will not want to continue doing them because we love Christ. "He that hath my commandments, and keepeth them, he it is that loveth me: and he that loveth me shall be loved of my Father, and I will love him and will manifest myself to him" (John 14:21).

There is nothing more basic to happiness than peace of mind. But it is ours only as we are free from guilt. There is no solution other than salvation. And when we know Christ, we have the assurance that our sins are gone forever and that we can have cleansing for our daily walk. This brings complete freedom from guilt. This is THE WAY TO HAPPINESS!

4

Belonging

SOME YEARS AGO the *New York Times* printed a human interest story entitled, "He Would Like to Belong." The article told about a small boy who was riding on a downtown bus. There he sat, huddled close to a lady in a gray suit. Naturally, everyone thought he belonged to her. Little wonder, then, that when he rubbed his dirty shoes against a woman sitting on the other side of him, she said to the lady in the gray suit, "Pardon me, but would you please make your little boy take his feet off the seat? His shoes are getting my dress dirty."

The woman in gray blushed. Then giving the boy a little shove, she said, "He's not *my* boy. I never saw him before."

The lad squirmed uneasily. He was such a tiny little fellow, his feet dangling off the seat. He lowered his eyes and tried desperately to hold back a sob.

"I'm sorry I got your dress dirty," he said to the woman. "I didn't mean to."

"Oh, that's all right," she answered, a little embarrassed. Then, since his eyes were still fastened upon her, she added, "Are you going somewhere—*alone*?"

"Yes," he nodded, "I always go alone. There isn't anyone to go with me. I don't have any mommie or daddy. They're both dead. I live with Aunt Clara but she says Aunt Mildred ought to help take care of me part of the time. So when she gets tired of me and wants to go some place, she sends me over to stay with Aunt Mildred."

"Oh," said the woman, "are you on your way to Aunt Mildred's now?"

"Yes," the boy continued, "but sometimes Aunt Mildred isn't home. I sure hope she's there today because it looks like it's gonna rain and I don't want to be out in the street when it rains."

The woman felt a little lump in her throat as she said, "You've a very little boy to be shifted around like this."

"Oh, I don't mind," he said. "I never get lost. But I get lonesome sometimes. So when I see someone that I think I would like to belong it, I sit real close and snuggle up and pretend I really do belong to them. I was playing that I belonged to this other lady when I got your dress dirty. I forgot about my feet."

The woman put her arms around the little fellow and "snuggled" him up so close that it almost hurt. He wanted to belong to someone. And deep in her heart she wished that he belonged to her.

This little boy, in his artless, childlike fashion, had expressed a universal need. And it does not matter who he is or how old he is: *everyone wants to belong.*

THE DESIRE TO BELONG

"It is not good that the man should be alone."

God spoke these words at the very beginning of human history. You remember the story—how God created the first man, Adam, and then, because man needed companionship, God created Eve, the first woman.

"And the Lord God said, It is not good that the man should be alone. I will make an help meet for him" (Gen. 2:18).

This desire to be with others is innate. It is a "built-in" psychological need placed there by God. We see its evidence on every hand. People cling together as families, they cluster together in communities and towns and cities, they give their allegiance to their country and even sacrifice their lives to preserve its unity. A "man without a country" is a pathetic case; and the man, woman, or child without a family, or without friends, is the object of sympathy. There is no one to whom he belongs.

People need each other and want to "belong." Many are concerned about getting married because they do not want to live alone. We all like to feel that we are related in some way to others and that we are part of a group. We feel secure when we think that we are included and we are happy when our interests and feelings are shared by others. So we form countless organizations and clubs for people to join. There are societies, brotherhoods, lodges, sororities, fraternities, leagues, unions, trusts, fellowships, gangs and guilds. They are service clubs, hobby groups, sports clubs, professional groups, cultural societies, religious groups, and political organizations. We find clubs for tall people, clubs for short people, clubs for single people, clubs for married people, clubs for young, clubs for old, clubs for everyone. These efforts on the part of man to form into groups are merely further indications of his basic psychological need—that of *belonging*.

Yes, all normal people like to *belong*. It is a God-given desire—and it is a satisfying experience.

WHEN YOU DON'T BELONG

But what about the person who feels that he just does *not* belong—he would rather be by himself? Is this a wholesome attitude?

No, and this is usually a serious symptom. Because it is a psychological fact that we are social beings and we need social relationships if we are to maintain good mental health.

The person who is a "lone wolf" cannot adjust to society. It is abnormal for people to want to be alone. Naturally, everyone needs to be alone *part* of the time —but always to prefer your own company to that of other human beings is not a healthy attitude. The proverbial hermit who lives alone in an isolated shack is tabbed "peculiar"—and of course, he is. When a person loses contact with others and cannot fit into a desirable social pattern it is a danger signal. Psychiatric social workers look upon "aloneness" as an unhealthy sign.

School psychologists are constantly on the alert for children who are isolates, boys and girls who are always on the outer edge of activities. They know that such tendencies in childhood often lead to real trouble later on. If these children are spotted, they can be helped to fit into groups situations and thereby develop into normal, healthy members of society.

How does it feel to *not* belong?

Here is the answer in the words of thousands of people who experience it, "No one wants me." I'm not good enough for them." "I can't please anyone." "No one cares and there's no use trying." "There must be something wrong with me." "No one understands, and I'm all by myself."

It is not a comfortable feeling, is it?—always to be left out, standing back along the fringes and never finding your way into the center. It's lonely; it's desolate.

This barren, rejected feeling can gradually push a person closer to a serious breakdown. Psychologists and psychiatrists find that many of their clients have long histories of not belonging.

How well I remember a woman who suffered from this very thing—she never belonged. True, she had tried desperately to be accepted by others; she had joined nearly every club in town. Oh yes, she attended the meetings, paid the dues, and went out of her way to get into the whirl of things. But still she was never really one of them. She didn't seem to fit. In time this "left out" feeling caught up with her in the form of physical aches and pains.

People feel it keenly when they think no one wants or understands them. It is not enough to say that those who are overwhelmed by "aloneness" do not develop fully. Frustration caused by this unmet need can lead to severe psychopathology. Indeed, this unmet need is the cause of various neurotic symptoms—many of which can become very serious. Excessive daydreaming, stuttering, loss of appetite, depression, and various forms of obsession—these and other symptoms often develop when people continually feel rejected or isolated. Some people actually develop stomach ailments, palpitations of the heart, and muscular aches and pains without knowing what caused them.

During the recent World War, I had an experience which I shall always remember. While serving as a naval officer I was sent to a small island in the North Atlantic, the country of Iceland. There, stretched across the bleak, desolate lava fields not far from the Arctic Circle, lay the Keflavik Air Base. The winter was dreary and dark. The long nights stretched into the days, crowding out the sunlight. Life for the most part was dull and lonely. Apart from the Air Base there were no houses, no trees, no vegetation—just endless nothingness. To our boys in blue and khaki the culture of the people was different. The harsh, Viking tongue was different. The cold, arctic climate was different. Everything was strange and different.

Many of our American boys found that psychologically they couldn't take it. Shortly before I arrived, ships sailed back across the North Atlantic to the United States, carrying a large number of American military personnel who were forced to leave because of poor mental health. For the most part, their mental illnesses were attributed to the fact that these men could not adjust to the strangeness of that land. Life there seemed so remote—so different from anything they had ever known. Familiar sights were missing, the countryside was barren and forbidding, and the language seemed impossible to learn. In the lives of these men, one thing was apparent: *they did not belong*. The basic need of "belonging" was not being met in their lives and the result was an emotional breakdown serious enough to send them home.

Not to "belong" usually leads to trouble. We cannot ignore this psychological need without reaping the consequences.

HELPING OTHERS BELONG

What makes you like your closest friend? Is it wealth? Looks? Education? Fame? No, none of these. True friendship hinges on something much more basic and important. You like your friends because they make you feel comfortable. They appreciate you. You feel that when you are around them, *you belong*.

And just as you enjoy having others make you feel that *you* belong, so others appreciate your making them feel that *they* belong.

One of the secrets of happiness is to invest yourself in others—to use every opportunity to make them feel wanted.

The techniques for helping people feel that they belong are sometimes subtle. It is so easy to unwittingly make people feel that they do not belong. The thoughtful person is alert to the things he should avoid.

(1) *Undue or continual criticism.* This is one of the most effective ways to make a person feel that he does not belong. Criticism tells a person, "We don't like the way you do things and we would be happier if you weren't around." Criticism sets up a barrier between ourselves and the other person and he feels that we are not pleased with him.

(2) *Unfavorable comparisons.* These have much the same effect as criticism. We seldom solve people's problems by comparing one person unfavorably with another. Parents and teachers especially need to guard against this. Unfavorable comparisons do three things: They cause us to dislike the one with whom we are compared; they cause us to resent the one who did the

comparing; and they make us dislike the place where it occurred.

(3) *Assigning unsuitable tasks.* When people are given jobs which they do not understand or which they find too difficult, they become embarrassed. They feel that they have lost "prestige." They think that others must hold it against them because they were not able to come through with the expected results.

(4) *Thoughtless teasing or embarrassment.* Whether the "remark" is about clothing, mannerisms, speech, finances, appearance, accomplishments, friends, or ideas, the result is much the same. A person feels, "I don't suit them: I just don't fit in here."

(5) *Taking a person for granted.* Failure to recognize one's contribution and accomplishments makes him feel that you do not appreciate him and that you do not accept him. In whose progress are most people interested? Their own, of course. So when we ignore other people's efforts, we tell them, in a sense, that we are not interested in them.

These are practical, everyday concerns—and not one of us can afford to overlook them! In our homes, churches, schools, communities and various other organizations we have a responsibility to encourage and help those about us. This brings happiness to others, but it brings even more to *us*!

Today's alert classroom teachers are beginning to take special note of children who do not seem to belong. Through sociometric techniques, classroom teachers are learning to identify boys and girls who are not chosen or who are avoided by others. Misfits? Perhaps, but the teacher knows that these youngsters may be heading toward serious maladjustments unless steps are taken to help them.

Of the more than one million juvenile delinquents in America this year, most of them feel that they are not really wanted! No one knows exactly how many boys and girls in the United States run away from home, "floating" from one section of the country to another. But the California Director of Youth Authority says that in the State of California alone, two thousand youngsters escape to his state *every month*. Law enforcement agencies declare that without exception these young people are convinced that they do not belong.

Parents have a special responsibility. When children feel that they are "rejected," they usually resort to undesirable behavior in order to gain some recognition. Strange? No, belongingness is such a basic need that it must be met, either acceptably or unacceptably.

As I counsel with people I find that many marriage problems stem from this basic cause—a husband or wife does not feel that he or she is wholeheartedly accepted by his mate. The Miltons were an example of this. When they came to my office they were on the verge of separation. As I worked through on the case I found that the husband spent most of his time criticizing his wife. Did he love her? Yes, but because he constantly found fault, his wife felt as though she could never do anything to please him. Day by day the husband destroyed his wife's feeling of belonging to him.

"I think," she said, "that we would both be happier without each other." Actually Mr. Milton did not realize how rejected he was making his wife feel.

"Belongingness"—yes, it is a basic psychological need that must be met in the lives of people of every age—including those who are *older*. How much healthier and happier our grandparents would be if they were made to feel that they were wanted, loved, needed and appreciated.

The same thing is true with all our relationships in life. Whether it is at home, at school, on the job, or at church—we can and should make other people feel that they belong.

This is a challenge. And a serious responsibility. Our cues, then, are: compliment, notice, listen, appreciate, encourage and cooperate—the cues for happy and useful living.

BELONGING TO GOD

"It's mine," the boy said, holding his little boat with loving satisfaction and pride. "I *made* it myself!"

There was no question about it. He had made it for himself—for his own enjoyment. The boat *belonged* to him.

And so it is with God. He created man for Himself—for His own pleasure. "Thou has created all things, and for thy pleasure they are and were created" (Rev. 4:11).

Although God created people for each other (ordaining marriage, blessing the home, and sanctioning human government), His primary purpose in creating human beings was for fellowship with Himself. "And God said, Let us make man in our image, after our likeness . . . So God created man in his own image, in the image of God created he him; male and female created he them" (Gen. 1:26, 27). Rightfully then, man belonged to God because He *made* him.

Belonging to God! What could be more complete; what could be more satisfying? Man enjoyed a perfect bond of fellowship with God, his Creator—*until man wilfully broke this relationship by sinning.*

After that, everything was changed. Man had given himself over to Satan and was now controlled by sin. His nature was sinful and he was alienated from God. "Your iniquities have separated between you and your God, and your sins have hid His face from you, that He will not hear" (Isa. 59:2). Man no longer belonged to God: he was now "of his father, the devil" (John 8:44). A severe statement? Indeed. But also a very severe *fact*.

Could any tragedy be greater—to be estranged from the One who made us for Himself? Separated from God—here, during our life span on earth, and for eternity. How it must grieve the heart of God. And what a complete void is left in the heart of man. For although people can and should belong to one another, they were created as spiritual beings. They *need* to belong to God.

God knows this. And He wants us to belong to Him. Although mankind has chosen *not* to belong to God, in His divine love and tender compassion, He has chosen us. "Ye have not chosen me, but I have chosen you" (John 15:16). The great heart of God has provided a way that makes it possible for us to *belong* to Him— now and forever. But we must *accept* His provision.

What is this provision? It is God's own beloved Son, Jesus Christ. "For there is one God, and one mediator between God and men, the man Christ Jesus" (I Tim. 2:5). "But now in Christ Jesus ye who sometimes were far off are made nigh by the blood of Christ" (Eph. 2:13).

The boy who held his little boat and said, "It's mine, I made it," suffered a keen disappointment. One day, with exuberant anticipation he carried his boat to the shore of the lake and sailed it on the clear, blue water. The little boat skimmed along as the gentle breeze blew its sails across the rippling waves. Then suddenly a gust of wind caught the little boat and snapped the string the boy was holding. On, on—out further and further the little boat sailed until at last it had vanished from sight.

Sadly the boy made his way home—without his prized possession. It was lost.

The weeks and the months went by. Then one day as the boy passed by a toy shop, something caught his attention. Could it be? Was it really? He looked closer. *It was.* Yes, there in the display window was his *own* little boat.

Overjoyed, the boy bolted into the store and told the owner about the boat on display. It really belonged to him. He had *made* it, hadn't he?

"I'm sorry," the shopkeeper said, "but it's *my* boat now. If you want it, you'll have to pay the price for it."

Sad at heart, the boy left the store. But he was determined to get his boat back, even though it meant working and saving until he had enough money to pay for it.

At last the day came. Clutching his money in his fist, he walked into the shop and spread his hard earned money on the counter top. "I've come to buy back my boat," the boy said.

The clerk counted the money. It was enough. Reaching into the showcase, the storekeeper took the boat and handed it to the eager boy.

The lad's face lit up with a smile of satisfaction as he held the little boat in his arms. "You're mine," he said, "*twice* mine. Mine because I *made* you—and now, mine because I *bought* you."

So it is with our relationship to God. We are His twice. His first because He made us. Then because we turned away from Him, Satan took over. "All we like sheep have gone astray; we have turned everyone to his own way" (Isa. 53:6). But God wanted us so greatly that He paid the price to buy us back. The price was tremendous—the highest price that ever could be paid. It was the sacrifice of His own Son, Jesus, upon the Cross of Calvary. "Forasmuch as ye know that ye were not redeemed with corruptible things, as silver and gold . . . But with the precious blood of Christ, as of a lamb without blemish and without spot" (I Peter 1:18, 19).

Think of it. God paid the price of sin through the shed blood of His own Son so that He might *buy us back*—redeem us. And because of this, *we can belong to Him*. Today. Tomorrow. Throughout eternity.

It is an overwhelming thought when we consider the close, intimate relationship which God provides for those who accept Christ as their personal Saviour! In this wonderful relationship with God, we are His *sons*

—His very own. "Beloved, now are we the sons of God, and it doth not yet appear what we shall be: but we know that, when He shall appear, we shall be like him; for we shall see him as He is" (I John 3:2). What could be closer! What could be sweeter! We belong now because we are *"accepted in the beloved"* (Eph. 1:6).

God reminds us that He is the vine and we are the branches (John 15:5). In other words, our relationship with Him is so close that it would be impossible to remove one without taking part of the other. He also tells us that He is our shepherd. But most intimate of all is the fact that we are actually *indwelt by God's Holy Spirit!* "Know ye not that ye are the temple of God, and that the Spirit of God dwelleth in you?" (I Cor. 3:16).

When we belong to God, He promises that He will never leave us nor forsake us. Man may be fickle, but God is sure. He is steadfast. And when we belong to Him we can say with the Apostle Paul, "For I am persuaded that neither death, nor life, nor angels, nor principalities, nor powers, nor things present, nor things to come, Nor height, nor depth, nor any other creature, shall be able to separate us from the love of God, which is in Christ Jesus our Lord" (Rom. 8:38, 39). Could any "belonging" be more satisfying than this?

Truly, when we belong to God we have His fellowship and His companionship. Nothing can meet man's need for belonging in any fuller or richer degree. The Irishman expressed it well when he and his Christian friend were talking.

"It's a grand thing to be saved," the friend said.

"Aye," answered the Irishman, "it is. But I know something better than that."

"Better than being saved?" the other asked in surprise. "What can possibly be better than that?"

"The companionship of the One who has saved me," was the reply.

There is nothing sweeter. Fellowship with God exceeds all other joy here on earth or in heaven. And is ours to enjoy forever.

BELONGING TO GOD'S FAMILY

Whenever I travel throughout the United States or in foreign countries, one significant fact always stands out: there is a close-knit bond of fellowship among true believers that exists in no other area of society. It is a *kinship* of one Christian to another. They all belong to the redeemed family of God.

Even though they may be complete strangers, when a child of God meets another of "like precious faith," they feel a oneness and a genuine warmth. They have much in common. They *belong*. The closeness they feel is not only because they share similar experiences, but because the same God, in the person of the Holy Spirit, indwells each of them. In other words, they are "spiritual relatives"—God is their Father and they are "brothers" or "sisters" in Christ. And this tie is far stronger than any human tie could possibly be: it is a relationship that will last for eternity.

Two brothers were traveling together in Europe. One was a Christian but the other was not. The unconverted brother was a member of the Masonic Lodge.

Like most Americans, they were always on the lookout for other U. S. citizens. So when they heard that there was an American in the town where they were staying, they visited him and learned that he was a gospel missionary. Immediately the two Christians began talking about the blessings of the Lord. What a time of fellowship! After a short visit the brothers went on their way.

They had no sooner stepped into the street when the Mason said to his brother, "Say, I didn't know you knew him before. When had you met him?"

"Never saw him before in my life," answered the Christian.

"What!" exclaimed the brother.

"That's right."

"Well, I've never seen the like. You never saw him before and yet for the last hour you've been talking like long lost friends."

"That's because we both know the Lord," the Christian replied. "We are brothers in Christ."

The Mason was silent. Then a moment later he added thoughtfully, "Well, John, I must admit, this sure beats Masonry."

And he was right. The bond of Christian fellowship surpasses all other human bonds. God speaks of this relationship (that of one Christian to another) as being parts of one body—His Church. Nothing can be in closer harmony than the parts of the body. They work together with minutest precision, they cooperate with each other, they "sympathize" with each other. In short, they operate as one because they *belong* together. And Christians belong together because they are *in Christ*.

During the last World War, a report from China told of a Japanese soldier who entered a Chinese Christian church at service time. His entrance created considerable apprehension and alarm until he stood up and said, "I am a conscript soldier, but I am also a Christian. If I may, I would like to worship with you."

The congregation breathed easily once again. Of course he was welcomed.

At the close of the service the Japanese soldier shook hands with the Chinese minister and asked him to sign his Bible.

The pastor gladly obliged. And beneath his signature he wrote in Chinese, "There is neither Jew nor Greek, there is neither bond nor free . . . for ye are all one in Christ Jesus" (Gal. 3:28).

How true! Neither Jew nor Greek; neither Chinese nor Japanese, nor American, nor any other earthly division—in Christ. There are no barriers of language or birth when we are children of the King. We are all "one in Christ Jesus." The poet expresses it beautifully in the following lines:

> In Christ there is no East or West,
> In Him no South or North;
> But one great fellowship of love,
> To show His glories forth.
> In Him do true hearts everywhere
> This sweet communion find;
> His service we do gladly share
> In love to all mankind.
>
> Join hands then, brothers of the faith,
> Whate'er your race may be:
> Each one who loves the blessed Lord
> Shares in His victory.
> In Christ now meet both East and West,
> In Him meet South and North:
> All blood-bo't souls are in Him blest,
> Thro' them his love flows forth.
>
> —J. Oxenham

What is the tie that binds our hearts together in Christian love and unity? What is the basis of our fellowship? God gives the answer in His Word; "But if we walk in the light, as He is in the light, we have fellowship one with another, and the blood of Jesus Christ His Son cleanseth us from all sin" (I John 1:7). That's it. We must *walk* in the light—the Christian walk. Then it is that we have fellowship "one with another." Then it is that we sense our state of belonging—"one with another."

Belonging. How well I remember my own experience in Iceland. Just shortly before I arrived there as an officer in the Navy, a shipload of military personnel was transported back to the States because those men did *not* belong. The mental strain had been too much.

Now I was to be stationed there. But I wasn't alone. God, my Father, was with me. Soon I discovered that many of God's people were there. And although the country was different, the climate was different, the language was different—our God was the same. And I *belonged*.

I had only been there a few days when someone knocked at the door of my quonset hut. I opened the door and before me stood two fair complexioned young men—typical Icelanders. They smiled and cordially introduced themselves as Christians. A friend from the States, Krist Gudnason, had written about my coming to Iceland.

This was the beginning of a blessed time for me. It wasn't long before these two friends introduced me to many more Christians. I attended church with them and visited their homes. We spent many happy hours together —hours that were a spiritual blessing and an inspiration to me. Our bonds in Christ became so strong that when my tour of duty in that country came to an end, it was with reluctance that I said "goodbye" to my many Icelandic Christian friends.

As I left that little land that I had come to love and appreciate, I thought of the contrast between my tour of duty there and that of my fellow service men. They were shipped home for treatment and observation because they could not belong.

Indeed, man's need for belonging is best met in the Christian life. Because Christ has redeemed us by His blood, we belong to God. This is the ultimate in belonging. Nothing can exceed the satisfaction of knowing that God is our Father and we are His children— the object of His love and care.

And when we belong to God, we belong to each other—*in Christ*. This is the key to genuine fellowship. It unlocks the hearts of true believers around the world—and causes us to *belong*. Such belonging is not only human: it is divine. For when we belong to God's family, the relationship never changes—and we belong forever!

Knowledge That Satisfies

THERE HE LAY—just a tiny, sweet bundle of babyhood as he trustingly looked up into his mother's face. The age of innocence? Ah yes, but more than that. He was completely uninformed. You see, tiny Tommy hadn't lived long—*and he had a lot to learn.*

But it didn't take him long to start learning. And once he began, there was no stopping him for the rest of his life. Tommy soon learned that when he cried, he got attention. And as time went on, he learned new and better ways of expressing himself. He learned about this strange and wonderful world in which he lived: about people and plants and water and weather and animals and ants—yes, about *all sorts of things.*

But interestingly enough, the more Tommy learned, the more he wanted to learn. And the more he studied, the more he began to realize how much there was to learn, and how little he really knew. Tommy went through elementary school, then high school—and college. But he never finished learning.

Was Tommy an exception? No, not at all. People are made like that. It's human nature to want to learn and gain knowledge. Like Tommy, every individual starts from "scratch." And like Tommy, the desire to learn, understand and gain knowledge is one that will continue as long as he lives. Why? Because it is one of man's basic psychological needs—an "inner hunger." Truly, we are *born to learn.*

That is why every normal person wants to learn. And why the happiest and healthiest people are those who have an opportunity to satisfy their God-given curiosity.

Naturally we do not all seek the same information. The interests of the bank clerk may differ widely from that of the circus acrobat. And the primitive tribesman does not search for knowledge in the same way the atomic scientist does. Nevertheless, everyone wants to learn the things that seem important to him.

This basic psychological need, the desire to learn and gain knowledge, is one of the primary characteristics that distinguishes man from the animal kingdom. Here is a quality that sets him apart from other forms of life. Animals don't crave education. In fact, they resist it. Most animal trainers use one of two methods to persuade animals to learn their routines—sugar or the whip. But not so with people. With them the incentive is knowledge itself. And people will go to all extremes in order to learn, to develop intellectually. God created man to think, to perceive, to make decisions, and man is not happy unless he is learning.

Is it surprising then, that your personality develops as you learn? Those who want education but who have never had the opportunity to get it are often frustrated. Other things being equal, when you have had the opportunity to investigate and acquaint yourself with facts, you are more interesting. You have a finer personality and you can better face the demands of life.

Learning Is Big Business

Not long ago an elderly man with whom I was counseling told me, "Dr. Narramore, if I had it to do over again, I would get more education."

As he spoke, his voice carried a tone of regret. Actually, this man echoed the thoughts of thousands of his fellow men. People are seldom satisfied with what they know. They want to know more—and more—and when they have learned more, their thirst for knowledge is still not quenched.

That is why learning has become such important business—BIG BUSINESS. In our civilized world education is a giant concern of man. Various schools are open "around the clock." Day schools, night schools, colleges, universities, institutes, summer schools, correspondence schools, trade schools, nursery schools, graduate schools—yes, schools and courses that fit every age and need. But schools are not all. The printed page fills men's eyes and minds with facts, figures and fancies. Books, magazines, newspapers and literature of every description fly off the presses by the millions. What a tremendous effort people make to meet this inner hunger in their lives—the basic psychological need of inquiring and gaining knowledge!

A few years ago while I was in New York I was invited to speak at a banquet in the Hotel Astor. For my speech I wanted to know the number of books and periodicals published each year in the United States. So I phoned some of the so-called authorities. But no one knew the answer.

Finally, I went to the well known source of authority, the radio "Answer Man," who answers questions on every subject. But after talking to several of his secretaries, and finally getting through to the "Answer Man" himself, I learned that this time I had stumped the "Answer Man." Not even *he* knew how many books and periodicals were published each year.

But he *did* give me some sources that I could contact in order to come up with my own findings.

By contacting the publishers and other sources suggested, and by adding the various figures, I arrived at the staggering answer. I found that if all the books and periodicals published in the United States in one year were placed on top of each other, and if they were each an inch thick (many are more than that), they would reach up to the top of the Empire State Building which is 102 stories high—not just once or twice but 3,200 times! In other words, stacked skyward, these books would make 3,200 piles, each as high as the Empire State Building.

My mind was running rampant now, stimulated by the overwhelming mountain of books published annually—so I sharpened my pencil again. This time I discovered that if these books were all placed end to end they would extend far enough to build a causeway across the ocean to Paris—and then back again to New York. And what's more, there would be enough books left over to reach all the way from New York to Chicago.

Reading material? Miles and miles of it. Books written on every subject imaginable. But with all of this, we still want to learn more. And we always will. Solomon wasn't exaggerating when he said, ". . . of making many books there is no end . . ." (Eccl. 12:12).

Today, more than ever, people feel the need for knowledge. Because of widespread educational opportunities, radios, television, literature and other means of communication, in all probability people possess more information than they have in any other generation in the history of mankind. But are they content with this vast store of knowledge? Hardly! For there is always more to learn—and people are always craving to know it.

So it is that the business of *learning* truly is BIG BUSINESS. And, as the British writer, Lawrence Sterne, has expressed it, "the desire of knowledge, like the thirst of riches, increases ever with the acquisition of it!" Who can deny this?

INCENTIVES

In today's world ignorance is *not* bliss—it is a decided handicap. And those who could climb to the top must have something to offer: either knowledge or skill. A few of the incentives that spur us on to get more education are quite obvious, while others are more subtle.

Some people travel the path of knowledge believing

that it will eventually lead to happiness. They feel that if they learn more, their lives will be enriched and they will have more capacity for enjoyment. In a sense, this is true. For we *do* improve our personalities and gain self-confidence and poise as we become better informed.

Others pursue education and training because they believe that they have *unusual gifts or talents* which deserve to be developed. Singer, artist, playwright, or salesman—a man's innate ability needs polishing and refining if it is to be a scintillating jewel instead of a rough piece of rock. Talent isn't enough. It takes a lot of ambition and good solid training to bring out its luster.

In most cases, those who have more education and training get the *better jobs*. Advanced degrees usually demand bigger pay-checks. A real premium is placed upon knowledge, giving its owner a distinct advantage in life. Many times it is the password that permits a person to start on the road to success. So people are willing to sacrifice if necessary, in order to obtain the education that will eventually afford a *higher standard of living*.

Then there are some who are spurred on to higher learning because they want prestige—the *admiration* of their fellow men. They realize that recognition and acclaim usually go to those who have more knowledge.

Still others seek knowledge because they believe it is the key to *freedom*. And it is true that when people have the facts, they can make wiser choices. Education and Democracy have always been allies—while on the other side of the wall, bondage and ignorance go hand in hand.

There are people who know that knowledge is a source of *power*. Power to control, force and sway. This authority complex rules them until they rule others.

Some men realize that if they are to make any

contribution in life, they must know something. Effectiveness and ignorance are not compatible. And people want and need to feel that they are useful, that their service in life is fruitful. Henry Ford, the great industrialist, once said, "Anyone who stops learning is old whether this happens at twenty or eighty. Anyone who keeps on learning not only remains young but becomes constantly more valuable, regardless of physical capacity."

But that's not all. Among the millions of inhabitants of the earth, many seek knowledge with a much deeper motive than any of the ones discussed. People are looking for the "*why* of life." Just what is man's role upon earth? Why did God put us here? Is there any purpose in life? With these vital questions still unanswered they enter erudite halls of learning in search of "truth" that will answer the riddle of life.

HELPING OTHERS

We need not study people long to realize that deep in the heart of every man is the innate desire to learn. But many people have never thought about their responsibility to help others meet this basic need.

Not long ago while walking down the corridor of our headquarters I met one of the new secretaries.

"Hell, Miss Smith. Are you enjoying your work?"

"Oh, it's just wonderful. I've never been so happy in my life."

"Fine. I'm glad you like it."

"There's only one thing . . ."

"Yes?"

"Sometimes I think I should be paying them instead of their paying me."

"Why is that?"

"Well, it's just that I am learning so many important things I never knew before. Dr. Johnson, who gives me dictation, always explains the work, and by the end of the day I feel like I've been going to college and getting paid for it too!"

Later that day I began to think about what she had said. What a contrast between Dr. Johnson and most of us. By taking a little time to explain things to his secretary, he was helping to meet a basic psychological need in her life—the desire to learn and to understand.

Actually, we *all* have the responsibility (and privilege) to open lines of communication and to create an atmosphere in which those with whom we live and work can learn and gain knowledge. And in doing so, we also help ourselves.

In a sense, we are *all* teachers. What a challenge! It's up to us to help children and young people to learn. Whether they are in our family, our community, or in some other sphere of our influence, our responsibility remains.

We should never tell a child that he is too young or too stupid to understand. And when he raises the questions that are embarrassing or difficult for us to answer at the time, we should accept the child and his question, and let him know that we will think it over. It is no disgrace to admit that we do not have all the answers.

Much more important than the answer we give is the cordial, encouraging way in which we react to those who are inquiring. So many people grow to adulthood feeling that no one has time for them, that others are not interested in their questions. Such feelings can increase to a point where serious maladjustments develop; and the results are physical and emotional disturbances.

Often I have found that teenagers and adults who had serious behavior problems or who, for example, have committed sex crimes, are really the victims of ignorance. They have done these things because they never had the opportunity to gain wholesome, factual information. This is to the shame of parents, schools and churches. Yes, we *do* have definite responsibilities to others—and in this way we also serve society.

Husbands and wives encourage each other to keep growing intellectually. Since gaining knowledge is one of the basic needs of man, meeting this need will help each marriage partner to be a happier, healthier person. Reading, taking courses, attending lectures, traveling, experimenting—these and many other activities will help keep your marriage zestful and romantic. They will add sparkle and interest to your home. And your children will admire you for it.

INFORMATION PLUS

The most important dimension of knowledge is the "kind." To be sure, there is learning that yields great satisfaction. But much of our learning merely demands more learning. The man who plumbs the depths of learning doesn't always come up with a satisfied heart. How well we know that some of the most unhappy people in the world are those who have walked down graduation aisles to pick up impressive pieces of the "alphabet" by "degrees."

A few years ago I had the privilege of taking graduate study at Columbia University in New York City. During that time I became well acquainted with scholars from many parts of the world. If secular learning itself could make people happy, I was in the right place to see it. Nearly everyone I met was reaching a pinnacle of accomplishment—the doctor's degree! But I noticed little relationship between secular intellectual achievement and genuine peace and happiness. Something was lacking.

One fellow, John was typical. He often talked about how happy he would be when he completed his dissertation. When at last the University handed him the coveted sheepskin, I asked, "Well, John, how does it feel?" His answer did not surprise me. "I'm glad it's over," he said, "but it doesn't make me feel any different."

John's learning (volumes of it) had added up to innumerable facts and figures but not to immeasurable joy and gladness. Why? Because it revolved around the creature, not the creator. Its center was materialistic. God was forgotten. And the deep longings of the mind and heart still went begging.

The twentieth century is characterized by great advances in knowledge—unprecedented communication, sources of power, space travel, and many fantastic discoveries.

We pride ourselves in having made great strides. But for all this, it has not lessened the corruption of our society. The more we learn, the more clever we are at killing each other.

General Omar Bradley, the distinguished military leader, made this classical statement: "Our knowledge of science has clearly outstripped our capacity to control it. We have too many men of science; too few men of the Sermon on the Mount. The world has achieved brilliance without wisdom, power without conscience. Ours is a world of nuclear giants and ethical infants. We know more about war than we do about peace, more about killing than we do about living. This is our twentieth century's claim to distinction and progress."

In a recent book Charles A. Lindbergh wrote, "To me in youth, science was more important than either man or God. I worshipped science. Now I understand that spiritual truth is more essential to a nation ... The more urgent mission of our time is to understand these (spiritual) truths and to apply them to our way of modern life."

When six Nobel prize winners, all top men of science representing five different nations, met in New York a few years ago, they gave this statement to the press: "Science has nothing to give men to change their nature so that they will stop fighting wars."

But the greatest statements about human learning and knowledge have been made by God Himself in the Bible. Describing people who live in the "last days," he says they are, "ever learning, and never able to come to the knowledge of the truth" (II Tim. 3:7).

Man-made satellites, guided missiles, space stations, and round trips to the moon! These are wonderful. But they do not bring satisfaction. And the heart of man still cries out, "Unsatisfied!"

KNOWLEDGE WITH SATISFACTION

Is there any knowledge that can satisfy the human heart? May our desire to learn, to gain understanding be gratified?

Yes, there is Truth that sets you free, "knowing" that brings peace and happiness, knowledge that never disappoints the learner. This truth challenges all ranges of intelligence ...

One evening several years ago I was glancing through the daily newspaper when suddenly a familiar name caught my eye. Immediately I followed the column with keen interest. We knew this man:

"Listen to this, honey," I said to my wife. And then I read the article about our friend.

How thrilled we were! This man was an educator, a man of degrees—but best of all, he was a born-again believer. As we read the news item it stated that he had taken the qualifying examination for the doctor's degree in a certain great university. Then it went on to say that he had come out with the *highest* I.Q. score ever recorded in that institution.

Several days later I saw this brilliant man. As we fellowshiped together and talked of the things of God, he said in all sincerity and humility, "Narramore, I am constantly amazed at the inexhaustibility of the Bible. I may study one chapter thoroughly, but the very next day I can study the same chapter again, and it will still unfold something that I had never seen before.

"Sometimes I wonder how I could have missed these marvelous things. But that's the way the Word of God is. I can study the same portion of Scripture day after day and month after month—and through the years there is always something more wonderful that I had not discovered before."

Yes, the Bible challenges man's highest intellect. And it is not until he follows Christ that he faces the greatest challenge. It is then that new vistas of knowledge open before him and he finds access to unlimited Truth.

What is this *knowledge*? What is the *Truth*?

Interestingly enough, Truth is a *Person!* Not facts? Not information? No, a Person. Jesus spoke with Divine authority when He said, "I am the Truth." (John 14:6). And in Colossians 2:3, the Bible tells us that in God and Christ "are hid all the treasures of wisdom and knowledge."

All the treasures of wisdom and knowledge—in God! That means, then, that if we are to have true wisdom, the kind that satisfies, we must go to the source, to God Himself. The Bible says: "The fear of the Lord is the beginning of wisdom." (Ps. 111:10).

Notice that we do not even *begin* to have wisdom until we reverently recognize God. Knowledge without God is built upon a wrong premise. Therefore, it is faulty. When God is left out, there is a God-sized vacuum in the center of man's knowledge. And all other knowledge is out of balance because the hub is missing.

In order to understand the "why of life" we must *first* realize our condition as sinners, unfit to stand in the presence of a Holy God. Then as we learn the truth of the Gospel—how God sent His only Son, Jesus, to die on the Cross for our sins—it is our responsibility to act upon this knowledge and accept Christ as our Saviour. When we have done this, we can experience the joy and peace of knowing that we belong to God—

that we are truly His redeemed children. Only when we know the Giver of life can we understand life. It then takes on meaning and purpose. "And we *know* that all things work together for good to them that love God, to them who are the called according to His purpose" (Rom. 8:28).

After we have been saved, we have an even greater incentive to learn. We want to be our best for God. Furthermore, learning is easy because our thinking is straight. It is God's command to "Study to shew thyself approved unto God, a workman that needeth not to be ashamed, rightly dividing the word of truth" (II Tim. 2:15).

As we grow in spiritual wisdom and understanding, guided by the Holy Spirit, we can say with the psalmist, "I have more understanding than all my teachers, for Thy testimonies are my meditation" (Ps. 119:99).

More than *teachers?* Yes, that is exactly what this verse says. It sounds strange, yet it is true. Your teachers may be loaded with systematized facts; they may be walking encyclopedias. Yet, if they do not know Christ, the fountainhead of all knowledge, they are sadly lacking in truth and in wisdom!

Man's knowledge does not last long. It is temporary at its best. Man may learn "facts" today but find them changing tomorrow. He goes from one bit of knowledge to another—groping, struggling and striving to find his way through the dark maze.

Yesterday's great knowledge is no longer great today. The newspaper is thrown away the day after it is printed. Encyclopedias are sold for a "song" after they are a few years old. One great invention passes into oblivion after another great discovery is made. So it is that information today is not what it was yesterday—or what it will be tomorrow.

But God's knowledge is not so. It lasts forever and ever. Man constantly strives to gain insight into even the "ABC's" of God's great wonders. Take the atom for example. Have you ever realized that the root words for "atom" means, "impossible to be split?" But the most interesting part is not that we have split the atom. It could have been done centuries ago. The significant fact is that man has split what he said was absolutely "unsplittable"! And so the word "atom" stands as a monument to man's unreliable, transient knowledge.

How God must smile as He looks down and sees us gloat in our own "great findings." God knew all the answers from the beginning, because "All things were made by Him; and without Him was not anything made that was made" (John 1:4). He knows the unknown!

But the believer is never left to the mercy of man's vacillating, changing theories. The Christian can say, "I will bless the Lord, who hath given me counsel: my reins [inner self] also instruct me in the night seasons." Regardless of world conditions, we can be sure that God's wisdom and knowledge shall be the stability of our times. God promises, "I will instruct thee and teach thee in the way which thou shalt go. I will guide thee with mine eye." And when God is "instructing" us we can know that we are on the right track.

Our library shelves are lined with encyclopedias and other books dealing with almost every conceivable subject—volume after volume. Yet, as complete as these may seem to be, they are still pitifully inadequate. They tell us only a smattering of truth—simply because they are the outgrowth of our limited, finite minds.

But there is one Book that stands apart from all others. This continual best-seller astounds the greatest scholars: it withstands the test of time. It is not of human origin; it is divinely inspired *without errors*. Down through the years it has been miraculously preserved. God's Book of knowledge, the Holy Bible, is as sure as God Himself because it is His Word. "Heaven and earth shall pass away but my Word shall not pass away" (Matt. 24:35).

The poet (author unknown) who penned the following lines pays sincere tribute to the BOOK OF BOOKS.

There are books in the making and books in the
   store,
There are books on the table, and books on the
   floor.
The library and stockroom have books piled up
   high,
There are more to be written and more I must
   buy.

Historical novels, biographies too;
Each week brings a dozen exhausting "Who's
   Who,"
There is fiction that's truthful, and fiction that's
   trash,
There's an orderly volume and another mere hash.

There's a new book of science and a book of the
   play,
There's the book of the year, and the book of the
   day.
There are books to refer to and some to ignore,
There are books that will thrill you and others
   will bore.

But the Book of the ages, of balance and power
Is the Book called the Bible, the Book of the hour!
Exhaustless its treasure, eternal its store
All the best of the others you'll find here—and
   more!

It is true that to be healthy and happy we should keep on learning. This desire to gain knowledge is a basic psychological need that cries out to be satisfied. But knowledge and education given solely from the minds of men are not adequate. We can search the libraries of the nations, gain all of the world's understanding and yet never find fulfillment in the empty shell of knowledge.

Not until a man accepts the Christ of the Bible as His own Saviour and lives a dynamic Christian life is this need completely satisfied. It is only then that the veil of understanding is lifted: his learning is no longer centered in his own finite little world, but in eternity. Now he can look "beyond"; now he has access to divine knowledge because God, his Father, is the very Author of knowledge!

6
How to Handle Fear

While working in my office one day, I received an urgent phone call. "Dr. Narramore," a young lady said, "my name is Jane White. I'm a Christian and I've read your articles in magazines. I need help—badly. May I speak to you for a minute?"

"Surely, are you free to talk from where you are now?"

"Yes," she gasped. "I'm in a phone booth. I just got off the bus. And please forgive me if I sound like— well, if I don't seem to make sense. But for weeks I've been having terrible fears. And just now while I was riding to work, that dreadful, frightening feeling began to come again. I tell you, I almost became hysterical. I didn't know who to call or what to do. But I knew of you so I got off the bus and phoned. I'm afraid I'll do something terrible if I don't get help. May I see you right away?"

I arranged an appointment. And as I put down the receiver, my heart went out to her in pity. True, I had worked with similar cases. But I was reminded again that there are *many* who suffer from fear, although their cases may not be as serious as Jane's.

Unrelieved fear is damaging to the mind and body. And it causes real *pain* and suffering.

God says, "Fear hath torment." It is a devastating thing. We may feel sorry for those who are fearful, but we cannot fully realize the torture that fear inflicts unless we have experienced it ourselves. True, fear knocks at everyone's door—no one is exempt. But unless we are fearful much of the time, we cannot know the mental anguish it brings and the toll it takes on the human body.

WHAT DOES FEAR DO?

In his publication, "Your Emotions and God's Word," Harvey C. Roys, prominent medical doctor, illustrates the effect of fear. He tells of a laboratory experiment in which an animal was purposely frightened. Here are Dr. Roys' findings: "If you take a cat into the x-ray room and give it a special meal of Barium Sulphate, you can study by means of a fluoroscope the action of the cat's stomach. You will see that there are nice muscle waves which mix the food and cause the digestive processes to be carried on. Then if you bring a *dog* into the room, something happens. All of those beautiful muscle waves stop. The digestive processes cease, and the cat has indigestion. If this experiment is repeated enough times, the cat may develop a peptic ulcer."*

If this can happen to a cat—a mere animal, what then takes place when a complex, sensitive human being is subjected to fear? The answer is real suffering—physical as well as mental.

Fear takes on many physical symptoms. For years we have recognized such signs as upset stomach, headaches and nervousness. But today, the list is growing longer. Medical books are filled with ailments that stem from emotional disturbances such as fear.

Fear silently robs people of good health and happiness. They sense that something is wrong but they do not know the cause. So when this basic psychological need, *being relatively free from fear,* remains unmet in your life, you are certain to suffer the consequences— torment, mental anguish and physical damage.

*Your Emotions and God's Word, Harvey C. Roys, M.D. (Seattle Gospel Publishing Service, Seattle, Washington). Quoted by permission of the author.

And the results of such emotional conflicts finally pile up, showing themselves in a variety of ways.

Have you ever wondered whether fears and anxieties can actually turn a persons's hair white? It can! Researchers have found that severe emotional stresses can cause a rapid formation of microscopic air bubbles in the hair. These displace the natural pigment and cause the hair to appear white. This only emphasizes the profound and far-reaching effects of fear and worry.

In many cases, low scores on vision tests have been traced to anxiety. We find that in fifty out of every one hundred people, the ability to see is definitely impaired when they are even slightly frightened.

Fear can actually "scare the wits out of you," causing the thought processes to come practically to a halt. Even mild anxiety can hamper your ability to think. Unless you are forced to do so, it is foolish to tackle a tough problem or to make an important decision when you are anxious or fearful.

When a person is afraid, he cannot think as clearly or as rationally as he is ordinarily capable of doing. This is why fear interferes with learning.

Teachers who use fear to discipline students defeat their own purpose because it sets up mental blocks and hinders the learning process. Fear makes students "clam up," forgetting the things they already know: it also discourages creative thinking and reasoning. Actually, fear is a form of "mild panic"—you temporarily lose control of yourself. Such a condition never encourages learning.

How well I remember "Miss Larson," one of my high school teachers. I can see her yet—straight and austere with steel gray hair and cold gray eyes. She was there for business. She would tolerate no foolishness—and everyone knew it. When Miss Larson entered the room a peculiar spell came over the entire class. Cold chills ran up and down our spines. One thought flooded our minds, "I hope he doesn't call on me." But the inevitable was bound to come. And when it did, fear gripped not only our minds but also our vocal cords.

"Robert," she would command, "stand and report."

Like the others before him, Robert stood up in a daze of fear—his mind a complete blank. He had prepared his lesson and he knew it well. But under the circumstances, he simply could not remember.

It's a wonder he learned *anything* in that class. But I'm sure of this: the little we absorbed was *in spite* of her and not *because* of her teaching. Oh yes, she knew her subject and she was capable of teaching it, but the *fear* she instilled *prevented* us from learning.

How Fear Begins

Where does fear come from and how does it begin? Is it from training? Or through experience?

The answer is *both*. We learn fear from both training and experience. And it is important that we do.

Training? Yes. And a reasonable amount of caution is desirable. Children must learn to avoid hazardous traffic, fires, hot stoves, high places, and many other situations involving danger.

There is a limit, of course. Some parents go beyond this reasonable limit, instilling needless fear into their children, warning them of situations which are *not* actually harmful. Overcautious and oversolicitous adults sometimes protect children from imaginary dangers.

We as parents and teachers may have fears, and whether we realize it or not, by our actions and reactions we can impose these same fears upon our children. Fear is contagious. Children are especially susceptible when fear is imparted to them by their parents.

Take Phyllis, for example. She was afraid of many things—things her mother had feared. Oh yes, Phyllis was a grown woman, now married and with a family of her own. Although she realized that many of her fears were ungrounded, she couldn't seem to break her pattern of reactions.

Phyllis was horrified of spiders. If one should even come near her, she would become almost hysterical. Why? Because her mother had reacted that way.

And electrical storms—how they terrified her!

One day in my office, Phyllis began to talk about her fears. "I remember," she said, "how it was when we were children. Whenever there was a bad storm with thunder and lightning, mother would grab my sister and me and take us to a closet. There, all three of us would huddle, hide our faces and tremble until the storm had passed. You see, mother's uncle had been struck and killed by lightning. That was probably the reason for her intense fear.

"But as for my sister and me—well, I suppose mother 'taught' us to dread lightning and thunder. And although I realize now how foolish it is to become so panicky over an electrical storm, that terrible fear still grips me."

As Phyllis and I continued to talk about her fears, I admired the mature attitude she was taking in regard to her own small children.

"I'm determined not to make *my* children suffer from fear just because I do," she told me. "And no matter how frightened I am, I try to act as though it doesn't bother me at all."

"And are you successful?" I asked.

"Oh, yes," answered Phyllis. Then, as her face lit up in a radiant smile, she added, "And what's more, when I tell my children that these so-called fears are nothing to be afraid of, I not only help them, but I help *myself.*"

And Phyllis was right! She was not only helping her children to develop healthy, normal attitudes, but in so doing, she was helping herself.

But what about *experience*? Don't people develop fears because they have been frightened themselves?

Yes, and sometimes this is good. We *should* fear real danger. But it doesn't always end there. It may cause serious difficulty later on. Severe fright—either from a real cause or an imaginary one—if not relieved, understood, or realistically resolved, may be forgotten after a short time with no apparent reactions. But it is not at all uncommon for this fear (or a related one) to rear its ugly head again months or even years later. The person may develop a phobia that persists in spite of its irrationality—and the basic cause is none other than the frightful experience that left its hidden scar sometime before.

Bob, a young business man, was the victim of a hidden, unresolved fear. Symptoms: (1) although he had talent and training, he had a dread of speaking in public, and (2) he had a distressing dream that visited and revisited him. It was always the same—he couldn't remember his lines in a play.

Bob, like many people, had never told anyone about his fear. But it was a constant annoyance that kept him from being his best.

One evening while he was thumbing through a magazine, an article caught his eye. It was entitled, HIDDEN FEARS. He eagerly read every word. That did it!

I know what I'll do, thought Bob as he put down the magazine. *I'll go see a psychiatrist. Maybe I can get help like the fellow in this story.*

It was all set—every Tuesday at 4:00 o'clock. But Bob got cold feet and just before the first appointment, he almost backed out. However, once he broke the ice, he looked forward to the other interviews.

"Bob," said the psychiatrist at the end of several sessions, "what do you think? Do we need to get together any more?"

"No," Bob replied. "I think my problem is worked

out now. In fact, I'm *sure* it is settled. And thanks so much for all your help."

What had happened? During their sessions together, Bob had talked to the psychiatrist about his fears. The psychiatrist had encouraged him to discuss them in detail. Simply emptying his heart and mind gave Bob a great deal of relief. But the psychiatrist did not stop there. He skillfully arranged and guided the discussion so that Bob could explore in detail the possible causes of his fears. Bob examined each cause carefully and looked for a connection between it and his present condition. Little by little he uncovered the roots to his problem. He traced back into his own experiences until he found the beginnings of his fears. Then he brought them out into the open, examined them, talked about them until each one was finally whittled down to its true, insignificant size. Now that the causes were understood, resolved and "aired," Bob cleaned out both large and small particles of fear residue that had quietly and secretly haunted him for years.

What causes fear? Unfortunately, as in Bob's case, the causes are not always obvious. In fact, they may be extremely subtle and difficult to uncover. Since fear is an emotion, it is often tied up with other emotional problems. Studies reveal that people who are from broken homes, or who have personality problems, are much more likely to have ungrounded fears. But in extreme cases, a person needs individual study and diagnosis before intelligent treatment or therapy can take hold.

Fear does not always develop suddenly. And although it may *seem* to have just arisen, more often it is the result of a series of experiences which accumulate until they seem like mountains.

Take Marjorie, for example—a nice looking girl with a sincere, pleasant personality. People liked Marjorie because she liked them. Her difficulty did not show up until she was married.

Her mother had always "taken care of things" and was recognized for her efficiency. But after Marjorie began housekeeping for herself, she found she had a problem. She was afraid to entertain guests. Oh yes, she wanted to be sociable. She and her husband Dick were popular with their age group at church. But Marjorie had no confidence in her ability to cook or graciously serve guests in her home. Sound foolish? Yes, to some, but not to Marge.

The reason for Marjorie's fear: from the time she was a little girl, her mother had never allowed her to help in the kitchen. "Now run along, dear," mother would protest when Marjorie wanted to help. "I don't want to be bothered when I'm cooking. I can do this much better and faster than you can—so run along and do something else."

That was not all. Marjorie's older sister was a "natural" at cooking. "My, how well Roberta does," people would remark. "She just seems to have a knack."

But not Marjorie! She just *didn't* have the "knack" —*nor was it ever developed*. When she tried her hand at cooking, it usually ended in failure. But worse than that, the family laughed at her. The result: Marjorie was *afraid to try*.

Yes, our childhood fears often carry over into adulthood, causing maladjustments in later life. If a person has never developed self assurance as a child, he cannot suddenly expect to have it when he is grown. And so it was with Marjorie.

But Marjorie's story *does* have a happy ending. Dick proved to be an understanding husband who was able to help Marjorie gain the self-confidence that had been denied her for so many years. He encouraged her to talk about her problem. He tried never to ridicule her, either privately or in public. And Dick's approval of her efforts became a real "boost" to Marjorie. He was always on hand to compliment her (even if her cooking wasn't like "Mother's"). Not only that, he encouraged her to take a course in home management. This gave her the "know-how" she lacked. With this kind of encouragement from her partner, it wasn't long before Marjorie's self-confidence began to blossom. And her fear? Well, that slowly disappeared.

Yes, as in Marjorie's case, we can help each other. We have a responsibility to our children—and to our marriage partner. Since people are not perfect, it is possible that an excellent marriage may have one partner who lacks self-confidence and is beset by fear. But if the other one is patient and understanding and works intelligently, a great deal can be done to alleviate these fears. How much better to help a person than to blame! Fear is always caused: but if we do our part, we can help others overcome their fears and be more like the people God intended them to be.

Nipped in the Bud

A wise man once said, "The best remedy for fear is to meet it before it happens." How true this is. When you fear something, don't run away—analyze it. Then you can decide the course of action to take. Truly, inaction is fear's greatest ally, and action is the most effective antidote.

Since "an ounce of prevention is worth a pound of cure," Christian parents and teachers can do much to prevent boys and girls from developing phobias. How? By candidly examining their methods of control, making sure that they rarely use *fear* as a means of discipline. The "fear method" is not only unsound; it is *unkind*.

"Do it or I'll tell the bogey man to get you!" "If you don't behave, I'll give you away to someone else!" "If you say that word again they'll cut your tongue off!" "If you don't do it, I'll lock you in that dark closet!" "If you don't act nicer, I won't love you any more!"

We have all heard people use ultimatums of this kind —and perhaps we've been guilty of resorting to similar ones ourselves. True, fear-laden threats such as these may bring immediate results. But they can inflict emotional damage that will leave a permanent scar.

How much better it is to honestly spank a child or take away his privileges than to dangle the weapon of fear over his head—a force with which he cannot cope.

Naturally, we should teach chidren to respect common dangers. But we should do all in our power to prevent them from being unduly fearful. When a child is fearful of a definite object or situation, we can help by entering the situation with him, minimizing the danger, and little by little showing him that there is nothing to fear.

UNDERSTANDING MINIMIZES FEAR

Have you ever realized that we seldom fear the things we understand? That is why it is so important for parents to talk with children about their fears. Understanding may not cause us to like certain things, but it does keep us from fearing them.

A young lady named Beth once told me her experience.

"When I was a little girl we lived on a street lined with huge trees," Beth said. "I don't remember what kind of trees these were, but I *do* know that in the spring of the year they dropped strange reddish blossoms—about as big around as a pencil and approximately two or three inches long. When people walked down the street and stepped on them, these blossoms would squash on the sidewalk and make what to me looked like a disgusting mess.

"I was deathly afraid of these blossoms," Beth continued, "because I did not realize what they really were. I thought they were ugly worms. And I had no special love for worms.

"I hated to go outside as long as those 'worms' were there. And when I walked to and from school I can remember hopping from one clear spot to another in order to avoid stepping on those repulsive 'creatures.' They almost made me sick.

"Then one day my kind, understanding mother found out about this strange fear that haunted me. She did not ridicule, but lovingly took me aside and explained that these were *not* worms at all but blossoms that preceded the leaves. 'Soon,' she told me, 'they will come out in all their glory to dress the barren trees in a lovely green robe.' Then picking up one of these blossoms, she held it gently in her hand. 'See, it is not a worm at all,' she said sweetly. 'It is a flower. See how pretty it is!'

"And for the first time in several springtimes, I saw beauty, not ugliness, in these fallen blossoms. Yes, they *were* rather pretty when I looked at them closely.

"I still did not *like* these blossoms, but now I was no longer afraid. I saw them in a different light. And, in time, I did not mind them at all."

PREPARATION REDUCES FEAR

People are fearful of the unknown. And the unknown does not necessarily mean any more than the untried. Actually, it makes little difference whether the untried is a person's first airplane ride or a child's first day at school.

Adults should prepare children for new experiences —getting them ready to accept rather than fear them. It is an important aspect of good social development.

I cannot help but think of Jimmie. His reaction to a new experience was a common one.

It was a beautiful clear day in early September. But as Jimmie walked beside his mother up the broad stone steps of the Westwood Elementary School, a strange apprehension gripped him. Jimmie reached up, grasped his mother's hand, and squeezed it tightly. He shuddered.

"What's the matter, Jimmie?" asked Mother.

"I'm cold. I don't feel well. I want to go home."

"Are you sick?" Mother looked at Jimmie half anxiously—half inquiringly—and a little bit dubiously.

"Yes," he blurted out, "I'm sick. I don't want to go to school."

"Oh, so that's it! But darling, you *have* to go to school."

"No, I don't want to."

"But why?"

"Because—because I'm—I'm afraid!"

Jimmie wasn't putting on. He really *was* afraid. Afraid because he was facing a new situation—afraid because he did not know what to expect.

When Jimmie stepped into the classroom and saw all the strange faces, he did not feel any better. He stuck close to his mother, still insisting that he did not want to stay.

"But you *have* to stay, Jimmie," persisted his mother.

"Then you stay *with* me. Don't leave me, Mommie. Don't leave me." Jimmie's pleading was earnest as he clung to his mother.

By this time Mother was becoming disgusted with her young son—but in an effort to calm him she promised that she would not leave.

Jimmie was satisfied. With Mother near, he felt safe.

But she had no intention of staying. So as soon as the teacher had Jimmie's eye, Mother slipped away.

The next morning Jimmie and his mother started out for school again. But the situation had not improved. Jimmie was more insistent than ever: *he did not want to go*. And today, *two* fears confronted him—the fear of a new situation (the classroom) and the fear that his mother would not keep her word.

Many children are afraid of new experiences. But the problem is never solved by deceit. Parents should *talk* with children and *explain* in a quiet, positive manner just what to expect. Then be sweetly firm—but *always* honest.

The Wrong Methods

Ridicule and teasing do not help a person who is afraid. It offers no solution—only adds embarrassment to the present fear. And the fear of being embarrassed is a most uncomfortable one. It is psychologically unsound to try to embarrass people out of their fears. It does no good—only harm—to drag a person's fears out in front of his friends. It makes him feel that he "loses face" with them. And fears are never overcome by tearing down confidence.

Some people think that they can help a frightened person by "forcing" him. Or perhaps they may take the unsuspecting victim by surprise to try to prove to him that he need not be afraid. But this is wrong. No doubt the people who do these things are well meaning—but they are not aware of the consequences. Because fear is not resolved by shock—rather, it is intensified. And this kind of "help" only makes matters worse.

I will never forget Diane's case. She did not like feathers. In fact, the repulsion was so intense that she actually feared them. No, she could not be coaxed to touch even the tiniest feather.

This seemed silly—especially to her brothers, Phil and Dan. "Imagine," they said, "being afraid of a little, soft, harmless feather."

At first Diane's brothers laughed and teased about it, but when their sister continued to be afraid, they became impatient. "We must do something to make her get over this crazy notion," they said.

Oh, they meant no harm—but it was not only *what* they did but *how* they did it. And the damage they inflicted was permanent.

It was Saturday noon. Diane had been playing with some neighbor children. Phil and Dan waited until Mother called her in for lunch. Then they hid behind a bush near the front door. The trap was set, and Diane was the unsuspecting victim.

A minute later, Diane, bubbling over with joy, arrived at the front door.

And then it happened!

Phil, standing behind the door, held a feather pillow that he and Dan had opened on one end. And as Diane entered the house, they showered her with feathers, shaking the entire pillow over her head!

What a joke! The boys roared—for a minute.

But it wasn't a joke to Diane. It was a horrible, frightening nightmare. Phil and Dan grew serious when they saw their sister's terrified expression and heard her hysterical screams. What had they done?

Diane was beside herself. She lost all control as this awful, traumatic experience seized her. Nothing the boys or their parents could do would calm or quiet her. Diane became weak—nauseated—a severe chill shook her entire body. She was a sick girl.

When the doctor arrived, his diagnosis was "a severe case of shock." It was several days before Diane was well enough even to sit up in bed.

But physical damage was not the only result. The extreme emotional upheaval that took place within Diane was of far more lasting consequence.

She is a grown woman today. But she still breaks out in a cold sweat whenever she sees a feather. And as a result of this ill-timed experience, she developed several other fears that she has never been able to conquer. Confidence in her brothers and in her whole world was shattered that fateful day—it lay at her feet in a shamble of tiny, white feathers—confidence that was never restored. Nor did the horror of this experience ever cease to linger in her mind. The result? It added to her insecurity. And today, she is a restricted fearful personality—because someone tried to "force" her out of her fear.

Another foolish way to handle fears is to simply say, "Relax!" Merely telling a person to relax is no solution. If he *could* relax, he would. Admonitions to relax neither change the facts nor one's attitudes. They merely leave a frightened person where he was—frightened without a sympathetic friend. But talking it out *does* help.

So let him do the talking. Encourage him to tell you how he feels. It's much more effective. After all, what *you* think doesn't automatically change *his* feelings. Fear is a gripping thing—you can't get away from it. And no matter how foolish it may seem to others, it is real to the one who is caught in its clutches.

How can we help people overcome their fears? Certainly not by ignoring them. Just saying, "You shouldn't be afraid," is pure folly. People must be reassured, comforted and put in a more secure situation. Then they will be able to see things in a clearer perspective. Then the feared circumstance will not seem so foreboding.

Take the case of little Timmy. He was afraid of the dark.

Every night it was the same. Daytime was a happy time, but when darkness came, something happened inside of Timmy.

When it was time to go to bed, he would stall as long as he could—a story, a drink of water—and, of course, the bathroom! And so it went, until his exasperated mother would finally corral him into his bed, give him a final goodnight kiss, and tuck the covers snugly around his little shoulders.

Then came the dreaded moment when mother reached to turn out the light.

"Oh, Mommie, please don't! Please don't turn off the light!"

"But Timmy," rebuked his mother, "it's time to go to sleep." She reached again toward the lamp.

"No, Mommie. Please!" There was real urgency in Timmy's pleading voice. His eyes portrayed a look of terror as he gasped, "I'm—I'm afraid! It's so dark when the light is out."

"Afraid? Afraid of the *dark?* Why Timmy," she chided, "a big boy like you *afraid* of the dark. How silly! What would your friends think of you if they knew? I'm ashamed of you."

And with that she reached determinedly for the light, clicked it off, and strode out of his room, closing the door behind her.

Timmy buried his head under the covers and shuddered. Deep, insistent sobs shook his little body. His throat felt strangely dry. He was afraid. He didn't want to be—but he was. And he was suffering *needlessly*—and alone.

Little wonder that Timmy hated bedtime. And little wonder, too, that he developed many other fears which followed him all through his life and kept him from being the well adjusted man he should have been.

How much wiser Timmy's mother would have been had she taken a cue from Susan's mother.

Susan was afraid too. But when her mother found out what was troubling her, she bought a little night light and put it in Susan's room. And sometimes, when Susan seemed especially fearful, her mother sat by her bed and talked with her reassuringly.

"Everything is all right, honey," she would tell her. "Mother and Daddy are here in the next room and we'll leave the door open. Then if you need us, you can call us. But even better than that, Jesus is right here with you all of the time. You know that He loves you. We all love you, darling, and we're going to take care of you."

It wasn't long until Susan forgot that she had ever been afraid—and all through her life she learned to combat fear with confidence.

GOD AND FEARS

Yes, there are many reasonable, effective ways to minimize fear, both in our own lives and in the lives of others. And God expects us to use the intelligence that He has given us.

But human techniques are not enough. At best, our wisdom and understanding are hampered by human limitations. Psychological needs met solely on this level are never met adequately. *It is God who completely understands our basic needs.* And He has made provision to meet them in ways far superior to man's.

Several years ago I received a telephone call that I shall always remember. As I picked up the receiver, a lady's voice said, "Dr. Narramore, I'm Mrs. Newton. I have some serious problems and I would like to make an appointment to see you."

I explained that my schedule was filled for some time ahead and I told her that I was sorry but I would be unable to see her.

Yet she persisted. She went on to say that she had heard me speak over the radio and felt that I was the only one who could *really* help her. She told me how she had gone to "nearly everyone in Hollywood and Los Angeles" but how she was "no better off" than when she started.

Since I receive many calls from Christians who need counsel, I took it for granted that she too was a believer. But in the course of our conversation, I remarked, "I suppose that you know the Lord."

"Who?"

"I suppose you know the Lord."

"No, Dr. Narramore, I don't believe that I do. I don't believe I've ever met him. Does he live around here?"

I was taken back. I knew then that God would have me arrange my schedule so that I could see her at least for a short time.

"Hold the phone," I told her, "I'll see what I can do to squeeze in an appointment for you." So I shaved off a little time here and there from several of my appointments and managed to scrape up half an hour that I could give her.

Three o'clock the next afternoon found Mrs. Newton seated in my office. She was a middle-aged lady, rather tall, well dressed and nice appearing. As we talked together, I found that she was a forthright, intelligent, reasonable person. After a few minutes I asked her to describe her difficulty.

"Well," she said, "I don't know what's wrong, but something is. Things aren't going right in my marriage. But that's not the only trouble. I am never satisfied and I don't have any peace. I seem to feel afraid inside, but I can't put my finger on any one particular thing. Oh, my fears aren't big—but just little ones that keep nagging at me all the time."

"What have you done about it?" I asked.

"Well," Mrs. Newton replied, "I made up my mind I had to do *something*. So I talked with a friend of mine who told me she thought my trouble was all personality centered, and that I ought to take a course in personality development. So I followed her suggestion and enrolled in a class where nearly fifty people met each week. We spent a lot of time talking about our problems, and we also wrote a short autobiography. A little later on we used much of our class time in public speaking. Most of us gave several short talks while the other members of the class evaluated our speeches in terms of self-confidence and personality development."

"How did you get along?" I asked.

"Very well," she said. "In fact, at the end of the first term the class voted me as having made the most progress in the group. Well, that was encouraging, so I decided to take the second term. This time I got along so well that the teacher asked me to be her assistant. When she wasn't there, I took over the class and taught it myself. And once again, when the term was over I was chosen as the one who had made the greatest improvement. In fact, they gave me a lovely pen and pencil set as a prize for having won this honor."

"Do you feel that you were really helped?" I asked her.

"Certainly not!" Mrs. Newton replied emphatically. Then shaking her head sadly, she continued, "If *I* was the one who had made the most improvement, I pity the others. Of course, I learned a little about speaking in public and I learned that other people have similar problems to mine. But I can't truthfully say that I felt any different after the courses than I did before I started."

"What did you do after that?"

"Well, at first I didn't know what to do. But after a while I got to thinking about the teacher of the class. We had become quite friendly during the course of the year and I thought that perhaps she could help me. So I went over to see her."

"And what happened?"

"Oh, not much! It was really kind of silly now that I look back on it. You see, when I told this lady about my fears and how I was afraid that I was losing my husband, she said she feared that she was losing hers too. She told me how she had let her first and second husbands slip right through her fingers. 'But,' she said, 'I'm not going to let that happen again. And since we are both afraid that we may lose our husbands, I'd suggest that we each set up an *ironclad* program to hold them.' "

Ironclad! I had to smile to myself. "That's strong," I said. "Did you do it?"

"No, Dr. Narramore. I realized that if she had such a serious problem herself, surely she wasn't in any condition to help *me*. She needed help more than I did."

"What did you do then?"

"To be very frank," she continued, "I didn't know what to do. I thought I had tried everything. Then yesterday I heard you speak over the radio and I decided that it might help if I could talk with you."

As we delved into her problem, I found that her childhood had been quite normal. Although her marriage had a few ups and downs, it was evidently fairly successful. Her financial condition was average. But the most important aspect of her life, the *spiritual*, was essentially blank. Except for a little Sunday school and church attendance now and then, nothing had ever happened.

Here, then, was my cue. I knew that this spiritual void in her life was the underlying cause of *all* her problems. So I started from the beginning and explained to her that God created man for Himself. People were never intended to go through life without the fellowship of their Maker. Without God, we have no purpose in life. We are like a ship sailing through a treacherous sea without a pilot. Destination—disaster! I explained how man, in his natural state, can have no communion or fellowship with God because God has a righteous, holy nature, and man has a sinful nature.

"But, Mrs. Newton," I added, "God loved us *so* much that He made a plan to bridge the gap, thus making it possible for us to get right with God."

Then I went on to tell her about God's plan—how He gave His only Son to atone for our sins and make peace for us. I told her that the Bible says, "Christ is our peace." In other words peace is not a state of mind. Peace is a Person. And that Person is Christ.

"Mrs. Newton," I asked, "have you ever invited Christ, the Prince of Peace, to come into your heart and life?"

She lowered her eyes for a moment, then said, "No, Dr. Narramore, I don't believe I ever have."

"Are you interested?"

"Oh yes," she answered. "It's all new to me, but I am *very* interested. In fact, I think this spiritual lack in my life may be the cause of my problem."

Then I asked her if she would like to accept Christ as her Saviour and invite Him to come into her heart and life.

"I surely would," she said. "I think this is just what I need."

So right then and there Mrs. Newton and I knelt in my office. "Dear God," she prayed. "I'm a sinner but I need You. Please come into my heart and save me. I promise that I'll serve You the rest of my life. For Jesus' sake. Amen."

When we stood up, her eyes glistened with moisture but her lips wore a smile. A look of peace swept across her face. I talked to her a minute more about what she had done in accepting Christ as her personal Saviour. Then I suggested that she read through the Gospel of John and memorize some verses—John 1:12; John 5:25 and John 10:28 were all excellent ones for a new Christian.

Mrs. Newton was a happy woman when she left that afternoon. She knew now that she was right with God and she was confident that He would guide her.

The following week I saw her once again. What a difference! She didn't even *look* the same. Now her countenance beamed with a radiance that reflected the peace and contentment of her soul.

As we talked she told me how she had already read several books of the Bible, had memorized a number of Scripture verses and had talked with God each day in prayer. No wonder she was growing—no wonder there was a change!

She looked up and smiled as she said, "Do you know, Dr. Narramore, I've had more *peace* this past week than I've had in my whole life!"

Her problems? Oh yes, she still had some. But now she had peace of heart and mind, knowing that God would help her over the rough places.

This fine lady found what she needed. True, her fears had not been too evident—but they were deep-seated in her nature and in her soul. She was not at rest, she had no peace—until Christ came into her heart. So it is with every human being. And not until we have been reconciled to God through His Son, Jesus Christ, can we ever know real peace and joy and the "perfect love that casteth out fear."

Life has its pleasant places—but it is far from a "bed of roses." As people reach adulthood they learn that life holds many tragedies. When confronted with illness, dread diseases, war, sudden failure, hunger, insecurity, severe injury, loneliness, old age and death, there is *cause* for fear. Our generation is rapidly distinguishing itself by the development of frightening new weapons of war. Earth satellites, guided missiles, interplanetary travel do not reassure the fearful heart of man.

But God, our Father, promises never to leave us nor forsake us. In our weakness He speaks to us, "Fear thou not; for I am with thee; be not dismayed; for I am thy God; I will strengthen thee . . ." (Isa. 41:10). And when tragedy comes God reassures us by saying, "When thou passest through the waters, I will be with thee; and through the rivers, they shall not overflow thee . . ." (Isa 43:2).

God does not promise escape from every fearful situation, but He does promise to walk with us through every experience! And we can be strong and unafraid because God is the strength of our life.

God tells us to "be *anxious* for *nothing*, but in everything by prayer and supplication with thanksgiving let your requests be made known unto God" (Phil. 4:6).

Here then, is a much better solution than being anxious. This solution is workable, while anxiety works nothing but havoc.

Just what does anxiety do? It does not empty tomorrow of its sorrow; but it does empty today of its strength. It does not make you escape the evil, it makes you unfit to cope with it when it comes. It does not bless tomorrow, but it robs today.

One basic fear common to all mankind is the fear of *death*. This is natural because deep inside the soul of every living creature is a strong desire to keep living. And indeed, death is grim, stark and unevasive. From childhood, every person knows that he is born to die. And when a person faces an unknown, uncertain eternity, he is a fool if he does not fear it.

I'll never forget the comment made by one of my professors at Columbia University. He was lecturing to a psychology class when he admitted that he was at a complete loss to know how to counsel about death.

"Students," he told us, "in all other cases of counseling I am confident, but in the face of death, there is *nothing* I can say."

Nothing? How hopeless! No wonder people are afraid!

But it doesn't need to be like this. Because Christ has *conquered* death, thereby taking away its sting and ugliness. And when we trust in Christ as our personal Saviour, eternity is a *bright and glorious prospect!* Death no longer is something to be feared—but rather something to be anticipated. Why? Because the child of God knows that to be absent from the body is "to be present with the Lord."

So for the Christian, death should hold no fear. And like the apostle Paul we too can say, "For me to live is Christ, but to die is gain" (Phil. 1:21). At death, the unsaved man has everything to lose. But the saved has everything to gain!

God has given us a wonderful promise—one that can dispel all fear. He says, "Lo, I am with you alway, even unto the end of the world" (Matt. 28:20).

This means, then, that circumstances cannot sever us from Him. It means that surroundings cannot hide God's face from us. He is always near and dear to those who are truly His own. Tests may come. He is

near. Trials may come. He is still near. Sickness may
lay us low. He is by our side. Death may come, He still
says, "Lo, I am with you alway." Nothing will be able
to separate us from His love. Truly, we can say with
the psalmist, "Yea, though I walk through the valley of
the shadow of death, *I will fear no evil. for thou art*
with me" (Ps. 23:4).

Peace of mind? Yes, it's part of the Christian's
built-in blessing. Yet there are some Christians who do
not appropriate this peace. True, they belong to God—
but they do not *rely* on Him. They take affairs into
their own hands and become upset and fearful. How
unnecessary. How foolish. Happiness is at their command if they will only "cast their burden upon the
Lord." Then, they too can say, "The Lord is my *light*
and my *salvation;* whom shall I fear? The Lord is the
strength of my life; of whom shall I be *afraid*?" (Ps.
27:1). What does God give us? Light. Salvation. But
that is not all—He gives us strength and *no* fear!

Dr. Gilbert L. Little is a prominent physician with
years of experience as a private psychiatrist and as
head of a large American hospital. In his book, *Nervous Christians,** Dr. Little throws light on the subject
of Christians who have fears. He emphasizes the following causes and solutions.

1. *Fear begins to enter a Christian's life the moment he starts losing close fellowship with God.*

Where does fear come from? Not from God. God is
love. And "there is no fear in love" (I John 4:18).
When we move away from God we leave the center of
love and peace. God never creates disturbance in the
heart of the consecrated believer. "For God is *not* the
author of confusion, but of peace . . ." (I Cor. 14:33).

With God we have nothing to fear. He is our Father.

---

* Little, Gilbert L., *Nervous Christians* (1956, Good News Broadcast-
ing Association, Inc.). Now published by Moody Press. Used by permission.

He cared for us in His infinite wisdom and love. What could be more reassuring? What could be more complete? Truly, when we "*abide* under the shadow of the Almighty" we have nothing to fear. So it is that the Christian who is in close harmony with God has no real cause for fear.

Is there fear in your heart? Then check your fellowship with God.

2. *When a believer begins to lose his close fellowship with God, he usually tries to cover up, seek his own devices, make excuses and use various compensation mechanisms.*

Adam did. And so did Eve. When they turned away from God, they attempted to cover up their guilt, fear and sin. And their descendants (you and I) are no different. We are still doing this today.

Adam and Eve did not turn back to God—the One they had offended. They did not beg forgiveness. Instead ... "they sewed fig leaves together, and made themselves aprons" (Gen. 3:7). This was man's solution to hide his nakedness and sin. Christians are busy sewing "aprons" today—church "aprons" and many other kinds of "aprons."

We have no record that Adam feared while he loved God and communed with Him. He feared *after* he sinned. Spiritual Christians testify to this Scriptural truth today: as long as they love God and follow His will for their lives, they have no fear.

3. *When a Christian develops rather serious fears, he may tend to avoid counsel from a deeply spiritual person.*

When the Lord asked the disciples if they also would go away (to the world) Peter answered the question by saying, "Lord, to whom shall we go? Thou hast the words of eternal life" (John 6:68).

"To whom *shall* we go?"

Spiritual Christians should not expect non-Christians to help them with their problems of fear and anxiety, because non-Christians cannot understand soul problems. It is unfair to expect them to grasp spiritual things, which can be discerned only by the Spirit of God within the Christian.

It seems that most Christians, after suffering for many years, just assume that God has overlooked and forgotten the time when they turned to the world and forsook their "first love." Most of these people have really not repented of their backsliding, but have taken on religious or other works as a covering for sin. And when they do attempt to return to God, Satan discourages them by blocking their prayers and hindering the reading of the Word.

It is not unusual for Christians to decide quite suddenly, even during the period of psychotherapy, "I think I can go home and work out my problem by myself. I know what I should do." But sooner or later they go elsewhere for treatment.

Clients who have been "let down," in prior consultations tread warily the next time. Their complaint is, "I told him everything, but he didn't do a thing for me." These situations are unfortunate, but Christians should *not expect* the ungodly to help them resolve problems that have a spiritual cause. It is rebellion on the part of God's redeemed children, who are blood-bought, to turn from Him and go to the world with their spiritual problems.

The spiritual Christian trusts Christ to lead him much like a child trusts his father to lead him by the hand through difficult and fearful places. This does not take away the *object* of fear, or make him forget it. But now he is no longer afraid, because he trusts his father. And since God is our Heavenly Father, He leads us to overcome our fears.

4. *The way back to peace of mind is through confession, turning to Christ and walking daily with Him.*

Most people who are fearful would give anything to have their minds free from anxiety and worry. But this is not accomplished by treating symptoms. One must confess the things that made him anxious and guilty. Confession, however, must have a basis more substantial than a psychological release, which many people experience by merely confessing something. If there is to be a lasting therapeutic value in confession, man must come to the understanding that only confession from the heart and repentance toward God will bring healing to his soul and peace to his mind.

Confession does not imply a lengthy analysis of the subconscious memory. But the Christian does need to see how he was led to stray from God and how to find his way back to Calvary.

One of psychotherapy's big problems is to help a person see that his suffering developed over a long period of time, and that he cannot expect a few psychiatric consultations to do anything miraculous for him. He needs to go back ... back; for it is usually a long way back to the place where he lost his "first love." The Lover of his soul has been pushed into the background and now he is preoccupied with himself.

The Christian who is afraid must turn his thoughts back to Calvary and get a fresh vision of Christ's redemptive love for him. *He must meditate, moment by moment*, on what Christ did and how He overcame for him.

In addition to Dr. Little's four basic considerations of fear, there are undoubtedly some fears that may be traced in part to physical origins. Remember the case of Jane White, the young lady who in desperation got off the bus and called me from the phone booth? Diagnosis indicated that her serious emotional and fearful state stemmed partially from a glandular malfunction. Medication not only gave her temporary relief, but it also undoubtedly helped to restore a proper chemical balance in the body. She also responded favorably to counseling from a Christian psychologist. Yes, Jane was a believer, but little did she realize how far she had strayed from God. The road back to Calvary was long and tedious. But through complete confession and submission she entered God's glorious joy and light.

True consecration to God, abundant prayer, and a continual feeding upon His Word provide the Christian with a way of life that dispels fear. It is then that "the peace of God, which passeth all understanding, shall *keep your hearts and minds* through Christ Jesus" (Phil. 4:7).

Surely, when we trust in Christ and lean hard on Him, we can say, "God hath not given us the spirit of fear; but of power, and of love and of a sound mind" (II Tim. 1:7).

Economic Security

ICE CRACKLED beneath the sleigh as the swift team of huskies pulled across the frozen terrain. Only the occasional bark of the dogs or the snap of the driver's whip interrupted the sound of the howling wind. Although it was only mid-afternoon, the sky was dark against the gleaming whiteness of the barren glaciers. This was Winter. And in Eskimo land the sun had gone to bed for the season.

Two fur-clad figures clung to the rear of the sleigh— Roy Atungurach, the driver, and his ten-year-old son, Tom. The sleigh was mostly filled with their cargo— a polar bear, two large seals and a barrel of fish.

A hunting expedition? Indeed! But these two Eskimos were not returning from an excursion that had been planned merely for pleasure and sportsmanship. They were struggling for the bare necessities of life—for food, shelter and clothing. And in their primitive culture, fishing and hunting supplied these needs.

True, Eskimos like Roy and Tom Atungurach do not spend a minute worrying about money for a new car or for dental bills or for health insurance or for education. But theirs is a day-to-day battle for food and clothing. Their quest for economic security is starkly real and brutally exhausting.

And while Eskimos are battling the economic problems of an unkind climate, the oil company executive in California is maneuvering just as fiercely against the economic forces he confronts. His college-age daughter demands a new sports car and Fifth avenue clothes to keep up with her sorority sisters. His insurance premiums are staggering. Taxes have soared. The upkeep on his $75,000 home is more than he bargained for. And in the shadowy background is the uneasy fear that he may lose his high-paying job, or if he does keep it, he will be unable to live on a retirement check of $750 a month.

Fortunately, these extremes don't affect the majority. Most of us are somewhere in between. But wherever we are—whatever our station or rank, *we all have a genuine need for at least a measure of economic security*. And this need is basic—not only to our physical well being, but also to our mental health. It is more than materialistic; it is psychological as well.

We *all* like to believe that some day we will be financially secure, that we will be able to retire comfortably in old age. We are hopeful that as the "rocking chair" days come, we will be able to pay our own way —not to be a burden on others. This is a natural desire of the human heart. And it's commendable.

But even a quick glance at our world tells us that people often go to *extremes*. This one insatiable drive seems to control their motives: "We must have financial security!"

THE SCURRY FOR SECURITY

Every day millions of people feverishly expend their energies in activities which they hope will make them economically secure. With one eye on the bank account, they work days, nights, Sundays and overtime to bring in a few more dollars.

Some are overly concerned about the success of their business. They try nearly every trick of the trade to make their profits soar.

Housewives bravely fight the battle of the bargain. Anything to save a few pennies—even if they have to go out of their way to do it!

Others worry about stocks and bonds. Each day a

great network of communication advises people when to buy and when to sell. Blood pressures rise and fall with the temperamental fluctuations of Wall Street.

Insurance salesmen use countless "confidential" techniques to persuade the average man that he "cannot afford to be without adequate protection." After all, the salesman argues, "You owe it to yourself and to your family."

So it is in every realm of life. People work, strive and connive to assure themselves that they will be secure. True, we *do* need to provide for today and save for a "rainy day"—but most people seem to forget that God owns the cattle on a thousand hills. And so they eagerly stash away money and possessions without even giving God so much as a second thought.

After that it is only a matter of time: money looms up so big and important that it blots out real values and it practically becomes a god. This is the beginning of trouble. Because God warns that "the *love* of money is the root of all evil" (I Tim. 6:10).

ATTITUDES AND HEALTH

Man's inner drive to accumulate wealth usually goes far beyond the desire to meet his actual needs. It passes the point of "making a living." If possible, most people will settle for nothing less than protection against every emergency. And it is this ceaseless human search for financial security that often leads a man into difficulty. Hard work and constant struggle take their toll on the human body. But an even greater menace is hidden in the worry and concern involved. These affect both man's physical and mental condition.

Ralph Blake, for example, was such a victim. He was only in his thirties but he had complained of extremely poor health for some time. After a thorough physical examination, his doctor diagnosed the illness as one that was undoubtedly brought on by emotional tensions.

"Ralph," the doctor explained, "you need the services of a psychiatrist."

"What?" Blake exclaimed. "I may be sick, Doc, but I'm not crazy!"

"No, you're not crazy, and you probably never will be," assured the doctor. "But I think your worries and tensions have become so firmly fixed that you will need a specialist to help you find your way out. I doubt if you can get to feeling like you should until you resolve these feelings."

As Blake took trips to the psychiatrist's office the truth came to the top. The major causes of his nervous condition were the constant fears of not being able to support his family and not being able to handle financial emergencies should they arise.

Since the time he was a small boy, Blake's father had impressed on him the need for financial security. "Son," his father would admonish, "life is a very serious matter, and if you don't want to starve to death, you'd better work and save every cent you can." His parents often reminded him that people who were not able to pay their bills were taken to jail. They warned him against getting married early and having a family for whom he couldn't provide. In short, they filled his mind with so much concern that they were partially responsible for bringing about a condition in Ralph's life that he could not handle.

Like Ralph, there are many people who are disturbed by the fear of not being able to meet their needs throughout life. This serious, insistent worry takes its toll on both mind and body. For most of these people there are only "a few ways out." Very often it's sickness—and sometimes even suicide.

ADULTS CAN HELP

Parents and teachers are key people. They have the privilege of helping children and young people develop healthy attitudes toward financial matters.

Children should not be exposed to embarrassment because of low economic status. Neither should they be catered to because their father "owns the town." Adults can point out that greatness does not depend upon finances. Children should learn that many great people have had meager, humble beginnings.

Interestingly enough, the size of a family's bank account does not necessarily determine the attitudes that prevail in the home. Wise parents, whether rich or poor, do not subject their children to needless anxiety about economic security.

True, children must learn the value of money. The sooner they discover that money doesn't "grow on trees," the better off they will be. But when parents place *undue emphasis* on finances, unhealthy attitudes are fostered. The home should not put a premium on the accumulation of money; rather, it should encourage stewardship. Parents should teach children to pray for their needs. When boys and girls are impressed with the fact that God has unlimited resources and always cares for His own, they naturally learn to *trust* instead of *worry*.

Financial pressures visit most families at one time or another. But these need not throw them off balance. In fact, parents can take difficult times and turn them into opportunities to build constructive, positive attitudes toward finances. Two children from different homes, yet with similar financial means, may develop completely *opposite* attitudes toward financial security. The difference? Their parents. One child was give a materialistic outlook. The other received a confident point of view based upon trust in God.

OUR PART

We have all heard the saying, "God helps those who help themselves." And this is largely true. God never endorses laziness. He does not intend that we should do nothing, then expect Him to supply our needs. The

Bible tells us that if we do not work, neither should we eat (II Thess. 3:10). We must do our part. And this not only includes earning a living but also wise financial planning.

Wise planning? Indeed! This is just as important as earning power. Thoughtful planning is the oil that makes the wheels of success run smoothly. It prevents us from getting into financial difficulties.

Because we live in a free country, we have the opportunity to do something about our economic security. Most of us have a fairly constant income. Starting with this figure, it's a wise person who sets up a budget. And don't be afraid to do it!

You don't have to be a mathematical genius to develop a workable plan. "Workable" because if you try to follow a budget that is unreasonable, you will only add to your sense of insecurity. Be realistic. Note your fixed expenses—rent or house payments, utilities, food, installment payments. Then allot something *each* month for clothes, medical expenses, insurance, automobile maintenance. Always leave a certain amount for miscellaneous. You'll be glad you did!

Most dedicated Christians set aside at least a tenth of their total income for the Lord's work. This should come first. And it is a good plan to put at least a small amount into a savings account each month.

This is just a rough outline. Each person will want to adapt it to his own needs.

The main thing is to be *realistic*. One young couple I know nearly wrecked their marriage because they were not. Bill was a school teacher. He and his wife, Mary, had been married only a short time when they began to dream about a home of their own. They started saving, and when they thought they had enough money for a down payment, they started looking. Both had come from fine homes and naturally they wanted something nice themselves.

However, they found that new homes in the area

where they wanted to live started at $20,000. Realizing that they could not handle anything that high, they finally settled on a 12-year-old house with a rustic beamed ceiling and two used brick fireplaces. Price: $16,950.

They didn't have enough down payment to qualify for a lower interest FHA loan so they had to use conventional methods. A reputable company loaned $11,950 and after the down payment there was a second trust deed of $3,000 at 6.6 per cent interest. The realty broker said they could pay it off at $25.00 a month with a three-year due date. Payments on the first and second deeds totaled $124.00 a month, not including taxes.

They moved in. And three years moved by all too rapidly. Each year taxes climbed higher until the monthly tax bill alone was $30.00. This meant house payments of $154.00 a month.

Then came the shock. The three-year due date on the second deed was up. They had been paying $25.00 a month on it but some $16.00 of that had gone into interest. They now owed a lump sum of approximately $2,500.

They hadn't been able to save a penny since moving into their home. Now it was almost impossible to refinance the loan. Tension was tight and under the strain Bill developed an ulcer. Mary blamed him for not getting out of the teaching profession and into a job that would provide more money. In time, trouble spread from one area of their marriage to another. The picture wasn't pretty.

Fortunately, before their marriage went completely to pieces, they sat down with pencil and paper and together they did some old-fashioned figuring. For the first time since their marriage they took a realistic attitude toward their present and future economic status.

The problem was so simple that afterward these two

intelligent young people were amazed that they hadn't seen it long before: They sold their house and bought a cheaper one where the total payments, including taxes, were within their budget.

Bill and Mary, however, are not the only ones who have found themselves in this kind of deep water. People are constantly falling into the snare of buying beyond their means. They think they must "keep up with the Jones'." This makes them easy prey for the "easy payment plan." After a while it takes an accountant to keep track of all the payments. And the victims find that they are trapped: there are just *too many* bills to meet. The "easy payments" have become hard ones.

Almost all of us have times when we face difficulties. It is one of the most common problems of mankind. But the measure to which God will bless us depends largely upon how much common sense we use to face the situation realistically and honestly.

God expects us to plan for the future. Remember the story of Pharaoh? God warned him in a dream to save in the time of plenty for the lean years that were to come. The dream went like this: seven fat cattle were devoured by seven lean ones, and seven full ears of corn were consumed by seven thin ears. When Joseph was called upon to interpret this dream, he told Pharaoh that God was warning them to save in the time of their prosperity for the period when famine would visit the land. They did just that. And not only were the people of Egypt spared but they were able to help those who came to them from surrounding countries (Gen. 41).

Should we do less? When God blesses us financially, we need to remember that as His stewards it is our God-given responsibility to use our money wisely. Planning for the future makes sense. And just as God advised Pharaoh to do this, so He would have *us* save for the lean years.

Everyone makes mistakes—we don't always plan

wisely. And when this happens we must be mature enough to face the situation. The first step is to admit our error and ask God's forgiveness. Then we must call upon Him for guidance. Having done this, we are in a position where God can bless us.

GOD'S PART

Although man spends much of his life in quest of security, it is sobering to realize that *there is actually no such thing as absolute financial security*—even for the richest. Any one of a multitude of tragedies may visit a family, leaving it financially destitute. And with the development of atom bombs, hydrogen bombs, cobalt bombs and intercontinental ballistic missiles to carry them, people are brought gravely face to face with the stark fact that their savings will not guarantee them the financial security they had carefully planned.

What then is the answer? Is there no way for man to be economically secure?

No, not on a human level. But this answer is *not* hopeless. We *can* be economically secure—without any threat of failure. How? By committing our lives to the providence of God through His son, Jesus. The Bible tells us that "God shall supply all your need according to His riches in glory by Christ Jesus" (Phil. 4:19).

"All"—"According to *His riches* in glory!" Could anything be more complete? However, we must realize that God promises to supply our *"needs"*—not every whim and selfish desire.

That He "shall supply" is a *guarantee* made by God to His own children. If we trust in Christ as our personal Saviour He forgives us our sins and gives us eternal life. It is then that God becomes our Father. Because He is holy and cannot look upon sin, we must first settle the sin question by asking forgiveness and taking Christ into our lives. Not until then can we claim this "guarantee"; not until then do we have the right to expect His blessings.

God loves His own and He always cares for them. David attested this truth when he said, "I have been young and now am old; yet have I not seen the righteous forsaken, nor his seed begging bread" (Ps. 37:25).

When the Israelites journeyed through the wilderness, God met their needs—not just once, but for the entire forty years. He fed them manna from heaven, gave them water from the rock; and clothed them with garments that did not wear out. "Thy raiment waxed not old upon thee; neither did thy foot swell these forty years" (Deut 8:4). Security? This was it!

And when the multitudes, hungry and weary, thronged about Christ, He did not ignore their physical need. But He took the lunch of a little lad, blessed it and fed them all. Not only did everyone have ample to eat but there was food to spare—twelve baskets full.

God has never ceased caring for those who trust in Him. He is doing it today.

It was during my college days that I became acquainted with a woman who was a living example of this truth. Mrs. Coldwell, a widow with two children, lived near the campus and often invited Christian students into her home for fellowship. This refined, deeply spiritual lady was a great blessing to all of us. She made her humble living by giving music lessons. At times when her pupils were ill and unable to come for lessons, she could not meet her expenses. But Mrs. Coldwell was never defeated—she trusted in a *great* God.

"God knows, and I'm not worrying," she would often say. "Surely He who changed my life, can somehow send in the insignificant sum of thirty dollars."

And God always did!

Years ago, George Mueller, one of England's great Christians and a mighty man of faith, established an orphanage. At times the money ran low and circumstances were trying. But George Mueller believed in prayer and trusted God to meet their needs.

One morning as he and the children sat down for breakfast there was no milk for their cereal. But a small thing like *milk* didn't alter his faith.

"Children," he explained, "although we don't have any milk as yet, we are going to go right ahead and thank God for it just the same. Our Heavenly Father knows about our needs and I am sure He will provide."

Then as they bowed their heads in grateful thanks for something that as yet they did not have, a sudden, loud knock at the door interrupted their prayer.

George stopped praying. "Children," he told them, "this may be God's answer to our prayer."

The door swung open and there stood a milkman. He explained that his wagon had broken down in the street and that he was having to dispose of the milk.

With a smile on his lips, George Mueller lifted his eyes toward heaven and whispered, "Thank You, Lord. I *knew* You would provide."

George Mueller had remarkable faith. But we too can believe God. When we trust Him implicitly, we find a sweet, intimate fellowship which is beyond description. It is then that we find real peace because we are confident that God will not fail us.

Happiness is not dependent upon financial reserves or other types of so-called securities. The happiest people in the world are those who daily trust God to provide their needs, realizing that His storehouse is unlimited and that He cares for them.

Does God care? Enough to be interested in the details of our need? Yes, indeed. Christ said, "Are not two sparrows sold for a farthing? and one of them shall not fall on the ground without your Father. But the very hairs of your head are all numbered. Fear ye not therefore, ye are of more value than many sparrows" (Matt. 10:29-31).

The very hairs of your head are all numbered! Such

detail! Surely, if God is *this* interested in you, He will not neglect your needs. He *wants* to care for you.

If you are a Christian worried about economic security, pour out your heart to God and ask Him to undertake for you. Ask Him to transform your mind so you can see that ultimate security lies not in money but in *Himself*. When He gives you this new transformed attitude, He will flood your heart with peace.

Worry about financial security is like a little stream of fear trickling through the soul. But faith will dry up this annoying stream. Faith and worry do not go together. They cannot both share the same heart or mind. The child of God who believes sincerely that all things work together for his good cannot worry very long. Worry never blesses; it always blights. It upsets digestion and robs of sleep. It makes one irritable. It destroys peace and embitters thinking.

The solution is (1) earnest, daily prayer (2) continual reading of His word and (3) trusting completely that God will not fail. *Prayer and Bible reading build faith.* If we are children of God, let us stop worrying. Why worry when we can *read, pray* and *believe?*

As a child of God we have resources that are hidden to the world. Let us never permit fear of the future to rob us of our joy today.

When we are in the place where God wants us to be, we have no real reason to be concerned about our needs. God promises to provide. With His leading comes His provision. He never separates the two. When we make our own decisions we are on our *own*. But when we follow Him, our present and our future are with God.

Vance Havner, prominent Christian leader, points this out in the story of Elijah, the prophet: "When God told Elijah to go to Cherith and hide there by the brook, He added, 'I have commanded the ravens to feed thee *there*.'

"Later God told Elijah to go to Zerephath and

'dwell *there.*' And added, 'I have commanded a widow woman *there* to sustain thee.' No, He did not promise to feed Elijah just *anywhere.* He did not say, 'Just ramble over the country anywhere you like and I will feed you.' It was limited to *there,* the place of God's will.

"God provides only where He guides. The place of his purpose is the place of His power and His provision. But we must be *there.*"

God does provide if we have the right relationship to Him and are obedient to His will. It is sometimes difficult to take the steps of faith necessary for God to reveal His power and wisdom.

Paul and Louise Gates, a young married couple, were meeting their regular monthly expenses when suddenly an emergency came. It demanded considerable money. And they just didn't have that much. For as long as they had been Christians, they had tithed. God had always blessed them. But now an emergency!

"Honey," Paul said to Louise, "what shall we do? If we skip our tithe we can meet our bills. We can make up our tithe later."

"No, Paul," Louise answered. She shook her head as she added, "That wouldn't be right. Our tithe belongs to the Lord *first.* We've always paid our tithe and I don't think we should stop now. I believe that if we honor God and obey Him by paying our debt to Him, He will somehow see us through this financial struggle."

Paul thought a moment. Then stepping over and placing a kiss on his wife's forehead he agreed, "You're right, dear. I'm glad you feel this way about it. We'll pay our tithe as usual and we'll trust the Lord to meet our need."

That evening a friend dropped in to say "hello." After a few minutes he said, "By the way, my wife and I received an unexpected check in the mail the other day. We've prayed about it and we feel led to give a portion of it to you folks. Use it in whatever way you wish."

Paul and Louise looked at each other in utter amazement. How delighted they were—and grateful! When they opened the envelope they saw that the check was made for exactly the amount of their need. God had not failed them. And they were glad that they had not failed Him.

It always pays big dividends to be obedient unto God. The widow of Zarephath is an example of this (I Kings 17:8-16). Things were in a terrible condition— famine and drought in the land. People were dying of hunger every day. Yet, when Elijah came and asked that she prepare him a cake with her last handful of meal and last cup of oil, she was obedient to God. She could have said, "I'm sorry, Elijah, but I'm awfully hard up and I need the food for my own family. Charity begins at home, you know."

How fortunate for her that she did not. Because if she had refused to feed Elijah, she would have been spelling her own doom. She could have saved the meal and the oil for her own use—but after they were gone, she and her son would have starved to death. But because she obeyed God and left her security in His hands, He honored her by continually replenishing the source.

Notice that God did not give her a full year's supply of meal and oil at one time. Instead He met her needs day by day. "And the barrel of meal wasted not, neither did the cruse of oil fail, according to the Word of the Lord" (I Kings 17:16).

So it is today. God may not shower us with large sums of money all at once (although He might), but He does meet our needs as they arise. It is precious this way. We do not become so interested in our financial prosperity that we forget about the Giver. Instead, we trust Him for our "daily bread."

Plan wisely? Yes, prayerfully plan for the future.

But always realize that true economic security stems only from God. He alone knows your needs and is able to provide day by day. "For your heavenly Father knoweth that ye have need of all these things. But seek ye first the kingdom of God, and his righteousness, and *all these things shall be added unto you*" (Matt. 6:32, 33).

Yours is a great God, and the future is safe—*in his hands!*

Your Unique Contribution

IT WAS MONDAY morning when Susan Williams spied the postman coming down the street. As she hurried out to meet him he greeted her with, "Good morning, Mrs. Williams. You must be expecting something special."

"Well, I am . . . in a way," Mrs. Williams said.

The postman thumbed through his letters and smilingly handed her one.

"Oh," she said, "it's just the one I was looking for!"

She tore open the envelope and read the letter two lines at a time. "Oh, it's wonderful!" she exclaimed. "They accepted it. They've *really* accepted it!"

"Accepted what?" he asked.

"My song!" she said. "For some time I've been working on a composition, and now a publisher has agreed to publish it."

"Well, isn't that just fine," said the postman. "I didn't know you wrote music."

"Oh, yes," she replied. "I've written many songs but they've never been published. You don't know how I've always wanted to write something that would live on and on—and now my dream has come true!"

Actually, all of us are like Mrs. Williams. Deep down in our hearts is a desire to make some worthwhile contribution to life. Men and women want to be remembered as having given something unique to the world. The engineer dreams of spanning a great gorge —a bridge that will be acclaimed for years after he has gone. The athlete trains arduously to win and set a record. The artist strives for a masterpiece. Parents like to instill into their children thoughts and sayings which will influence generations to come. And who among us hasn't secretly wished that he might write a book? Or even a story? Or perhaps just a poem (if not more than a few lines), which would distinguish us from others?

People everywhere are seeking some magic key that will unlock the door to a more meaningful life. Little wonder then that psychologists and psychiatrists are in general agreement that one of the basic psychological needs of all human beings is to make a worthwhile, unique contribution to life. And unless this need is met, we cannot be our best—physically, emotionally, or spiritually.

How It Affects Us

Dr. Foster knew the Mason family well. One morning when he was out for a walk we passed by the Mason home and noticed Grandma Mason sitting on the porch. "Good morning, Mrs. Mason," he greeted. "How are you feeling?"

"Not so well," she replied.

"Oh no?" the doctor inquired. "What's your trouble?"

"I don't know. I guess I'm just wearing out. Nothing to do. Children all raised and gone. Nothing to occupy my mind. I'm just a burden, I suppose."

As the doctor walked on down the street he kept thinking about Mrs. Mason. *When I see her children,* he thought, *I'll tell them what she needs. Not medicine, but a feeling that she still has a worthwhile place to fill in life.*

The wise doctor wasted no time in getting this message across to the rest of the family. "But what should we do?" they asked. "Grandma isn't strong enough to do any physical work. Anyway, she doesn't need to. We're happy just to have her with us."

"I know," the doctor assured them, "but there are other things she can do."

Then he went on to suggest that they ask her advice on the decisions they make, that they let her know how they count on her prayers.

The Masons took the doctor's advice. And it wasn't long before Grandma began to feel much better. Now she had some real incentives. Out of the wealth of her rich experience she was able to guide and counsel her loved ones and to have a real ministry of prayer. She now felt that she was making a worthwhile contribution. Life took on renewed zest and meaning.

Yes, this is a basic psychological need. We all need to feel that we are contributing something worthwhile. And failure to meet this need is as serious in adulthood as it is in childhood. Such neglect is often reflected in one's physical and mental health. To be happy, to have a dynamic balance amid stress and strain, to be at one's best, each of us needs to feel that day by day he is accomplising something worthwhile. It is important to our personalities, our mental attitudes, and to our physical health.

Boredom is a pitiful thing. It gnaws at the center of our sense of well being. And many people are bored. Bored with routine work. Eight hours a day. Uninspiring job. No challenge. The same thing over and over. Day in and day out. If it isn't a time clock, it is the monotonous task of washing dishes, fixing lunches, washing clothes and cleaning house! It matters not the setting—the routine task is there. And it's drab. Boringly drab.

This is an unhealthy state. Continued boredom warps our personalities. We become sour and uninteresting. To draw the best out of us, we need to be challenged. So the things we do should be significant.

Yes, life without purpose *is* dull. But when we have a goal in life, the world takes on a different perspective. And as the things we do become meaningful, they give us real dynamic. It's the stuff that dreams are made of. And it adds zest and interest to life.

LIFE CAN BE MEANINGFUL

We have all heard the phrase, "Life can be beautiful!" But life can never be beautiful unless it is filled with n.eaning. This is the difference between significant living and ordinary, empty living.

The world is filled with people who strive to do some "great" thing. But after they achieve their goal— so what? They have made very little contribution to life. Why? Because their goals had little, if any, real significance. The purposes were too flimsy.

One night I attended a meeting of outstanding Christian educators. On my way home I turned on the car radio and tuned in on the news. A newscaster read a "Hollywood bulletin" about a seventeen-year-old screen star who had been awarded a year's contract for nearly one hundred thousand dollars. *What a contrast,* I thought. *The educators are moulding the minds and hearts of our future generations, but this "starlet"— well, what difference does it really make* whether she is *on* or *off* the stage?

To say that there are many important contributions to be made in life would be a gross understatement. The atomic age offers innumerable opportunities for investing our lives and influence. Human resources are sorely needed in every sphere of life. And the world is waiting for men and women who will contribute something significant.

You may have read the delightful book, *The Small Woman,* by Alan Burgess. This is a true story about Gladys Aylward, who at 26 was a parlor-maid in London. She longed to be a missionary to China but she lacked the education to pass the necessary examinations. One night in simple, child-like faith she took all the money she had—two pennies and one halfpenny— and laid it on her open Bible. Then this little parlor-maid prayed this sincere prayer: "O God, here's my Bible. Here's my money. Here's me. Use me, God."

And God did!

She arrived in Yangcheng penniless and unable to speak a word of Chinese. The people hated her because she was a foreigner. Even the children cursed her and threw cow dung at her. But Miss Aylward stuck it out and gradually the people began to trust her. She filled a home with orphans and ministered to their pysical needs as she gave them the Gospel. Her witness to our Saviour was so powerful that eventually even some of the proud, old Mandarin of Yangcheng publicly confessed their faith in Jesus Christ.

In a few short years this determined girl had risen from a humble parlor-maid to the exalted position of: Ambassador for Jesus Christ to the People of China.

But there is another side to this business of making a worthwhile contribution in life! For every one that should strike boldly out on a new course like Gladys Aylward, there are thousands who should stay right where they are.

The majority of us may never find life to be a stirring adventure of great deeds. For the most part, life is work. And much of it consists of routine, uninteresting work. Someone has to sack groceries at the market. Someone has to type letters and keep up the office files. Someone has to grease cars. Someone has to work at a drafting board. Someone has to mop kitchen floors.

Escaping from routine jobs is not the answer. Avoiding responsibility doesn't make a person happier.

When psychologists look into case studies they find that many unhappy people skip from job to job and even from town to town. But it seldom solves anything. Because the basic problems are usually not found in the job or the climate, but in the person. So no matter where the people go, their problems are still with them.

The solution then is: Be realistic. An old Latin proverb states it in this way, "A man cannot give what he hasn't got" (*Nil dat quod non habet*). So it is with us. We cannot give the world some great masterpiece of artistry if we do not possess the natural talent. Yes, we can only give what we have. "For unto whomsoever much is given, much shall be required" (Luke 12:48). God does not judge us by how many talents we have: *it is how we use the ones we do have.*

The Bible tells the story of a widow who did not have much to contribute. But she gave all she had and the Lord was pleased. "And Jesus sat over against the treasury . . . and many that were rich cast in much. And there came a certain poor widow and she threw in two mites, which make a farthing. And he called unto him his disciples, and saith unto them. Verily I say unto you, That this poor widow hath cast more in than all they which have cast into the treasury: For all they did cast in of their abundance; but she of her want did cast in all that she had, even all her living" (Mark 12:41-44).

We can't all be big, ostentatious chandeliers in the main lobby. Some of us must light the little back hallway. But the lesser lights make just as significant a contribution as the flashy chandelier. In fact, many times they are needed more.

There is no honest task that can't be done to the glory of God. Brother Lawrence in his classical book of the sixteenth century, *Practicing the Presence of God,* tells how as a cook he was humbly delighted to stir a cake or pick up a straw from the floor for the glory of God.

When we see our station in life through the eyes of a Brother Lawrence we are getting close to the secret of making a genuinely worthwhile contribution in life. "Whether therefore ye eat, or drink, or whatsoever ye do, do all to the glory of God" (I Cor. 10:31).

Do all to the glory of God! What could be a greater challenge! What could be more significant! This means that the most humble job in the world can become a glorious mission for our Saviour. And when we realize this, happiness is at our command.

NEVER TOO LATE

It's never too late to start doing something worthwhile.

Like the story of Mae Watson. From the time she was just a little girl, she had wanted to be an educator. She enjoyed children and had a real gift for teaching. But circumstances had kept her from attending college.

The years had passed all too quickly. And Mae became more and more dissatisfied with her routine office job. "I want to work with people," she said. "I want to help children."

Then one day she shocked all her friends. She left her desk and headed for college. "But Mae," her friends suggested, "aren't you a little *old* for college?"

"No," was Mae's plucky answer. "Of course, I may be older than the rest of the students. But I can't start any younger. And the longer I delay, the older I'll be."

So Mae started college. She soon discovered that age made little difference. The four years flew by. When she stepped up for her diploma she knew it had been well worth the effort.

There are many people like Mae. Sometimes it takes courage to step out of a rut, but it is always gratifying when you head toward your goal—no matter what your age.

In Southern California there is a fine Christian high school, Culter Academy, that was founded years ago by Mabel Culter. In 1954 Miss Culter, age 60, decided that being the president of a noted Christian school was fine, but that there were other pressing needs in the world.

She confided to her friends that she wanted to be a missionary to Korea!

"What?" they thought, "she can't really *mean* it—not at *her* age."

Her friends tried to persuade her that she was needed at the academy. ('They were too polite to tell her that she was simply "too old" for any mission board to accept). But their discouragement could not hold back Mabel Culter. She knew what she wanted and she went after it. Sixty? It did not bother her in the least. She applied to the Evangelical Alliance Mission (TEAM) and explained that her experience was just what was needed. And to the surprise of everyone, the mission board agreed. So off to Korea she flew to help establish an orphanage, a hospital and a Bible institute!

The quality of a person's contribution in life does not depend on age. True, youth has vigor. But maturity has the advantage of experience. Challenges are for those who accept them. God does not limit the applicants to a certain age bracket. It is never too late to do the job if God is calling you to it.

ENCOURAGING OTHERS

The greatest joys in life come as we invest ourselves in others. And every day offers an opportunity to do this—especially through encouraging those around us. The difference between a man who makes a significant, worthwhile contribution in life and the man who does not, is often one word: "encouragement." The Bible says that "Where there is no vision, the people perish ..." (Prov. 29:18).

It might be a boy down the street, a lady at church, the man at the office or a husband or wife. But "big things" hinge largely on encouragement.

Discouragement may attack anyone. When things go wrong a person may think, "I might as well give up." But your word of encouragement will give him a new impetus.

Many people do not know their potential. It often takes that extra little "boost" to get the ball rolling. There are people with real ability who never do anything about it. Why? Because they need someone to

give them confidence—they need to know others believe in them.

John is a good example. After high school he started
driving a truck for a local firm. But a neighbor realized
that John had a lot to offer and that he could be
making a much greater contribution to life if he had
the training. So one day the neighbor had a long talk
with John. He encouraged him to enroll in college the
next semester.

John did. Engineering was his choice. And several
years later John graduated and joined a large equipment firm.

It wasn't long before he started working on a special
project of his own. And in a few years John had
perfected it—an important piece of heavy-duty earth
moving equipment. Roadbuilders everywhere began to
use it. And before long many more motorists were
enjoying big, new highways.

Now John was making a significant contribution to
society. But little did people realize that the man
responsible for this was the "neighbor" who had
encouraged a teen-age truck driver to do something
worthwhile.

CONTRIBUTING FOR ETERNITY

Billy Graham has repeatedly said that without the
prayers of faithful believers his campaigns would be
monumental failures. And this is true of all Christian
activity. Spritual work is energized by the Holy Spirit.
Christians who fail to pray, fail to make one of their
great contributions. Think of the contribution you make
when you daily remember your pastor at the throne of
grace. Think of the contribution you make when you
pray for that missionary in some difficult place of the
world. Think of the contribution you make when you
pray for that loved one who has not yet come to the
Savior.

In God's Word we are admonished to pray: "Confess

your faults one to another, and pray one for another, that ye may be healed. The effectual fervent prayer of a righteous man availeth much" (James 5:16).

Some people feel that because of ill health or family obligations, they cannot contribute much to the work of the Lord. But they can. Any believer can enter into God's holy presence and pray. And prayer changes things—and people. Some of the greatest prayer warriors that this world has ever known have been crippled with disease and broken in body. Martha Snell Nicholson, for example, suffered years from numerous infirmities. Yet her life was radiant because she kept in constant contact with God through prayer. This dear woman was an inspiration and a blessing to countless thousands.

Do the cares of the home interfere? Then consider Susannah Wesley. She had nineteen children. Besides caring for her large family, she gave all of the children their educational training, teaching them herself. A busy woman? That's stating it mildly. But she was never too busy to pray. She prayed every day with each one of the children individually, besides praying for them alone. But it was worth it. Her prayers produced two mighty men of God that stirred all of Great Britain. Hers was a great contribution through prayer —and the names of her sons, John and Charles Wesley, stand as a towering tribute to their praying mother.

Another eternal contribution in life is that of *giving*. Churches could not preach the Gospel, Christian colleges and Bible schools could not train future leaders, gospel broadcasts could not go out over the air, if humble believers did not give. There would be few missionaries on the foreign fields if Christians did not give. When God's people give their money to further the Gospel, they are investing in *eternal souls*. Such contributions are so great that they cannot be measured.

I once heard a man say that the most annoying part of being a Christian was receiving appeals for donations. "It seems as though every Christian organization in the world is out after your money," he said.

I thought to myself, *Giving is one of the greatest joys of being a Christian. It is a privilege.* Each month my wife and I look forward to giving our tithes and offerings to various Christian organizations. Naturally we cannot give to every need, but it is a wonderful blessing to help the ones that God has placed upon our hearts.

When a person gives of his income, it represents his talent, his time, his earning power and his thinking. In short, when a person gives his money, in a sense he gives *himself*.

Most of us realize that "the harvest truly is plenteous, but the laborers are few" (Matt. 9:37). But it is also true that the *money is scarce.* Missionary leaders have told me that the greatest barrier to reaching unevangelized areas is not personnel—it is lack of *finances*. There are young people applying to mission boards today who may never be sent out. Why? Simply because there is no money to send them!

Not everyone is privileged to become a missionary. And few of us have the opportunity to reach the millions by radio. But we can all be on the team. How? By systematically tithing our income and giving our offerings unto the Lord. In this way, our money will have lasting value because we have invested for eternity.

Money isn't the only commodity we can give, however. Our time and our talent is just as valuable—and sometimes more so. When we give generously of our time, our training and our ability, we invest ourselves.

Our time. This is a precious item. And a personal one. The moments are here—and then they are gone forever. But we are held responsible for how these moments are used. God tells us to "redeem the time" —to take advantage of every minute. There is no better way to do this than to offer our time to God. Perhaps God wants you to spend time visiting the sick.

He may want you to open your home for a Bible class, or sew clothing for a missionary orphanage. Whatever it may be, time given to the Lord is time gained.

And our talents. Christ tells us not to "hide our light under a bushel" (Matt. 5:15). Since God has endowed us with every ability we have, we should use it for His glory. Perhaps it may be singing in the choir, or doing children's work, or counseling with young people. Whatever your talent is, develop it and use it for the Lord. This is your contribution—individually and *personally yours*.

Our belongings should also be dedicated to the Lord. When our home, our car, yes, everything we own is surrendered to the Lord, He can and will use them for His glory. Our temporal possessions then become implements of spiritual blessing.

God calls some of us into full-time Christian work. This is an honor and a sacred trust. When God calls us to some specific task, we dare not let it go unheeded. We *must* obey if we are to be effective Christians.

As we walk close to the Lord and to His will, He makes us channels of blessing. It is only then that we make a lasting contribution—one that will count for eternity.

THE GREATEST CONTRIBUTION

Children are always talking about what they are going to be when they "grow up." A nurse, a fireman, a circus clown! And as they reach adolescence, the picture begins to take more form. They realize that it is a decision they must eventually make. When they pass through their "turbulent teens" they spend more and more time thinking about how they might use their lives. Dr. Henrietta Mears, noted Christian leader, has often said, "The paramount issue with every young adult is, 'What am I going to do with my life?' "

It is only natural that we should want to know what

our greatest contribution in life might be. And we *can* know.

To learn the answer, we must turn to God's Word, the Bible. There we see that the most precious commodity is *life itself.* God says that a person's soul (the life that lives on forever) is worth more than the whole world, and that there is nothing valuable enough to give in exchange for it (Mark 8:36).

God also says that nothing is more important than the salvation of a soul. Nothing, absolutely nothing can compare with leading someone to Christ. The proportions of this contribution are so great that they are measured not in time, but in eternity. To save a soul from hell, from a Christless eternity; to point him to the matchless Saviour who alone can satisfy on earth, and enable him to abide in heaven for endless ages—this, through the work of the Holy Spirit, is *the greatest contribution of which any human being is capable!*

In His Word, God has said, "He that winneth souls is wise." Every Christian can be actively engaged in soul winning. It is only reasonable to believe that God who has given us the desire to make a worthwhile contribution in life, also enables us to fulfill it.

Years ago in the city of Boston there lived an "insignificant" man by the name of Ed Kimball. Among other things, Kimball was a Sunday school teacher who realized that the greatest contribution he could make was not just to earn a living but to tell others about the saving power of Christ. So he kept witnessing to the boys in his class. Among them was a young shoe salesman, Dwight L. Moody. Every week Ed Kimball made it a point to visit him and talk to him about his soul. In time, Moody surrendered his heart to Christ.

Kimball's evangelism did not end there. He had touched a firebrand for Christ who was to be heard " 'round the world." Thousands upon thousands learned about his wonderful Saviour, the Lord Jesus

Christ. In fact, today D. L. Moody is known as the man who shook two continents with the Gospel of Jesus Christ. What a great contribution Kimball made when he reached this "giant" for Christ.

Another example is Steve Landon. At eighteen he was one of the roughest, toughest, football players that ever hit Washington High. Standing a little over six feet tall, he weighed 195 pounds and was every inch a man.

"How does he manage to stay in school?" people asked. "He breaks every rule in the book and he's not always sober when he arrives on the campus."

One Monday morning everything came to a climax. Steve had been drinking the night before. After a big family fight he stumbled to school ready to "whip the world."

Miss Barkley, his English teacher, greeted him as he made his appearance in the school library. She had always taken an interest in Steve. But Steve wasn't in the mood to talk to anyone. Sensing that Steve was in serious trouble, she followed him over to his locker. "It's no use talking to me," Steve snapped at Miss Barkley. "I've got my own life to live and I'm going to live it just the way I please."

Throughout the day Miss Barkley kept praying for Steve. *They're sure to expel him this time*, she thought. And they did.

That evening she called Steve on the phone and asked him to come over to her house. If ever he needed a friend, it was then. So Steve went over to see Miss Barkley.

She told him more about Christ and how He had died for people like Steve. She told him that he could have real happiness if he would only surrender his heart to Him. Then she invited him to go with her to hear an evangelist who was coming to speak at the city auditorium. Steve promised that he would go. A few nights later the service began with a packed house.

And Steve was there—slouched down in the very last row of the auditorium.

The evangelist brought a powerful message. And the Spirit of God touched hearts. At the end of the service Steve headed for the altar. "I felt," he said, "that I couldn't get there fast enough. I talked with a counselor after the meeting and right then and there I settled the whole thing. I told the Lord that from now on I was going to live for Him—and I never meant anything more seriously in my life."

That was the turning point for Steve. Miss Barkley helped to get him reinstated in high school. And this time things were different. It wasn't long until graduation. Then, on to university. Steve stayed true to the Lord all through his college days. A few years later he became an outstanding youth leader in his area. Today, young people are thrilled as they hear this fine young man of God give his testimony of how a high school teacher talked with him, befriended him, prayed for him and counseled with him until he came to know Christ as his personal Saviour.

It was true that Miss Barkley was making a worthwhile contribution as an English teacher. But she realized that there was an even greater contribution to be made. To her, the structure of a sentence was not nearly as important as the salvation of a soul. And although she did not neglect her job as a teacher, neither did she neglect her duty as a Christian. Grammar? Yes, she taught it. But even more than that, she influenced young people for God.

Preachers have no monopoly on giving out the Gospel. They do not have the "exclusive" on winning souls for Christ. That means that every Christian can have a part in making this "greatest" contribution. In fact, it is his responsibility.

Christ tells us, "Ye shall be witnesses unto me both in Jerusalem, and in all Judaea, and in Samaria, and unto the uttermost part of the earth" (Acts 1:18). We cannot all go to the *uttermost part of the earth,* but we can make certain that we cover the home base—our own "Jerusalem." It may be a business associate to whom we should witness, or the lady next door. Or perhaps we should speak to that classmate at school, or give a tract to the mailman. There are countless ways to witness effectively if our eyes are open to our God-given opportunities. Our "mission field" often consists of those with whom we work and play and do business. They are *ours* to win. You have heard it often, but it is nonetheless true: "Everyone knows someone else." Our immediate responsibility then is to those with whom we rub shoulders.

It was a pal who reached Jack for Christ. Jack was a New York boy. But that wasn't unusual, because there were thousands of young men living in New York City. Like most of the other fellows in his crowd, Jack was interested in everything that was going on—everything except his soul's salvation.

Jack's best friend was George Schilling. Both of these fellows played trombones in a jazz band and in the United States Cavalry. Out for a good time? Yes, and in a worldly sense, they usually had it!

But something happened to George. One night he walked into a downtown church in New York City where they were holding a New Year's Eve Watch Night service. That was the night for George. During the service Dr. Will Houghton brought a stirring gospel message, and when the invitation was given to accept Christ, George Schilling was the first to walk down the aisle. And he meant business. That night as George walked out of the church he was determined to live for the Lord.

Shortly afterward he talked to his pal, Jack, about how Christ had come into his heart. Jack was puzzled. This didn't sound like George. One night George gave him a New Testament. Jack was too polite to refuse it.

But before he reached home he tore it up and threw it away. None of that "sissy stuff" for him.

But George did not give up. He continued to witness to Jack and six months later they went off to army camp togther.

In this tough army crowd, thought Jack, *George will forget all about his religion. I know what George used to be and I'm sure he can't hold out.*

That didn't happen. George was man enough to stand up for Christ. Jack watched his buddy for full two weeks—watched him like a hawk twenty-four hours a day as they lived and worked in that army camp. Jack was amazed at the marvelous change in his friend's life. "George has something worth having," Jack decided. But still he did not give his heart to Christ.

A few weeks later when they had come back home, George persuaded Jack to attend an evangelistic service by asking him to play his trombone. Jack loved to play, so he went. But he was miserable. Although he did not make a decision when the evangelist gave the invitation, Jack couldn't get away from the pull of the Gospel. That night, alone in his room, he knelt by his bed and gave his heart to the Saviour.

The story doesn't end there, however. Jack knew that his main job in life was to witness for Christ. And he started right in doing it. A few years later Jack had to leave his regular employment because he was getting "too many invitations to speak for the Lord."

The years passed and through Jack's preaching and radio ministry many thousands have found Christ as their personal Saviour. The Lord led Jack Wyrtzen to establish several camps in the United States as well as in foreign countries, where young and old come to hear the Gospel. In addition, God has led Jack to help support over sixty missionaries throughout the world.

George Schilling, the young man who led Jack Wyrtzen to Christ, could have used his time doing many

other things. But he realized that the greatest contribution that one could ever make was to win a soul to Christ. So George was faithful. And through his consistent witness, Jack Wyrtzen found the Lord.

How about you? Are you making the maximum contribution in life? Or are you allowing the *good* to rob you of the *best*?

There are learned *educators* who have earned advanced degrees and who understand the psychology of learning. They have amassed great stores of information. They have devoted themselves to teaching mankind. Making a great contribution? Yes, but not enough. Since they have never come to know the Truth, Christ the Son of God, they cannot impart godly wisdom to their students.

There are *medical doctors* who have devoted years to specialized study of the human body. They understand much about anatomy, bodily functions, disease and the science of healing. And they are making a contribution to society. But they do not go far enough. They know nothing of the Great Physician who heals the soul. And they are unable to show their patients how to put on incorruption, how to have eternal life.

There are brilliant *psychologists* who can give an array of psychological tests to diagnose the causes of maladjustments. They can evaluate the human intellect and can detect the workings of the mind. But they fail to give their clients the "Mind of Christ."

There are well informed *attorneys* who can advise their clients about intricate details of national and international law. But because they are helpless to explain the law of God that converts the soul, the contribution they make is a limited one.

There are top *men of science* who help mankind "get off the ground"—to find their way to the moon. Yet they are helpless to point a man to heaven.

There are clever *salesmen* who can explain the advantage of their product and convince people of the

superiority of their wares. Yet they fail to show the advantage of the glorious Gospel—they cannot persuade people to accept the gift of God.

There are skilled *craftsmen* who build with utmost precision. But they fail to build a life for God.

There are artistic *homemakers* who understand how to beautify the home. They excel in the art of flower decoration, color design, furniture arrangement, and many other aspects of home management. And yet they forget the beauty of the soul; they completely neglect the beauty of holiness.

There are even *ministers* who present oratorical sermons—telling people "How to face life." And yet they never tell people how they can have *eternal* life—how they can face *both life and death*.

The contributions of men are worthy. It is right that we should help our fellow man. But unless we make the *greatest* contribution, we do not go far enough. For it is not until we help lead people to the Saviour that we can serve humanity on the highest level—the divine.

It is not just a matter of contributing if we feel like it. It is not like donating to charity. God's work is urgent. It cannot be turned aside. Since God is not willing that any should perish (II Peter 3:9), it is our responsibility to reach the unsaved with the Gospel.

If we are not working members of the team, we are missing out on the blessing. What can we do? We can give our time, talent and resources, and we can witness. We can study so that we will be ready to give an answer for the hope that is in us (I Peter 3:15). Some us will sow, others will water, and still others will reap. It matters little what part of the job is assigned to us. The important question is: Are we faithful in doing it?

The work of our hands will not endure. The great buildings that stand as proud monuments to our civilization will some day deteriorate and crumble. As durable as they are, stone and steel are not indestructible. The mighty bridges that span great waterways will some day fall into the abyss below. Scientific theories are ever changing. The great discoveries of today will be obsolete tomorrow.

Nothing we can do on a human level is permanent. The sound of our song will grow faint; the masterpiece we paint will fade; the books that we write will yellow and be forgotten. Our silver and gold that we have worked so hard to accumulate will tarnish. And this body that we carefully nurture and adorn will eventually lie in the grave.

Only when we deal with eternity can we expect the results to be immortal. So it is that there is *one* contribution man can make that will be of *lasting* value. Yes, the souls that we win for Christ will live on forever and ever. And through eons to come, those whom we have brought to the Lord will stand as a living memorial to our contribution here on earth.

True, one of man's basic drives is to make a worthwhile contribution in life. But the greatest contribution of all—the only one that will stand through eternity— is to have a part in bringing an immortal soul into the kingdom of God. This, indeed, is the way to genuine happiness.

Secrets of Success

WHEN I WAS a young boy I heard a neighbor say, "If a man's not a success by the time he's thirty-five, he'll never be one."

Immediately I perked up my ears. Not only did I swallow his statement but I supposed success was measured by wealth.

Years later I discovered that this was not true. No, it wasn't that this well-meaning neighbor had deliberately told a falsehood. He was sincere but he did not know the facts.

Actually, there is no age beyond which one can say, "He'll never be successful." Furthermore, contrary to what many people think, true success has very little to do with the size of a man's bank roll. But success and achievement *are* important—highly important. In fact, they are vital to our physical and mental health. Success draws the best out of a man and in return, it tends to fill him with normal, healthy attitudes. The result—a well adjusted person.

TONIC FOR YOUR PERSONALITY

Success is the tonic that puts zest into living—the "pay-off" for our efforts. That is why people who have never moved forward in life are seldom happy. They are suffering from an undernourished incentive—a malady that takes its toll in personality. People develop into interesting individuals as they achieve. And when they are *not* progressing, the results are bound to be detrimental.

Marie was an example of a person who was suffering from a "standstill." Due to unfortunate circumstances in her family, she had to leave high school and look for a job. In the community where she lived, employment was limited. So she took the only thing available, a filing job in a small office. Marie liked music and in this field she had unusual potential. But without training or experience her talent was held captive. Filing, filing, filing! How she hated it. This was not success and she knew it. Naturally, it reflected in her personality. No zest, little happiness, and constant conflict.

Nothing is more pitiful than the person who is standing still or going backward. His life is like stagnant water, unhealthy and undesirable. Stagnant water is motionless—has no outlet or source of refilling. And when people become inactive and are not taking in or giving out, they too become stagnant.

On the other hand, no one is more *interesting* and more vital than the person who is moving forward. Man was made to go forward, not backward. We grow, we develop, we mature. And as we progress, our personalities take on a vibrant sparkle. Progress is basic to all life: it is essential to every human being.

What happens to a person who continually fails? He becomes discouraged, taking the defeatest attitude of "Why try? I can't win anyway." There is nothing much more uninspiring and uninteresting than this kind of "wet blanket." He is likely to become suspicious, blaming people and circumstances for his lack of success. In short, he is extremely hard to live with because he has never found his "niche" in life. It is not uncommon for a person like this to complain of headaches and nervousness or other symptoms of emotional disturbance. Little wonder, then, that psychiatrists and psychologists agree that this basic psychological need, that of being successful, must be met if a person is to be his best.

In contrast to those who have not encountered much success, we find that people who are meeting with at least a measure of success in life are more likely to be interesting. They are usually optimistic and inspirational. Successful people look forward to the future. Why? Because the past has been profitable and the present is encouraging. As a result, they face tomorrow with confidence! When a person is achieving success, circumstances are not a threat to him. He has been able to overcome obstacles in the past so naturally, ho is *not* afraid of the future. Is it any wonder then, that people who are successful are easier to associate with than those who are failures?

Think of the people you know! In the office—that griper, always complaining about one thing or another. You can be almost certain he is not the vice-president of the concern; more than likely, he's a discouraged clerk who has been sitting at the same desk doing the same routine job for the past twenty years. And in school—it is usually not the "A" student who grumbles about too much home work and too strict discipline. In church—well, it's the same story. A person who is being used of God doesn't spend his time finding fault with the preacher or criticizing the deacons and elders. He's too busy doing something worthwhile. So it is that as we experience at least some success, our personalities improve and we become enriched, interesting individuals who are better able to get along with others.

SUCCESS MEANS MORE SUCCESS

Success *is* the basis for greater accomplishments. For when we succeed at little things we continue to succeed at bigger ones. Even the smallest success prepares us for further achievement.

You have heard the old adage, "Success is a ladder and those who attain must start at the bottom and climb to the top." Shopworn as this statement is, it carries a lot of truth. Each step up prepares you for the next rung. When you take one successful step, you look forward to the next—and the next—and the next. When most of your tries are successes, you can *take* a few bumps and bruises along the way. But when the failures outweigh the successes, it spells one thing —discouragement! And discouragement often breeds more trouble.

This is true of both young and old. Parents notice it. Teachers notice it, and so do employers.

I remember Sandra, a fourth grade girl who had been referred to me for special study. On her referral sheet, the teacher wrote, "I'm wondering if she's just lazy." When I observed the girl in the classroom, I readily saw that she was not interested in her school work. That afternoon I gave her a psychological examination and found that her intelligence was only low average. After studying her school records, visiting with her parents and talking with her former teachers, I felt that I had uncovered the roots of her difficulty. Sandra was not ready for the work that was being presented in her class. I was certain that her biggest problem was discouragement. She had run into it for years—both at home and school.

When I talked with the teacher, I suggested that she give Sandra work appropriate to her ability. We discussed ways in which the teacher could encourage her. Together we planned many ways to help Sandra achieve a degree of success.

A month or so later I saw the teacher again. "Do you remember Sandra?" she asked. "Well, she's doing much better. Her school work is improving. But even more than that, her whole attitude is different."

Like everyone else, Sandra thrived on encouragement. She had a basic psychological need—that of experiencing success and achievement. As soon as that need was met, she felt encouraged and happy. Now, for a change, she was meeting with some success. She was no longer a problem girl. Why? Because she had a new self concept. No longer did she think of herself as a "dunce." She had a new role—success.

It's not easy to be enthusiastic about the future when one has not been successful in the past. Failure dims our outlook. Tomorrows seldom look bright if our yesterdays have been marred by dissatisfaction. This was impressed upon me one summer when I joined Dr. Leo Phearman, an outstanding reading specialist, to conduct a reading clinic for boys and girls. These ten to fourteen-year-old children had at least average intelligence, yet they had never learned to read. By now they were so discouraged that they felt there was no hope for them. One of our biggest tasks was to convince them that they *could succeed*. Once this spark of hope had been fanned back to life, these youngsters were on the road to real progress.

There's nothing like failure to kill incentive and ambition. People don't mind working hard when the reward is accomplishment. But to work without results is no better than aimlessly marking time—going 'round and 'round in the same old rut, getting nowhere. Like a donkey on a treadmill. And that's when life becomes the "same old grind."

Yes, it takes more than *striving* to develop a well adjusted personality. It also takes some *arriving*.

SUCCESS AND HEALTH

Lois and her husband sat in my office one evening and told me their story. They had been on the mission field only a short time when she became ill. She seemed to lose all interest in life. Unable to sleep or eat, she lost considerable weight. Doctors on the field urged her husband to fly her back to America immediately.

After the young couple returned home, other medical doctors examined her, but found no serious physical causes of her breakdown. They advised her to get psychological help.

During the months that I worked with Lois she gained real insight into many of the causes of her illness. She had been raised in a family that was dominated by an older sister and by an unduly critical father. Lois' sister was not only competent; she was aggressive. Lois was made to feel that she could not do anything as well as her sister. Her father was always quick to criticize. "It's not good," he would say, "for children to get a big head." He believed that the best way to get them to improve was to point out how they should have done better.

The result? Lois grew up feeling dependent and inferior. She thought she was not capable of meeting things on her own. Although she accepted Christ as her personal Saviour a few years before leaving for the mission field, the more than twenty years of injurious experiences had caused profound damage. There were traces of these personality characteristics before she left America, but they did not become so dramatically apparent until she reached the foreign field. There Lois was exposed to undue stress and strain in a strange, lonely land where unusual hardships faced her every day. And to make matters worse, there was no one with whom she felt free enough to talk this thing out and to share her terrible feelings of depression. Naturally, the extreme emotional conditions that had prevailed through the years brought serious physical reactions so that she was finally unable to go on.

Through Christian psychological help and medical attention, Lois grew steadily better until she was able to carry on her regular duties in the home, then return to the field. But what a terrible price to pay for a needless experience! Yes, her parents had provided for her financial and physical needs—she had a nice home, nourishing food and good clothes. But she lacked that important element of success and achievement!

It takes more than fresh air and vitamins to keep a person healthy—a good emotional climate is needed too. Psychologists and psychiatrists continually re-emphasize the close relationship between the physical and the emotional—one affects the other. Since this is true, it is easily understood how success is basic to our well being.

The successful person is usually confident and he faces life with a wholesome mental attitude. He has a sound, emotional outlook and is not easily upset by disturbances. Because he has overcome other problems in the past, he is not overly concerned when new hurdles arise. This, in turn, directly relates to his physical condition. When a person runs into constant discouragement and defeat, it is injurious to his health. When failure continually operates in an individual's life, it can disrupt the body's glandular balance and cause headaches, backaches and many other physical ailments. Success then, at least to some extent, is essential if a person is to maintain good health—both mental and physical.

One day Mr. Burton came to my office. His face wore a tired, haggard expression. His whole attitude and bearing was one of dejection and defeat.

"I don't know what's the matter with me, Dr. Narramore," he confided, slumping down into a chair, "but everything seems to be wrong."

Then Mr. Burton told me his story. He had been a Christian for a number of years, had a fine wife and two lovely daughters. It would seem that he had everything to make him happy—but yet he was *miserable*.

"I'm *so* discouraged," he confessed. "I don't want to be like this but I'm terribly unhappy. I'm just a big failure, I guess."

He went on to tell me how dissatisfied he was—on the job, at home, in his church, yes, everywhere. And to him, life was intolerably dull.

"I'm tired all the time and I just don't feel well," Mr. Burton continued. "Yet when I went to our family doctor and had a complete physical check-up, he could find nothing wrong. But something *is* wrong. And whatever it is, I do hope you can help me find my trouble."

Poor health? Yes, but not from a physical cause.

As I talked with Mr. Burton I soon sensed that he was a brilliant man but was working at a job that almost anyone with no education could handle. Men with far less ability than he, were giving him orders all day. And in his particular company there was nothing he could do about it.

In the ensuing visits I gave him an intellectual examination and found that his intelligence was not only high but in the gifted class. After giving him several vocational aptitude tests we discovered that he had special ability in *several* lines for which he had no training or experience.

I encouraged him to start night school, and if possible, get a leave of absence from his work so he could take some summer work at a nearby university. He did this, and after two years he moved to a new company and into a position, for which he had unusual talent. Here he was able to utilize his recent training. Within a short time he gained recognition in his office, and a little later he was given a top executive position.

His poor mental health had disappeared. Now he was radiantly happy at home, at work, and at church. Success made the difference.

WE CAN HELP

Have you ever thought how much success depends upon our attitudes toward each other? When those around us recognize and encourage us, life is a place of satisfaction and success. When they do not, it is more than likely to be a place of defeat and failure.

Take Mr. Lane and Mr. Black, for example. They lived on the same street, had similar jobs, and both had small families.

But the similarity ended there. If you had known them personally, you would have realized a great difference between the two. Lane felt successful, but Black didn't. The difference? In their cases, it was due to their wives.

Mrs. Lane took nearly every opportunity to encourage her husband and to give him recognition. "Our Daddy is the best in the world," she would tell her children. "We love him, don't we!"

Then turning to her husband she would admiringly say, "Honey, you're just wonderful."

On the other hand, Mrs. Black seemed to take her husband for granted. Love him? Yes, undoubtedly; but she constantly pointed out to him the things they *didn't* have and the things they needed. She failed to give him the daily recognition that helps keep a man happy and healthy—the feeling that he is at least fairly successful.

After a number of years the two women had left permanent imprints on their husbands—one of success, the other, defeat.

We can't deny that recognition and status *are* important, not only in our marriage relationships, but in all phases of life. Children and adults alike need to feel that they are successful. At home—at school—at church—in the office—wherever we live, work or play, being successful is an important factor. We can help our children, our friends and our relatives feel that they are successful by our encouragement and support.

Yes, we *do* have a responsibility. But more than that, we have the joy of encouraging and recognizing others. When we let people know that we have confidence in them, we give them the "boost" that makes them feel successful. The by-products: good physical and mental health on their part and more happiness on ours. Consequently, success is not measured by some mythical yardstick. Rather, it is counted in terms of the recognition we receive from our friends, and the recognition we give to them!

SUCCESSFUL FOOLS

That a person can be successful and still be a fool is a paradox. But unfortunately, it's quite possible—and even more sadly, a common truth.

I'm thinking of a certain man who "made good" financially. In fact, he was wealthy. He had worked hard through the years and had made his fortune as a farmer. Everyone considered him a highly successful man and he prided himself on his own achievements.

One day as he was looking over his property and his belongings, he realized that he had more possessions than he had storage room. So he came up with a plan for expansion and proposed to pull down his barns and build greater ones where he could put all his fruits and his goods.

He smiled with evident satisfaction as he decided that he would now retire. "Soul," he told himself, "thou hast much goods laid up for many years; take thine ease, eat, drink, and be merry."

But God said unto him, "Thou fool, this night thy soul shall be required of thee: then whose shall those things be which thou hast provided?"

Fool? Yes, indeed! A fool because he was so short-sighted. He hadn't planned beyond the brief span of this life. And he hadn't reckoned with eternity or the fact that God holds the future in His almighty hand.

God tells us that "a man's life consisteth *not* in the abundance of the things which he possesseth" (Luke 12:15). But this man evidently did not know that. He had a wrong, an earthly sense of values.

The story of this "successful fool" is recorded in the Bible (Luke 12:16-21). Unfortunately, there have been thousands—yes, millions just like him. Today, as it has been through the ages, people are more *materialistic* than ever. They measure their successes by the false yardsticks of materialism and power.

"You can't take it with you," is more than a time-worn adage. It is a nugget of truth that we need to consider carefully. Not long ago two men were discussing a mutual acquaintance who had passed away. "How much did he leave?" asked one. "Everything!" replied the other.

How true this is. We leave *everything* we accumulate here on this earth. That is why God warns us to "lay not up for yourselves treasures upon earth, where moth and rust doth corrupt, and where thieves break through and steal: But lay up for yourselves treasures in heaven, were neither moth nor rust doth corrupt, and where thieves do not break through nor steal: For where your treasure is, there will your heart be, also" (Matt. 6:19-21).

Sometimes we may experience financial reverses or meet with trying circumstances. But to Christians, these losses are not too disturbing, because their treasures are laid up in heaven. Compared to the celestial glory of these riches, earthly treasures look insignificant and puny. And they are.

Yet there are countless numbers of people who foolishly stake their entire future on a mirage. Fortune? Fame? Love? Reputation? Are these the elements of success? Not really, because this kind of success is only on the surface. And when it crumbles, people's dreams crash with it.

Many have climbed to the top of their rainbows and have reached their pots of gold—popular acclaim, wealth, or other achievements. But once having reached this much sought goal, they still are dissatisfied and extremely unhappy. Why? Because they have left God out of their plans. Success obtained without the blessing of God is a farce—shallow and empty. And in God's sight, it's worthless. "For what shall it profit a man if he gain the whole world, and lose his own soul?" (Mark 8:36).

THE ROAD TO SUCCESS

The first essential on the road to success is to *start right*—*to put first things first*.

The very first verse of the Bible reads, "In the *beginning* God" (Gen. 1:1). Have you had a beginning with God? It's the only authentic starting place. God tells us to "seek ye *first* the kingdom of God and His righteousness; and all these things shall be *added* unto you" (Matt. 6:33).

So it is that the first step to success is found in accepting Christ as one's personal Saviour—coming to God as a repentant sinner and trusting completely in the work that Christ accomplished on the Cross for our salvation. When you have started on God's road, you have started on the road to true success. It's solid and it's sure. All other roads are treacherous, because no matter how great your success may be in this world, you will be doomed to eternal failure in the next.

People write books and give lectures on how to be successful. Yet, they often leave out the most basic element of all. Real success cannot be achieved anywhere but in the center of God's will. Some may appear to be achieving success but when we view them from God's perspective, we see that these people are really on little side lines and are not even in the running at all.

All ambitions, except one, end with life. They are only for the duration of human existence. The workman must lay aside his tools; the writer his pen; the surgeon his knife; the astronomer his telescope; the explorer his chart; the scientist his tube and acids; the musician his song.

God tells us that "the world passeth away, and the lust thereof: but he that doeth the will of God abideth forever" (I John 2:17). So it is that only one ambition will last for all eternity, only one ambition will demand all the ages for its perfect realization.

In the Old Testament it was said of King Uzziah that "as long as he sought the Lord, God made him to prosper." This is also true of us. As Christians we cannot expect to prosper unless each day is marked by sincere consecration.

But remember, success is never *dumped* into a person's lap. God gave us brains and brawn and He expects us to put them to use. So success also requires *action*. God expects us to do our part—to pray and to read His Word—and then to *work* in obedience to His will. Many people are not as successful in life as they might be because they are in the wrong vocation or profession. But here again, our relationship to God is significant. When we know Christ, He gives us new ambitions and desires. He guides us into the work He has chosen for us and for which we have ability. He graciously opens certain doors and closes others to insure our success. Actually, when God is directing our paths, we cannot fail! And God makes no mistakes.

I knew a teen-aged girl named Gloria. She was vivacious and pretty and her ambition in life was to become an actress and star in the theatre.

"Oh, Dr. Narramore," she sighed, "I can't think of anything more fabulous than to be a movie star. It's so glamorous and all. I *do* hope I have enough talent."

We talked for a little while about her plans and her ambitions, and I took the opportunity to tell her what Christ wanted to do in her life. She listened intently and tears filled her eyes as I pressed the claims of Christ. Although she didn't make any decision right then, it wasn't long until Gloria gave her heart and life to the Saviour.

And then things were different. She was a new person: old things had passed away and all things had become new.

A few months later I saw Gloria again and I asked her about her "Hollywood career."

"Oh, Dr. Narramore," she said, "stop kidding me. I

haven't the least desire in the world to be in show business. I want to serve the Lord."

And she did. After high school and Bible College, she went to a foreign country (with a handsome husband) to serve as a staff musician on a Christian radio station. Now Gloria is in a job where her talents actually lie. She has achieved *real* success. Think what would have happened if God had not changed her desire for a theatrical profession. Hollywood and Hell, divorce, heartbreak, sin, mental anguish—another precious soul on the ash heap of sin and sorrow.

Direction? Yes! God points the way to success. But even *more* than that. He walks the road *with* you. For when God comes into a man's life, He actually goes into *partnership* with him. Human beings were never intended to go through life alone. They need the fellowship of God, their Creator. And when they are in fellowship with Him, they can face life victoriously knowing that they are on the winning side with God and therefore cannot fail.

Bill is a good example of what happens when we are in partnership with God. Bill had struggled along, making little if any headway. Then one day he met a fellow who encouraged him to come to church.

Why not? Bill thought. *I've tried everything else.*

He came and was intensely interested; then he came again.

Not long afterward the church conducted special evangelistic services. Bill came but he was *most* uncomfortable—until midway in the meetings when he made a decision for Christ and was wonderfully saved. After the meetings ended, Bill began to study the Bible with his new-found Christian friends. He grew in the Lord and became a changed fellow. Everything seemed different now. And it was.

His job? Well, actually he was doing the same work as he had before but his attitude was different. Now

Bill was working for and with Jesus, his Lord and Saviour.

A few years later Bill was transferred to the great Northwest. Here he continued to work for the same commercial company to pay expenses, but he was also working for God. He bought a bus and on Sundays he filled it with children from rural areas and brought them to church and Sunday school. He started an active home missionary project, working evenings, Sundays and during vacations. Yes, Bill was doing a big job for God.

Now Bill is one of the most successful men in the world. And it all began when he went into partnership with God.

THE RIGHT KIND OF SUCCESS

Real success can only be measured by the dimensions of eternity, not by our tiny little piece of life here on earth. This is true because human beings have eternal souls that will live somewhere forever. The vital question is not "if." It is "where"—in Heaven or in Hell?

Things take on a different perspective and sense of values when we view them in terms of eternity. Our human view is so limited and so faulty. But God's view has an eternal dimension and it is as accurate as truth itself. This contrast between man's view and God's might be expressed something like this:

Life on Earth   *Millions and Millions of Years of Endless Eternity*

On earth we cannot always tell who is successful and who is not. But the facts come to light in eternity. A dramatic example is given in the Bible. God tells us that there was a certain rich man. (His name was not recorded. Evidently he wasn't successful enough to make God's "Who's Who.") This man had everything, a beautiful home, servants, fine clothes—and he lived off the fat of the land. By all the standards of the world, he was successful.

In contrast to this rich man was Lazarus—a poor, dependent beggar. He didn't have any of this world's goods. We do not know what unfortunate circumstances may have caused him to be in this pitiful state. But this we know, not only was he poverty-stricken but he was broken in health; and we are told that "the dogs came and licked his sores." A failure? In the eyes of his fellow men he was no doubt worse than that.

But in God's sight things were completely different. It took eternity to shed the proper light and perspective on the successes and failures of these two men. The rich man died and was buried. I can well imagine the elaborate burial ceremony for this man and the flowery inscriptions placed upon his tombstone. No doubt he was entombed with costly spices in a magnificent marble vault. But with all of this show of wealth, his soul was in hell suffering torment that exceeded all imagination.

On the other hand, when Lazarus died he was carried by the angels into Abraham's bosom. It is doubtful that this beggar even had a decent burial. But that didn't matter—that formality was only for the earthly body that was left behind. Now it was the *soul* that counted. And evidently his soul was in fellowship with God.

Was the rich man successful? Not in the light of eternity. His success was as short as his life. He had made no preparation for the soul that would live on forever.

No, Lazarus may not have succeeded in the eyes of men, but his success was measured by a heavenly goal. And throughout eternity he reaped the benefits of his wise choice. Did the wealthy man find no home in heaven because he was rich? Did the poor man find favor with God because he was poor? No, their bank accounts were not relevant, except for the impressions they made while here on earth.

So it is that in God's sight a seemingly insignificant person may be highly successful. In what way? Just think of that frail, obscure little old lady, who continually makes her petitions known before the Throne of Grace. A successful, joyous ministry? Indeed! Treasures? Yes, she has them—not in this earth, but in heaven where she can enjoy them for all eternity!

It Can Be You

Most of us have average ability, but it is surprising what great successes God can make out of very ordinary people. In His sight it is not the amount of talent that a person has that counts: rather, it is his yieldedness. And when God is moulding a life, you can be sure it will be successful.

I recall two high school boys who gave their hearts to Christ. As the months went by they both began to grow spiritually. Don was a tall, handsome boy who distinguished himself as an all-state athlete, and as an accomplished musician. He also had unusual abilities as a speaker. Everyone who knew him recognized his superior talents. In contrast, David was a homely boy from an extremely poor family. He had no special gifts or abilities. One might almost say that he was characterized by his mediocrity.

But the years following graduation brought many opportunities for life decisions. Christian friends began to see that Don was not including Christ in his plans while David sought the Lord in all that he did.

Some years later these young men presented an impressive comparison. It was evident that Don had not grown spiritually since his high school days. He was most unhappy, having had serious difficulties in several marriages, and not attaining success in either athletics or music. He had aged far beyond his years and was disillusioned and discouraged.

On the other hand, there was David, of only average ability—but what a contrast! He had not only received further Christian training, but he was happily married and busily engaged in a pastorate where he was being used mightily of God. David was thrilled with life, while Don could hardly bear it! David's happiness came not from natural attributes or from worldly acclaim but from being in the will of God.

Every sincere child of God can be and should be a success. For when God is in charge, there can be no failure. The apostle Paul said, "I can do *all* things through Christ who strengtheneth me" (Phil. 4:13). And we can say the same today.

What a wonderful thought—to know that we as believers have this special, supernatural help to make us successful. When we live close to the Lord, read His Word, pray and follow Him, we have the only recipe for genuine success. It is the promise of God: "This book of the law shall not depart out of thy mouth, but thou shalt meditate therein day and night that thou mayest observe to do according to all that is written therein; for then thou shalt make thy way prosperous, and then thou shalt have good success" (Josh. 1:8).

SUCCESS THAT LASTS FOREVER

"Laugh and the world laughs with you—cry and you cry alone."

How true! When we're on *top,* the world is with us: but let the picture change and we stand *alone.*

There is nothing much more vacillating than worldly success. Human nature is *fickle*—and since man measures success by the opinion of others, it becomes an insecure thing that can be lost in a minute's time.

Not long ago I heard a man give this definition of success: "Getting along with those you have to and keeping ahead of the rest of them." If this were true, a successful man is in the same precarious position as "humpty-dumpty." As long as he can sit on the wall, he is all right. But if he should fall off, his success is shattered.

I think of a friend of mine who was a great athlete. He was a famous miler—a runner who had set a new world's record and then, with lightning speed, had repeatedly broken his own record. He had won recognition and popular acclaim. Everywhere he went, people eyed him with admiration and asked for his autograph. He was crowned with success; he was riding the crest of popularity.

One day someone asked him, "How does it feel to be so successful?"

The athlete smiled wryly as he answered, "To be sure, there's a great thrill in being successful. And there's satisfaction in winning.

"But," he continued, "success doesn't last long. Sure —the crowd is with you, wildly applauding, screaming, stamping and yelling with enthusiasm; that is, as long as you're the winner. But when the day comes that you fail to knock off another fraction of a second from your time, or find that another runner can challenge your supremacy—then it's a different story. The crowd changes loyalties and, in no time at all, you are the forgotten man."

The forgotten man? Can this be true when only yesterday found him the world's hero?

Yes, it is true. One night we may shine with dazzling brilliance: but soon the spotlight is on someone else and we are not seen at all.

But there is success that doesn't fade! And God tells us about it in the Bible, His inspired Word. For in the book of Daniel, chapter 12, verse 3, we read: "And they that be wise shall shine as the brightness of the firmament; and they that turn many to righteousness as the stars forever and ever."

Here God shows us another dimension of success.

That dimension is "time." He says that the wise (those who win souls) and those who serve God by turning the unsaved to Him, shall SHINE! Not for a day, a year, or a season, not for a few years here on earth. But they shall shine through all *eternity*. Not only shall they shine as the stars forever and ever, but the quality of their brightness shall be as the firmament itself!

Have you ever watched a display of fireworks—perhaps on a Fourth of July night? Of course. The night is clear and starlit. Everyone is waiting. Then the fireworks begin! Some pop while others crackle, boom or shriek. But the noise is outdone only by the spectacular flashes of light. The rockets zoom upward, then burst into a blaze of multi-colored lights. Fountains of shimmering light fill the heavens. Beautiful streaks of fire blaze their paths across the midnight sky. Each one vies for prominence while the amazed crowd applauds with wild enthusiasm.

But an hour or so later the noise stops. The fireworks are gone. The rockets are silent and there is not a trace of the temporary display. And now, as you look into the sky again, you see the stars! There they are as bright and brilliant as before. And—permanent. Their glory was momentarily forgotten with the noise and success of the temporary flashes of man. But centuries later the *stars will still be shining*.

So it is with temporary, earthly success. At best it is only a feeble rocket which creates a momentary stir in the minds of men. Then it is forgotten. But, God promises that those who are godly and "wise" and those "that turn many to righteousness" shall be as the "stars forever and ever."

Sometimes we see godly men and women who seem to be insignificantly hidden by the razzle-dazzle of men. Perhaps a shop worker, a daily laborer, a school boy, an obscure preacher or a missionary, or a humble prayer warrior on a bed of suffering. And when we see these "little people of God" and compare them with the "big shots" of television, the prominent names of science, the luminaries of Hollywood or the "wheels" of politics, we wonder why God's own are not "successful."

THEY ARE SUCCESSFUL, but *we* are the ones who do not have the *eternal perspective*. For remember, God who speaks with eternity in view says that these lowly, godly saints shall *SHINE AS THE BRIGHTNESS OF THE FIRMAMENT, AS THE STARS THAT SHINE FOREVER AND EVER!*

Faith That Endures

"THERE I WAS, dangling in space. Millions of miles from nowhere.

"Oh, what a terrible, hopeless feeling! Nothing to hold on to, nothing to reach or grab. I didn't have the least idea where I was. There was no up, no down, no sides, no corners—just endless nothingness."

This is how one client described his dream—a veritable "nightmare" that troubled him night after night. But as we talked it through, he found that these dreams were the exaggerated "left-overs" of his daily feelings—distortions of his unresolved conflicts.

There is nothing worse than groping—"hopelessly dangling." Everyone needs to feel that he has something to which he can anchor. Continual uncertainty is mental torture.

Our space age society bears several trademarks. One of them is insecurity. People want to be secure. Financially secure, secure in their family relationships, secure in their jobs and secure in their social standing. But the most important security is often overlooked. Only in recent years have psychologists and psychiatrists begun to analyze man with a new dimension in mind. This new important dimension is "Faith." "Faith in a Supreme Being," they say, "brings stability and security." Indeed, an enduring faith in the living God is basic to all other "securities" in life. On this hinges the whole pattern of our life—now and for eternity.

As a psychologist, I realize that this is one of our basic needs. But it is not enough to have faith. We must have a *secure* faith—one that is certain today, tomorrow and throughout eternity.

It is a psychological fact that people are healthier and happier when they are *secure*. How would you feel if you were not sure that you owned your car? How would you feel if you didn't know whether you were married? How would you feel if you were indefinite about your employment—not sure of a pay check? To function normally and to function well, a human being must know where he stands. Extreme insecurity results in a disorganized mind which may lead to mental illness.

Yet there are many people (even sincere Christians) who are not *secure*. Their spiritual life is shaky, as though they were walking on the brink of a frightful precipice. Faith in God? Yes, but not a *secure* faith. They *hope* they are going to heaven. They *trust* that someday they will "make the Pearly Gates"; they *think* they may "cross over Jordan"; they *presume* they will some day see God.

But deep down inside they are not sure! In reality they are waiting until they die to see what actually will happen to them. And their fate is a mystery that is sealed until death.

No one knows better than God, our Creator, how harmful it is for man to continually feel uncertain. God never intended for His creatures to be insecure; and man never was—until he sinned and turned his back on God, the very source of all certainty and security.

God didn't let it go at that, however. In His great love, He made a marvelous provision for mankind, so that they need not grope blindly for something on which they might stake their future. Nor does God want them to. God made the supreme sacrifice—He gave His own Son, Jesus Christ, to die for our sins. When we trust in His shed blood we are forgiven. We are then the sons of God—and we are assured of an eternity with Him.

There is no guesswork about this. It is sure. As sure as God Himself.

If, of course, you are trusting in your own "good" works, or religious observances, or pious feelings, or your own moral standards—you are trying to get in by a back door and it will not work. Jesus spoke very plainly about this. He said, "I am the door: by me if any man enters in, he shall be saved, and shall go in and out, and find pasture" (John 10:9). He also said, "He that entereth not by the door into the sheepfold but climbeth up some other way, the same is a thief and a robber" (John 10:1).

A thief and a robber! If ever there is a picture of *insecurity,* this is it. When people look to themselves, or their relatives or to an organization or to some "great" leader for their salvation, they are by-passing the crucified Christ, the only means of security. And they will never know genuine security that leads to happiness.

There is only *one* provision for salvation. It is through a personal relationship with Jesus. God says, "There is none other name under heaven given among men, whereby we must be saved" (Acts 4:12). "Believe on the Lord Jesus Christ, and thou shalt be saved" (Acts 16:31). Believe! Not *do.* "For by grace are ye saved, through faith; and that not of yourselves: it is the gift of God: Not of works, lest any man should boast" (Eph. 2:8, 9).

Since salvation is the *gift of God,* could anything be more secure? All we need to do is to *accept* this gift and our souls are secure. With Him, there is no such thing as "dangling." Insecurity is completely opposed to God's nature. His is the author of all security: *He is complete security.* Nothing, absolutely nothing in this world can compare with the security we have in God.

I was born and raised on a western ranch. As a boy I was fascinated by the beautiful majestic mountains that surrounded our fertile valley. They were always there, and always the same. True, they changed their hues to blend with the moods of the day—blue in the morning, gray at noonday, pink and purple in the evening. But they never changed their form or their location. They were sure, they were solid—they seemed almost eternal. Other things changed. The trees and the shrubs grew or were cut down. New homes dotted the landscape, old ones were removed. New highways cut through the fields. The people grew older. Some moved away and others took their place. But through the years the mountains remained—unchanged.

Today when I visit the little community of my boyhood, I am still impressed with the mountains. The years have changed nearly everything else, but the mountains seem the same. Little wonder that writers and poets call them the "eternal" mountains. It is understandable why a great insurance company uses a famous mountain, the Rock of Gibraltar, as its symbol of dependability and security.

But rocks and mountains are *not* indestructible. Steadfast and unmovable as they seem to be, they surrender to nature and to man. Earthquakes can shake them, volcanoes can erupt them, wind and water can erode them, and man can blast them or mine them away.

There is nothing sure and certain except God. He is from everlasting to everlasting. His Word endureth forever. When our faith is placed in His hands, it is *secure* beyond our finite understanding.

I remember Phil's experience. Phil was one of my professional associates. Once a week several of the men from the office had lunch together in a nearby park. There, around a picnic table, we "munched" and had a little Bible study. One day while we were talking and eating lunch, Phil confided, "Well men, I hate to make this confession, but I don't know whether I'm really saved or not."

The men looked up, and one of them asked, "What do you mean?"

"Just what I said," replied Phil. "I've gone to church all my life. In fact, I've taught classes and I've even been the superintendent of the Sunday school. But I can't say for *sure* that I'm saved. And what really disturbs me is the fact that you men all talk as if you know definitely that you are saved. I might as well confess right here and now that I don't have that assurance."

"Let's take a look at what God has to say about it," I suggested.

So we opened the Book and looked at I John 5:12. "He that hath the Son hath life; and he that hath not the Son of God hath not life."

"Well," said Phil, "I never knew that was in the Bible."

Then we looked at the next verse, I John 5:13. "These things have I written unto you that believe on the name of the Son of God; that ye may *know* that ye have eternal life, and that ye may *believe* on the name of the Son of God."

We read the verse several times. "Phil," I said, "do you see at least two very important things in this verse? One is the fact that God has given us the written Word so that we might *believe* on His name. Another important fact is that He has given us this written Word so that after we believe on His name, we might *know* for sure that we have eternal life.

"*BELIEVE* and *KNOW.* Isn't that marvelous? God doesn't want us to be uncertain or perplexed. He says in His own Word that we can be saved and *know* it."

"That's right," agreed the other men.

Phil looked up. "Do you think there are many people who are saved and who don't know it for certain?" he asked.

"Yes," I nodded, "I'm sure there are. You see, it's one thing to be saved, but it's still another thing to have the assurance through His Word—to know beyond the shadow of a doubt that you have eternal life. Let's take one more look at God's Word."

We turned the pages to John 10:28 where we read:

"And I give unto them eternal life; and they shall never perish, neither shall any man pluck them out of my hand."

"That says the same thing three times," commented Phil. "God says that He gives unto us eternal life—life that never ends, then He says that we shall never perish, and then He says that no one will ever be able to pluck us out of His hand."

"That's right," the men agreed.

"Well," said Phil, "since I actually don't know whether I am saved or not I'd like to make sure right now."

Then Phil quietly bowed his head and prayed this simple prayer, "Lord, come into my heart and save me. If I have never before given my life to You, I am doing so right now. Please forgive me of my sins—and be my Lord. And thank You for doing it. In Jesus' name I pray. Amen."

That was a precious time for all of us.

From that moment on Phil was sure, not because of his feelings, but because God's eternal Word said so. Interestingly enough that day marked a great change in his life. Spiritually he began to grow and develop.

A few months later when I was talking with Phil I asked him whether he still had his "know-so" salvation.

"Of course I do," he said. "Ever since that day in the park when I settled it all, there's never been a doubt in my mind."

"But how can you be sure?" I questioned.

"Because God says so in His Word."

Absolutely! Phil was right. There is nothing more certain than God's Word—"Heaven and earth shall pass away, but my words shall not pass away" (Matt. 24:35).

But Phil's case was not at all unusual. Many people have this problem.

It was a real problem with Jon. A few years ago I flew up to Iceland on a speaking tour. The first day I was introduced to Jon, a tall, blonde fellow, typically Nordic, chauvinistic, and in every sense an Icelander. Jon was to be my pianist for our two weeks' stay. The first afternoon we got together and talked over our music plans. During the conversation I asked, "Jon, do you know for sure that you are saved?"

"Oh," he answered, "I know it as well as anyone could possibly know it *without dying.*"

"What do you mean?"

"Well, being saved is something that you cannot be positive about until you die."

"Oh, is that right? Listen very carefully tonight, Jon."

That night I brought a message on the assurance of salvation. And at the end of the service Jon came to me and shook my hand. "I want to thank you," he said, "for coming to Iceland. This is only the first night, but already your trip has been a success!"

"What do you mean, Jon?"

"Well, up until tonight I was not *certain* whether I was saved. But while you were speaking, God spoke to my heart and I realized then that I *could* know for sure. So I asked Him to come into my life and to save me. I knew that if I had never been born again before, I wanted to be, so I settled it right then and there. Now I am sure," he said, "and I am the happiest person in the world. This is what I've been looking for—and now I've found it."

"What's your basis for knowing?" I asked.

"The Bible," he answered.

And Jon was exactly right.

Yes, you too can trust in Christ and know for certain that you are saved.

"But," you may wonder, "*how* can I know?"

How? Simply by reading God's Word and believing it. If God says so, that is enough. You can depend upon His Word. It is settled in heaven—*forever!* See Ps. 119:89.

"Hath He said, and shall He not do it? or hath He spoken, and shall He not make it good?" (Num. 23:19).

It is not a matter of the quantity or quality of your faith. The question is how trustworthy is the person in whom you place your confidence. Is his character beyond reproof? Is he absolutely truthful? Is he 100% dependable? As much as we like our friends, we must admit that they are imperfect. By nature people are sinful and because of this even with all their fine attributes they are not always dependable.

But the character of God is beyond reproach. He is perfect: He is just: He is Holy. And God's Word is as sure as His character. "If we receive the witness of men, the witness of God is greater: for this is the witness of God which he hath testified of his Son . . . He that believeth not God hath made him a liar; because he believeth not the record that God gave of his Son" (I John 5:9, 10). "Abraham believed God, and it was counted unto him for righteousness" (Rom. 4:3).

A distressed lady once came to her minister. She was uncertain as to whether she was actually saved. "Oh pastor," she sighed, "I can't believe!"

"Can't believe whom?" the pastor asked.

She looked up, startled! She had never thought of it that way before. By refusing to believe, she was doubting God.

Faith is not something that we must feel within us. It is the committing of ourselves to someone else—to God. We may say that we have faith in a ship to carry us across the ocean. But it is not until we board the ship that we actually exercise our faith. Once we commit ourselves to the ship, it makes little difference how much we believe in its ability to sail safely to the other shore. It will carry the doubter just as securely as it does the one who completely trusts. But the worried doubter will miss out on the joy of the journey.

So it is with the Christian. When he trusts in Christ as his Saviour, he is saved even though he may feel uncertain about it. But unfortunately he misses out on the blessing. This is not God's will. Because in His Word He clearly tells us over and over again that we can *know* that we are saved.

Sometimes people ask, "Doesn't a person receive the assurance of his salvation at the time he is saved?" And of course the answer is: he may; but he may not. It depends largely upon whether the new convert reads this great truth in God's Word and whether the person leading him to Christ points it out to him.

Undoubtedly some people are saved who do not have the assurance of salvation. On the other hand there are people who do not have the assurance of salvation because they actually are not saved yet. But this is a fact: *Anyone who is saved can know it. And anyone who is in doubt can certainly make sure!*

I remember when I received the assurance of *my* salvation. I had trusted in Christ as my personal Saviour. And immediately afterward I began to read God's Word daily. It wasn't long until the Holy Spirit through the Scriptures began to witness to me about my salvation. God seemed to use one particular portion of Scripture to seal this truth to my heart. It was John 5:24. "Verily, verily, I say unto you, He that heareth my Word, and believeth on Him that sent me, hath everlasting life, and shall not come into condemnation; but is passed from death unto life."

"Heareth my Word, and *believeth* on Him that sent

me." Yes, I thought. *I've done that. I've truly heard His Word, the Bible, and I have believed.*

Then God spoke to me about the next word: "hath." I knew that "hath" meant "has." Has everlasting life! Tomorrow? Someday? When I die? No, *has right now!*

Then God led me to the next phrase: "And shall not come into condemnation." *No condemnation in the future*, I thought. *How wonderful! I shall not come into condemnation and judgment.*

Then God led me further to the last phrase: "But is passed from death unto life." *Is passed.* Gone. Already settled. Passed from what? From death unto life. "I have God's new life!"

Then I read the verse over and over. The truths flooded my mind: The one who hears and believes *HAS* eternal life—*now.* And he shall not come into condemnation but he *IS PASSED* already from death unto life!

Then I bowed my head and heart in prayerful thanksgiving. "I never need to worry," I said to myself. "It is settled forever. Now my responsibility is to serve Him the best I can as long as I live." Yes, that is how God spoke to me.

The story is told of two men who were journeying on their camels across the vast sandy regions of the Sahara desert. Slowly they made their way across the thirsty wilderness, following the footprints of an earlier caravan. Suddenly a violent sandstorm swept across the barren land and the two travelers were forced to take shelter in a nearby cave. The fierce, hot winds blew the sand and gravel until the men were scarcely able to see the camels by their side. At length the storm subsided, and all was serene once more. But as the men looked out across the wilderness the picture had changed completely. Every sand dune had shifted. Every shrub was covered. The few, meager landmarks were gone. One of the travelers, seeking in vain for some tracks, finally threw up his hands in utter dismay and exclaimed, "We are lost, we are hopelessly lost."

The other traveler had nothing to say. But that night after the sun sank beyond the western horizon, he gazed up into the star studded velvet of the night and said, "No, we are *not* lost. The stars are still there!"

So it is with us. The rapidly changing landscape of this stormy world may dismay us. The people we trust may fail us. And we may despair, feeling that we are hopelessly lost. But when we look up toward God rather than at our earthly surroundings, we can see that *the stars are still there*. Surely, if God can throw millions of stars into the sky, can hold all things together, and keep the universe moving with minute precision, we can rest assured that He is not haphazard about our eternal destiny. God's Word is more dependable than anything else in the universe. And when He is the guardian of our souls, we can be at peace knowing that we are indeed secure—without the shadow of a doubt.

This is *faith that endures*. This is God's way—to happiness!

THE CHILD
WHO RESCUED
CHRISTMAS

BY
JESSICA MATTHEWS

FIREFIGHTER WITH
A FROZEN HEART

BY
DIANNE DRAKE

MILLS
BOON

THE CHILD
WHO RESCUED
CHRISTMAS

BY
JESSICA MATTHEWS

Dedication

To my family, especially my husband, whose support never wavers.

First published in Great Britain 2011
by Mills & Boon, an imprint of Harlequin (UK) Limited.
Harlequin (UK) Limited, Eton House, 18-24 Paradise Road,
Richmond, Surrey TW9 1SR

© Jessica Matthews 2011

ISBN: 978 0 263 88612 2

Harlequin (UK) policy is to use papers that are natural, renewable and recyclable products and made from wood grown in sustainable forests. The logging and manufacturing process conform to the legal environmental regulations of the country of origin.

Printed and bound in Spain
by Blackprint CPI, Barcelona

Jessica Matthews's interest in medicine began at a young age, and she nourished it with medical stories and hospital-based television programmes. After a stint as a teenage candy-striper, she pursued a career as a clinical laboratory scientist. When not writing or on duty, she fills her day with countless family and school related activities. Jessica lives in the central United States, with her husband, daughter and son.

Recent titles by the same author:

MAVERICK IN THE ER
SIX-WEEK MARRIAGE MIRACLE
EMERGENCY: PARENTS NEEDED
HIS BABY BOMBSHELL
THE BABY DOCTOR'S BRIDE

Did you know these are also available as eBooks?
Visit www.millsandboon.co.uk

Dear Reader

Have you ever made a mistake that you bitterly regretted—to the point where you wish you could turn back time and make a better choice? My hero, Cole, had such a moment in his life, and it eventually came back to haunt him. Naturally I had to create a heroine strong enough to bear up under the pressure, and the following pages are the result. And what better time to set a story about love and forgiveness, goodwill and peace, than at Christmas?

So, as you take time to enjoy the season, I hope Sara and Cole's journey will touch your heart.

Happy reading!

Jessica

PROLOGUE

THIS day just kept getting better, Sara Wittman thought wryly as one of the morning headlines caught her eye.

Three people killed in medical helicopter crash.

She hated reading news like that—it was a horrible way to start her day—but morbid curiosity and a healthy dread drove her to read the few facts listed in the article.

En route from the University of Oklahoma Medical Center in Oklahoma City to Enid, the A-Star 350 helicopter went down in an open field thirty miles outside its destination for unknown reasons. The three people on board, pilot James Anderson of Dallas, Texas, Nurse Ruth Warren of Tulsa, Oklahoma, and Nurse Lilian Gomez of Norman, Oklahoma, died at the scene.

According to statements released by AirMed, the company that operates this flying medical service, the circumstances of the crash are still uncertain. The incident is under investigation by the Federal Aviation Administration and the National Transportation Safety Board.

As a nurse assigned to the medical-surgical floor of Nolan Heights Hospital, she occasionally cared for a patient who had to be flown to a tertiary care center for treatment and consequently had met the dedicated staff who flew those missions. Although Nolan Heights used a different company for their flying ambulance service, the men and women who specialized in providing that type of medicine were a special breed who'd garnered her respect. These people would be missed, not only by their families but also by the medical community as a whole.

"You're looking rather glum this morning." Cole, her husband of nearly three years, breezed into the kitchen wearing dark slacks and a rust-colored shirt—his usual attire for another busy day in his medical practice. He bussed her on the cheek before heading for the coffeemaker where she'd already poured a cup of the French roast she'd made strong enough to keep him running all morning.

She savored his husbandly peck before rattling the newspaper. "I was just reading about a medical helicopter crash in Oklahoma. Two nurses and the pilot were killed on the way to collect a patient."

"That's too bad," he remarked as he sipped from his mug and slipped a slice of bread into the toaster. "No one we know, I hope."

"No," she said, "although one of the nurses is from your old stomping grounds."

"Tulsa?"

"For being gone most of the night because of a patient, you're remarkably sharp this morning," she teased.

"It's all done with smoke and mirrors," he answered with a grin that after one year of dating, two years of living together and three years of marriage still jump-started her pulse every time. "But in answer to your question, Tulsa is a relatively large city. I didn't know every kid in my grade, much less my entire school."

"I suppose it would be surprising if you knew Ruth Warren."

He visibly froze. "Ruth Warren?"

"Yeah," she confirmed. "It doesn't give her age, though."

Then, because the news had obviously startled him, she asked, "Did you know a Ruth Warren?"

"The one I knew was a schoolteacher," he said slowly, his gaze speculative. "High school biology. Now that I think about it, she'd always talked about going into nursing. Maybe she finally did."

"Then it could have been your friend."

"I doubt it. Even if she did make a career change, the Ruth I knew was scared of heights. She'd always joked about how she'd never get on an airplane."

"There must be two Ruth Warrens," she guessed. "Both names are common enough and her surname could be her married name."

"It's possible," he murmured thoughtfully.

"Regardless, I'm sure her family, and everyone else's, is devastated."

"Hmm."

"And when a tragedy like this happens close to Christmas, it has to be even more difficult to handle," she commented, imagining how the season would never again be the same for those left behind. In the blink of an eye for these families, the holiday had lost its inherent excitement.

"Hmm."

Sara recognized his preoccupied tone. Certain his mind was already racing ahead to concentrate on the day's hectic schedule, she said offhandedly, "It's nice that we're closing the hospital at noon today."

"Yeah."

He was definitely not paying attention. "And Administration is doubling everyone's salaries."

"That's nice." Suddenly, his gaze landed on her. "What?"

"You weren't listening to me, were you?" she teased.

A sheepish expression appeared on his face. "Apparently not. Sorry."

"You're forgiven," she said lightly. "As long as you won't forget our annual anniversary getaway."

"I haven't," he assured her. "We have reservations for the weekend at the hotel in Bisbee, just as we decided, and we fly to Arizona on Thursday morning. It amazes me that you wanted to stay at that elevation and see snow when we'll be seeing plenty of it soon enough," he added in a mock grumble. "A sunny beach would have made more sense."

"We did the sunny beach last year," she pointed out. "This is different. Besides..." she gave him a sultry smile "...if we run into any of the resident ghosts that our hotel claims to have, we can bar ourselves in our room."

He grinned. "I vote we do that anyway."

As if on cue, Sara's watch beeped with her five-minute warning. Without looking at the time, she drained her mug and placed it in the sink. "Gotta run or I'll be late," she said as she stopped to give him a goodbye kiss.

He threaded an arm around her waist and pulled her close, his solid warmth comforting. "Do we have plans for this evening?"

She thought a minute. "No, why?"

The playful expression she recognized appeared on his face. "I predict I'm going to need a nap when I get home."

Ordinarily, the prospect would have thrilled her, but not today.

"Maybe we'll get lucky and make a baby tonight," he murmured with a feral smile and a seductive voice.

If only that were possible...

"We won't," she said flatly. "As of a few days ago, I'm not pregnant. It's the wrong time."

Her husband's appreciative gaze turned sympathetic. "Oh, honey. I'm sorry. Maybe next month."

Next month. It always came down to next month. For the last year and a half, those words had become her mantra.

"Yeah, maybe." Avoiding his gaze, she tried to pull out of his embrace, but he'd obviously heard the disappointment in her voice because he didn't let her go.

"Hey." His hand against the side of her face was gently reassuring. "It'll happen. Just be patient."

After all this time, her account holding that particular virtue was overdrawn. "I'm tired of being patient, Cole. We should see a different specialist." She finally voiced what she'd been contemplating off and on for the last month. "Dr. Eller could refer us to—"

"Sara," he chided, "Josh Eller is the best ob-gyn man in this part of the country. You know that."

"Yes, but another doctor might have a different opinion. He might take a more aggressive approach."

"A different doctor might," he agreed, "but Josh hasn't steered us wrong so far. You've gotten pregnant once. It's only been nine months."

Sadly, she'd miscarried within days after she'd learned she'd been expecting. Had she not been concerned about what she'd thought was a lingering stomach flu virus, she'd never have gone to the doctor, and when she'd miscarried, she would have attributed it to just another horrible period.

"But nothing's happened since," she protested. We should—"

"Be patient. Your body needs time to heal."

"Yes, but—"

"Josh said we should allow ourselves a year and we're close to that," he reminded her. "Life hasn't been so bad with just the two of us, has it?"

While their relationship hadn't sailed along on completely smooth seas—there'd been a brief ten days when they'd gone their separate ways because she'd despaired of him ever proposing and giving her the family and home life she wanted—she couldn't complain. "No, but a baby is like the icing on the cake when two people love each other. It—"

He stopped her in midsentence. "A baby will come if and when he's supposed to. You have to trust that Josh knows what he's doing. If he says not to worry, then don't."

She'd wanted Cole to be as eager to grow their family as she was, and his attitude grated on her. Didn't he understand how much she wanted this? Didn't he see that each passing month chipped away at her confidence and self-esteem?

And yet she understood Cole's propensity to maintain the status quo when it came to his personal life. Although he never said, she guessed that losing his parents at such an early age and the subsequent turmoil in his life had made him reluctant to modify an established routine. She didn't necessarily like his behavior, but it was a part of his character and she accepted it.

"Look," she began, "I know how difficult it is for you to change course when you're happy with the path you're on. After all, between dating and living together, it took you almost three years before you finally proposed, but you should be as excited about a baby as I am."

"I am."

"You don't act like it," she mumbled.

He raised an eyebrow. "Would wringing my hands and calling Josh every week, pestering him for information and advice, change things?"

He had a point. "No," she conceded. "But I want you to want this as much as I do and I'm not getting that impression from you." While she knew Cole was more reserved than most, she wanted to see a more enthusiastic response. "Sometimes I think you only agreed to have a baby to humor me."

"Oh, Sara." He patted her back as he hugged her. "I'll admit that I'm not eager for our lives to change because I'm happy with just the two of us. But I'd be happy if you got pregnant, too. A little girl with your pixie nose would be cute. So, you see, I'm basically a happy kind of guy." He winked.

His teasing tone defused her aggravation. "Oh, you." She poked him playfully. "Pixie nose, indeed."

"Seriously, Sara…" his gaze grew intent "…stressing out about the situation won't help matters. Josh won't steer us wrong."

Her husband's confidence soothed her frazzled nerves. Slowly, she nodded. "You're right, he won't."

"Good girl." He cupped her face with both hands and kissed her. "There's no doubt in my mind that it'll happen, so stop worrying. Before long, you'll be complaining about morning sickness, swollen ankles and not being able to see your own feet."

She offered a wan smile. "I guess. Now, I'd better run or I really will be late."

After she'd left, bundled against the cold, Cole noticed how quiet the house seemed without his bubbly wife's presence. He'd hated seeing her so downcast for those few minutes and he wished Sara would focus on what she had rather than what she didn't have. She'd always made it plain that she wanted a large family—two boys and two girls—like the one she'd had growing up, and while the thought of being responsible for four children—*four*—was enough to scare him spitless, he'd been willing to patiently *and thoroughly* do his part to fulfill her dream. He grinned as he remembered the last time they'd made love. They'd started in the kitchen then detoured to their oversize soaker tub before ending up in bed.

He enjoyed nights like those—craved them, in fact—and he wasn't in any particular hurry to lose them. Truth was, he liked having his wife to himself. The idea that he someday would have even fewer private moments with her than he did now only made him cherish those times all the more.

While he looked upon their inability to conceive as one of the temporary mountains of life some people had to face—and was, in fact, a little relieved because he'd had so little experience with a loving family—she saw it as a personal failure. She shouldn't, of course, because they were only in the early stages of the process. She'd gotten pregnant within six months of when they'd stopped using any birth control and although she'd lost the baby, only another nine months had passed. Consequently, they'd never thought they'd needed fertility testing, although if nothing happened soon, they would.

And yet he truly did believe what he'd told her. Mother Nature simply needed time to work and Josh would decide on the proper time for medical science to intervene.

Content to leave the situation in his colleague's capable hands, he sat down to polish off his toast and coffee. As he munched, he idly glanced at the newspaper his wife had discarded and the trepidation he'd felt when Sara had first mentioned the helicopter crash came back, full force.

Ruth Warren.

Surely the woman wasn't the same Ruth Warren from his youth—the same Ruth Warren he'd spent time with a few years ago at his fifteen-year class reunion. The same class reunion when he'd drowned his sorrows with far too many margaritas because Sara had left him.

In spite of his reluctance to take the step she'd wanted—

marriage—he'd come to his senses quickly. Accepting that his life would stretch ahead interminably without her, he'd proposed a week later. Sara had never pressed for details about his change of heart and he'd never offered them, except to say that he'd been miserable without her. Six months later, after Sara had planned her dream wedding, they had been married. Now, in a few more weeks, they'd celebrate their three-year anniversary.

Three years of the happiness and contentment he hadn't felt since he was eight.

Suddenly, he had to know if the Ruth Warren mentioned in the article was the girl who'd often sat beside him at school because their names fell so close alphabetically. Now that he thought about it, hadn't she mentioned during their reunion weekend that she'd turned her teaching certificate into a nurse's diploma? To be honest, there was a lot about those two days he didn't remember...

Determined to find an answer, he abandoned his coffee on his way to his office and powered up his computer. Minutes later, he'd found the online obituary at the *Tulsa World* website and scanned the details. Most, he already knew.

Age 33, preceded in death by her parents, attended the University of Oklahoma, earned a degree in secondary education and later in nursing before taking a position as a flight nurse.

Reading the facts suddenly made them seem familiar, as if she'd told him of her career change and he'd simply forgotten. He read on...

Survivors include a son, as well as many friends and former students.

She'd had a son? She hadn't mentioned a child, but she'd never been one to share the details of her personal life. He was certain he'd asked about her life—it had been a reunion, after all—but he'd been too focused on his own misery to remember the things she'd told him. Idly, he wondered if the boy's father was still in the picture. Probably not, if the man hadn't received mention.

A graveside service will be held at 10:00 a.m. Wednesday at the Oaklawn Cemetery.

Cole leaned back in his chair and stared blankly at the screen. The description of Ruth's life had been rather succinct, and certainly didn't do justice to the young woman he remembered. She'd lived through a horrible childhood, carried enough baggage to fill a plane's cargo hold and had a gift for defusing tense moments with a wisecrack, but she'd always been a great listener.

And now Ruth was gone. Of course, he hadn't talked to her since that weekend, but now he wished he'd contacted her and told her that he'd taken her advice. He'd faced his demons and followed his heart. Now it was too late.

Then again, Ruth had probably known…

It was hard to believe that someone Cole's own age, someone who should have lived another fifty years or so, someone with whom Cole had grown up with, was gone. Her death gave him a glimpse of his own mortality, and suddenly he wished he'd taken off the entire week to spend with Sara instead of just two days.

For an instant, he toyed with the idea of attending Ruth's funeral, then decided against it. Depending on how old her son was, offering condolences would either be overwhelming or wouldn't mean anything at this point. It would be better if he wrote a letter for the boy to read when he was ready—a letter telling him what a wonderful friend his mother had been.

And although he knew Ruth would never have mentioned their one-night stand to anyone even in passing, in one tiny corner of his heart he was relieved that now it would remain a secret for all eternity.

CHAPTER ONE

"WHAT do you say you run away with me this weekend?" Sebastian Lancaster asked Sara two days later as she straightened his bedsheets during her last patient round before her shift-change report. "I know this great little place for dancing. I could show you a few steps that will make your head spin."

Sara smiled at her eighty-five-year-old patient who relied on a walker and wheezed with every breath, thanks to his years of habitual smoking. No doubt the only head that would spin with any sudden move would be his.

"No can do," she said cheerfully, already anticipating her upcoming weekend away from the daily grind of hospitals, patients and housework. "I already have plans."

"No problem." He coughed. "What is it they say? Plans are made to be broken."

"I think you're referring to rules, not plans," she corrected.

He waved a wrinkled, age-spotted hand. "Same difference. It's been ages since I've tangoed and if I'm not mistaken, you'd be good at it. Got the legs for it."

Knowing the elderly gentleman couldn't see past his elbow, she let his comment about her legs slide. "I'll bet you were quite the Fred Astaire in your day," she commented, giving the top blanket a final pat.

"Oh, I was. My wife and I could have outshone these young whippersnappers on those celebrity dance shows. So whaddya say? Wanna spring me from this joint so we can take a spin?"

She laughed at his suitably hopeful expression, although they both knew she couldn't fulfill his request. Between his emphysema and current bout of pneumonia, he was struggling to handle basic activities, much less add a strenuous activity like dancing. However, his physical limitations didn't stop this perpetual flirt from practicing his pickup lines. Sara guessed his wife must have been adept at keeping his behavior in check, or else she'd turned a blind eye to his Romeo attitude.

"Sorry, but I'm already running away this weekend," she told him, glancing at the drip rate of his IV. "With my husband, who just happens to be your doctor."

He nodded matter-of-factly, as if not particularly disappointed by his failure. "Shoulda known. The pretty ones are always taken. Must say, though…" he stopped to cough "…that if Doc had the good sense to pick you out of the eligible women, then he's got a good head on his shoulders."

"I like to think so," she said lightly, aware that her relationship with Cole had endured some dark days. However, in spite of the usual differences of opinion between people of diverse backgrounds and ideas, in spite of his initial reluctance to commit and in spite of her miscarriage nine months ago, life had been good.

"You two just going away for nothing better to do or for something special?"

"It's our three-year anniversary," she replied. "Actually, we still have a few weeks before the actual date, but this was the only weekend we could both get away."

"Ah, then you're still newlyweds. I'll bet you're eager to

have your second honeymoon, even if it wasn't that long ago since your first, eh?" He cackled at his joke before ending on a cough.

Sara smiled. "It's always great to get away, honeymoon or not."

She'd been looking forward to this weekend for a month now and could hardly wait. Cole, on the other hand, had been preoccupied the last few days, which had been somewhat surprising because he'd been as eager to stay in the haunted historic hotel as she was.

"Too much to do before I can leave with an easy conscience," he'd said when she'd asked.

While that was probably true—as a hospitalist, he'd put in long hours to ensure the doctors covering his patients would find everything in order while he was gone—she had to wonder if something else wasn't on his mind. Still, she was confident that once they shook the dust of Nolan Heights off their feet, he'd leave those worries behind. And if distance didn't help, then the skimpy black lace negligee in her suitcase would.

"Well, go and have a good time," Sebastian said. "If he takes you dancing, dance a slow one for me." He winked one rheumy brown eye.

"I will," she promised. "When I come back to work on Monday, if you're still here, I'll tell you all about it."

"Do that," he said before he closed his eyes, clearly spent from their short conversation.

Sara strode out of the room, her soft soles silent on the linoleum. She'd begun to chart her final notes for her patients when another nurse, Millie Brennan, joined her.

"How's Mr. Lancaster this afternoon?"

Sara smiled at the twenty-six-year-old, somewhat jealous of her strawberry blond tresses when her own short hair was unremarkably brown. The only plus was that

Sara's curls were natural whereas Millie's came from a bottle.

"As sassy as ever. Given his medical condition, it's amazing how he can still flirt with us."

"Wait until he feels better," Millie said darkly. "Then he'll grab and pinch. When he does, it's a sign he's ready to go back to his assisted living home."

"I'll keep it in mind," Sara said.

"So," Millie said in an obvious prelude to a change of subject, "are you packed and ready to go tomorrow?"

Sara smiled. "Almost. I just have to throw a few last-minute things into my bag and I'm ready. Cole, on the other hand, hasn't started. I'm going to work on his suitcase as soon as I get home."

Millie grinned. "Don't forget to pack a swimsuit. And that teddy we bought a few weeks ago."

"Those were the first things in the case," Sara answered, already looking forward to modeling the lacy negligee under her husband's admiring gaze. While most people thought they were going to enjoy ski slopes and mountain hikes, Sara had planned a far more private itinerary—an itinerary that focused only on the two of them.

"When are you leaving?" Millie asked.

"Our flight leaves early tomorrow morning. We'd thought about staying the night at one of the airport hotels, but it depends on Cole. You know how he is." Sara added, "He can't leave if he doesn't have every *i* dotted when it comes to his patients." She was convinced that was why everyone thought so highly of her husband—he didn't cut corners for convenience's sake.

She sighed. "Sometimes, his attention to detail is rather frustrating, especially when it interferes with our plans."

"Yeah, but you love him anyway."

Sara had half fallen in love with him the first day she'd

met him, when he'd waltzed onto her floor as a first-year family medicine resident. She'd been suffering her own new-job jitters and he'd taken pity on her when she'd knocked a suture tray off the counter in obvious nervousness. The cup of coffee he'd subsequently bought her and the pep talk he'd delivered had marked the beginning of their professional and personal relationship.

"Yeah, I do," she said, returning Millie's grin with one of her own. "The only problem I have right now is knowing what to get him for Christmas. It's still two months away, but it'll be here before we know it."

"Has he mentioned anything that he wants?"

"Lots of things, but afterward he goes out and buys them for himself. I've told him not to do that, but so far it hasn't made an impression."

"It will when he wakes up on Christmas morning and there's nothing to open under the tree," Millie predicted. "Or you could just fill a box with socks and underwear."

"I could," Sara agreed, "but I couldn't be that cruel. I'm sure I'll get an idea this weekend."

"Well, good luck. As my mother always says, what do you get a man who has everything?"

What indeed? Sara thought. The one thing she'd wanted to give him—news that he'd be a father—wasn't something she could accomplish on her own, no matter how hard she wished for her dream to come true. Having grown up with a sister and two brothers, she wanted her house to ring with the same pitter-patter of footsteps as her parents' house had.

Be patient, Cole had reminded her. She'd try, she told herself. So what if it took them a little longer for their family to grow than she'd like? As long as it happened, as long as they loved each other, it would be worth the wait.

Fortunately, for the rest of her shift, she had little time

to dwell on her personal plans, but the minute she left the hospital shortly after six o'clock, her thoughts raced ahead to her upcoming weekend.

Her excitement only grew when she found the lights blazing in their home and Cole's SUV parked in the garage. Pleased that Cole had finished earlier than she'd expected, she dashed through the cold garage and into her cozy house.

"This is a pleasant surprise," she called out to Cole from the mud room as she tugged off her gloves and hung her parka on a coat hook. "I honestly didn't think you'd make it home before eight."

He rose from his place at the table as she entered the kitchen and kissed her on the cheek. "Things turned out differently than we'd both anticipated," he answered with a tight smile that, with his strained expression, set off her mental radar. "How about some coffee?"

He turned away to dump several sweetener packets into his own mug. "You never drink caffeine at this time of night," she said as she watched his movements with a knot forming in her stomach. "What's wrong?"

"It's cold outside. How about hot tea instead?"

He was trying to distract her, which only meant that something was wrong. *Horribly* wrong. The knot tightened.

"Cole," she warned. "I know it's cold, but I'm not thirsty or hungry. Something is obviously on your mind. What is it?" As a thought occurred to her, she gasped. "Oh, no. We can't go on our trip, can we? Something happened and Chris can't cover for you at the hospital. Oh, Cole," she finished on a wail. "Not *again!*"

"Sara," he interrupted. "Stop jumping to conclusions. This isn't about my schedule. Just. Sit. Down."

She sat. With her hands clasped together in her lap, she

waited. He sank onto the chair beside hers and carefully set his mug on the table. "An attorney spoke with me today."

Dread skittered down her spine. A lawyer never visited a physician with good news. "Is someone suing the hospital? And you?"

"No, nothing like that. Mr. Maitland is a partner in a law firm based in Tulsa."

"Tulsa?" Knowing he'd grown up in that area of Oklahoma, she asked, "Does this involve your relatives?"

"No."

"Then what did he want with you?"

"Do you remember reading the newspaper article about the medical helicopter crash the other day?"

"Yes. We'd talked about one of the nurses. I can't remember her name..."

"Ruth Warren," he supplied.

"Yeah. What about the crash?"

"As it turns out, I *did* know this particular Ruth Warren. Quite well, in fact."

His shock was understandable. She reached out to grab his hand, somewhat surprised by his cold fingers. "I'm sorry."

"In high school, we were good friends, although I've only seen her once since then. At our class reunion a few years ago."

She furrowed her brow in thought. "You never mentioned a class reunion. When was this?"

"Remember those ten days in July, after you and I had broken up?"

"Yes," she said cautiously.

"During that time, I went to my class reunion. It was over the Fourth of July weekend, and I didn't have anything else to do, so I went."

"Really? Knowing how you've avoided going back to

the area so you can't accidentally run into your relatives, I'm surprised."

"Yeah, well, it was a spur-of-the-moment decision," he said wryly. "Anyway, during that weekend, I met up with Ruth."

She touched his hand. "I'm glad you had a chance to reconnect with her after high school. Had you heard from her since then?"

"No. Not a word."

Sara had assumed as much because Cole had never mentioned her, but he was a closemouthed individual and often didn't mention those things he considered insignificant.

"Then what did the lawyer want?"

"He represents Ruth's estate. She named me, *us,* in her will."

Sara sat back in her chair, surprised. "She did? What did she do? Leave you her box of high school memorabilia?"

She'd expected her joke to make him smile, but it fell flat, which struck her as odd.

"She left us something more valuable than a box of dried corsages and school programs," he said evenly. "She entrusted the most important thing she had to us. Her son."

"Her son?" Of all the things he might have said, nothing was as shocking as this. "How old is he?"

"He's two and a half. His birthday was in April. April 2."

Surprise and shock gave way to excitement. "Oh, Cole," she said, reaching across the table to once again take his hand, her heart twisting at the thought of that motherless little boy. "He's practically a baby."

As she pondered the situation, she began to wonder why this woman had chosen them out of all the people she possibly could have known.

"Exactly why *did* she appoint us as his guardians? She

never met me and you said yourself that you hadn't kept in contact with her. What about the boy's dad? Or her family? Didn't she have friends who were closer to her than you are? I'm not complaining, mind you. I'm only trying to understand why she gave him to people who are, for all intents and purposes, relative strangers, instead of choosing substitute parents who were within her current circle of friends."

"She had no family to speak of," he told her. "Ruth grew up in foster care and as soon as she graduated, she was on her own."

"If you hadn't seen her for three years, it's especially odd she'd ask us to take care of him. There has to be a connection—"

"There is," he said, clutching his mug with both hands. "But to explain it, I have something to confess."

Once again, warning bells clanged. "Okay," she said slowly.

"Ruth and I—that weekend we were together at the reunion…" he drew a deep breath as if bracing himself "…I did a stupid thing. Several stupid things, in fact. I was angry that you weren't satisfied with our relationship as it was—"

"Just living together," she interjected for clarification.

He nodded. "I was hurt that after all those years of being a couple, you wouldn't be satisfied or happy until I put a ring on your finger."

"Oh, Cole," she said, disappointed that he hadn't fully understood why she'd pressed him to take their relationship to the next level. "It wasn't about flashing a gold band or a huge diamond. It was what the ring *represented*—a commitment to spend the rest of our lives together."

"I realized that. Later. But during that first week we were apart, while I was angry and hurt and feeling everything in between, I went to my reunion and…" he took another deep breath "…drank a few too many margaritas. A *lot* too many." He paused.

She was surprised to learn that Cole—a man who couldn't even be classified as a moderate drinker—had over-imbibed. While she wasn't condoning his action, she figured most people had done so at one time or another. His actions weren't smart or ideal, but drinking too much on one occasion wasn't an unforgivable offense, in her opinion, even if at the time he'd been old enough to know better.

"And?" she coaxed.

"When I saw Ruth again—we confided a lot in each other during our teen years—we talked. We both unloaded on each other and she helped me admit a few hard truths—"

"Do you mean to say that your friend *Ruth* convinced you to propose?" She'd always believed that he'd come to that conclusion on his own. It was disappointing to imagine that he'd been persuaded to marry her not because he loved her but because of a relative stranger's advice.

"Ruth didn't convince me to do anything," he insisted. "She pointed out what I already knew but couldn't quite admit—that I loved you and couldn't imagine my life without you—which was why I was so angry and hurt and miserable. And if I loved you, then I had to face my fears and propose."

Fears? He'd been *afraid?*

"Wait a minute." She held up her hands to forestall him so she could sort through his confession. "You'd always said that you wouldn't marry until you were ready, but now I learn that you were *scared?* Why didn't you explain? We could have discussed this."

"If you'll recall, we'd tried, but the conversation deteriorated and you walked out."

She wanted to protest that he could have stopped her, or that he could have called, or he could have done any number of things, but placing blame at this date was silly.

"Okay," she said evenly, "both of us could have done things differently, but truly, Cole, what were you afraid of?"

"That I couldn't be the husband you wanted or needed. That our relationship would change. We were doing great just living together and I had this...this *fear*...that marriage might ruin what we had."

"How was that possible?" she asked, incredulous. "We'd been living together for two years and dated for a year prior to that. How did you think marriage would ruin—?"

"You forget that the last functional family relationship I was in ended when I was eight. What did *I* know about how a healthy marriage should be? By the time I started college, I didn't know if the happy home I remembered was real or make-believe. Do you really wonder why I might be afraid our relationship would change, and not for the better? And when it did, both of us would be stuck in an untenable situation."

She fell silent as she processed the information. "Okay, I can respect that, but you obviously faced your fears because you found me at my friend's house and proposed." It bothered her to think that he could discuss his fears with a woman he hadn't seen in years instead of with her, but there was little she could do about it now. She only hoped he wouldn't tell her that at the time asking her to marry him had simply been the lesser of two evils.

"Proposing—marrying you—was the best decision I ever made. Don't ever forget that."

His vehemence both surprised and alarmed her. "Okay," she said warily. "But meanwhile you had your heart-to-heart with Ruth and because you two drowned your sorrows together, she wanted you to raise her child if something happened to her."

He visibly winced and avoided her gaze. "Unfortunately, we did more than talk and drown our sorrows."

The bottom dropped out of her stomach. "Oh, Cole. Please don't tell me that you— That you and this high school friend…"

He nodded, his expression grave. "We slept together. We didn't plan it, I swear. I didn't even know she was going to *be* at the reunion. The combination of everything from my insecurities and alcohol level to Ruth needing her own listening ear all coalesced until events just…happened. I've never done anything like that before or since and I regretted it right away. You have to believe me."

A part of her brain heard his near-desperation, but she was still too numbed by his newest revelation to grant him absolution.

"You should have told me," she said as her whole body seemed to turn into ice. "We should have had this conversation as soon as you rolled back into town. About your doubts and your…and Ruth."

"I couldn't," he admitted. "I was too embarrassed and ashamed. I didn't go to my reunion intending to do anything but meet with old friends. After my lapse in judgment—" his voice was rueful "—I knew this news would be devastating and even though we technically weren't a couple at the time it happened, I couldn't risk my mistake potentially destroying our future."

Would she have refused to marry him if she'd known he'd slept with another woman? Knowing how devastated she'd been at the time he'd stormed out after their argument, hearing that would have probably convinced her to count her blessings that he'd walked away.

At this point, however, she didn't know for certain what she might have done. She might only have extended their engagement until she'd been fully persuaded that he hadn't entertained second thoughts about marriage, but one truth remained undeniable. He'd taken away her opportunity to choose.

"I can't begin to tell you how sorry I am," he added. "If I could turn back the clock and live that night over, I would."

His remorse seemed genuine, but it did little to ease her sense of betrayal. "Sorry that it happened or sorry that you told me?"

He didn't have to explain, her little voice pointed out. *He could have simply let the story stand that they were old friends who'd reconnected during a class reunion. You'd still never know...*

"There isn't a day that goes by that I don't feel regret for my actions," he said, meeting her gaze. "That's something I have to live with for the rest of my life."

The pain in his eyes wasn't feigned; she recognized that. Unfortunately, his revelation made her question so many things. Had he *really* wanted to marry her, or had he only asked her because he'd found his courage in the bottom of a bottle?

How many other secrets had he kept from her? He probably had many, because there were so many personal topics he refused to discuss.

And yet, technically, they *had* severed their relationship, which meant he hadn't been required to answer to her. No vows had been broken at the time he and Ruth...

But it still hurt to know that he'd fallen into bed with another woman so quickly. Granted, the alcohol and his own anger had contributed to his decision, but still...

Although the truth weighed heavily, she had to give

credit where it was due. He'd been a faithful husband for the past three years and he'd been honest when he could have kept this secret forever and no one would have ever known. Yet he'd taken the risk and apologized profusely rather than simply brush off the incident.

Emotionally, she wanted to bristle and remain angry, but logically the incident was over and done with. Walking away from him because of one relatively *ancient* mistake committed when they'd been separated suggested her love must be terribly shallow if she couldn't forgive and forget.

"Sara?" he asked tentatively.

She exhaled a long, drawn-out sigh and offered a tremulous smile. "As disappointed as I am, as betrayed as I feel, even though some would say I shouldn't, I can't change the past. We'll leave it there, shall we?"

"Unfortunately, there's more," he said.

"More?" she asked, incredulous. "What more can there be? Isn't this *friendship* you had—" she chose that word instead of "affair" because she didn't know if a one-night stand fit the true definition "—the reason why she wanted you to look after her child?"

He didn't answer at first. "Sara," he said softly, "Brody is thirty months old. His second birthday came during the first part of April."

"Yes, you already told me."

He rubbed the back of his neck. "Do the math."

She did. Then, with a sinking heart, she knew. The apology on his face confirmed it.

"Oh. My. God. He's your son, too."

If Sara's face had revealed her shock before, now Cole only saw horror. From her sudden intake of breath, the oxygen in the room had vanished with the news, just as it had when Parker Maitland had delivered the same bomb-

shell to him a few hours ago. This news had knocked his
world off its axis, just as it had for his wife.

Eternity had only lasted forty-eight hours.

An unholy dread had filled him from that moment on
because he would have to explain the inexplicable to Sara
His confession had crushed her, just as he'd suspected it
would, and, just as he'd feared, the light in her eyes had
faded. Already she stared at him as if he'd become someone she didn't know.

How ironic to be in this position. After spending his
entire life always weighing his options and plotting his
course carefully to avoid potential pitfalls, *the one time*
he'd acted impulsively would haunt him for ever.

Oh, he could have ended this earlier without Sara ever
being the wiser. He could have told the lawyer that he
didn't want to raise Ruth's son—and his—and all this
would have vanished like morning mist on a hot summer
day. Yet he couldn't build one lie upon another, no matter
how enticing the idea was. Untruths always had a tendency
to be revealed.

"You had a baby with this Ruth person."

She sounded dazed, much as he had when he'd heard
the news. "Apparently so."

"Are you certain? I mean, if she slept with you at your
reunion, she might have spent time with someone else,
too."

Her faith in him was bittersweet and only made him feel
worse than he already did. He, too, had posed the question, hoping there'd been some misunderstanding, but the
possibility had died an instant death after Maitland had
presented him with undeniable proof.

"She didn't," he assured her, hating to destroy her hopes
but understanding how the possibility was a lifeline for
her to grab—a lifeline that their life wouldn't be turned

upside down so easily. "Maitland gave me a picture of the boy. There's a strong…family resemblance."

It was more than a resemblance. The phrase "chip off the old block" came to mind. If he compared photos of himself at that age, he'd think his image had been cut and pasted into a scene from today.

"And she wants you to look after her—your—child."

From past experience, Cole knew that Sara's reserved tone was merely a smoke screen, especially given the words she'd chosen. *Her. Your child.* Underneath her deadly calm was a churning cauldron of emotions held in check by sheer force of will. Cole would have rather seen her yell, scream or throw things, instead of seeing her so controlled.

"She wants *us* to look after him," he corrected. "She wanted Brody to have two parents, not one."

As she sat frozen, Cole hastened to continue. "Apparently, Ruth knew the situation would be…difficult…which was why she left a letter for you to read."

He dug in the manila envelope Maitland had given him and placed the small sealed white envelope that bore Sara's name in front of her. Next to it, he positioned Brody's photograph so that those impish dark brown eyes were facing her.

Sara didn't move to accept the envelope or glance at the picture.

"Ruth rightly believed you would play an important role in Brody's upbringing, which is why she stipulated that you also had to agree to take him."

"And if I don't?"

He paused, torn between wanting her to refuse and hoping she'd accept the challenge ahead of them. "Then the search will begin for different parents," he said evenly. "According to Maitland, Ruth hoped that wouldn't happen. He and his wife, Eloise, were Ruth's neighbors and they knew how much she worried about Brody going into the same foster-care system she had."

"If they knew Ruth so well, why didn't she appoint them as his substitute parents?"

"Parker is sixty-nine and Eloise is sixty-seven. As much as they love Brody, it isn't feasible for them to parent a child at their age." Parker had told him that he and Ruth had discussed this scenario and they'd both agreed that Brody needed younger parents who would conceivably give him siblings as well as live long enough to see him through high school and college.

"Where is he now?"

"He's with Maitland and his wife at a hotel." He paused. "Parker invited us to stop by at our convenience tonight. However, he did mention that Brody usually goes to bed at eight and with all the commotion of the past few days, he's been a little cranky if he stays up later than that."

The silence in the room became deafening and Cole watched helplessly as Sara rubbed her forehead with a shaky hand. "I don't know what to say," she murmured. "I'm tempted to believe I'm dreaming, that this is just an elaborate hoax or a misunderstanding."

"I know how you feel, but this…" he fingered the photo "…proves otherwise."

He stared at the snapshot lying on the table, picking out the facial features that seemed to be carbon copies of his own—coal-black hair, dimples, a straight nose and lop-sided grin. Yet, even with the proof before him, he was still hardly able to accept that he had a son.

A *son*.

While he'd been willing to add to their family—*some-day* in the future—knowing he had a son *now* was mind-boggling. It was one thing to feel guilty about his one-night stand, but quite another to know a child had resulted. He didn't know if he felt happy or sad, disappointed or excited, but he'd sort through those emotions later. At this moment, the reality had to be addressed, which was, namely, would they accept Brody into their home, or would Brody enter the same state-run children's services that Ruth had loathed?

He simply couldn't go against Ruth's wishes, but her way was filled with pitfalls. Having grown up in a situation where he hadn't been wanted, he'd always vowed to keep some sort of "escape clause" in his relationships, which was why he'd had so much trouble making a commitment to Sara. But now, if he accepted Ruth's child, *his* son, there would be no escape. If he intended to do this, he had to do so with the intent of being in it for the long haul.

This, at least, was the same decision he'd made before he'd proposed. And that had worked out, hadn't it? he told himself.

Or, it had, until he'd lost all common sense on that long-ago night.

He wanted to scream at the fates for putting him in this position, but what was done was done. There was only one way to escape this time, but as he glanced at Brody's photo, the idea didn't appeal as much as it might have. After all, if he'd been willing to face his fears and have a baby with Sara, how was this any different?

There was a big difference, he thought tiredly. Sara was his wife and she'd stand beside him, helping him, guiding him along the right path, correcting his mistakes. Now the question was, would she stay with him or not? Would he lose his son *and* his wife?

He studied her, wishing she'd say or do something rather than remain locked in icy calm. If only they had time to come to terms with the situation and what it meant to them as a couple, but time was a luxury they didn't have.

"Sara?" he asked tentatively. "We have to make a decision."

"Right *now?*" She sounded horrified.

"Maybe not this instant," he conceded, "but definitely within the next twenty-four hours. Brody's future has to be settled, one way or another. Keeping him in limbo isn't in his best interests."

He'd wondered if the prospect of having the baby she'd wanted would overshadow its origins, but she clearly hadn't reached that level of acceptance yet. He understood. He was still stunned and he'd felt the bombshell several hours earlier.

She nodded, almost absentmindedly.

Thinking that Sara would benefit from seeing Ruth's wishes in black and white, he pulled a copy of the will out of the manila envelope and flipped to the pages in question.

"Ruth had arranged for all of her assets to be placed into a trust fund for Brody and she named us as the trustees. She didn't want finances to factor in to our decision, so she left a modest nest egg for his care."

Not that he intended to tap into it if they chose to raise him. After all, Brody was *his* son, and his responsibility.

"There are a few personal things she asked that we keep for him, heirlooms if you will. Everything else will be sold."

"I see."

"She also asked that we legally adopt him so he carries our surname rather than hers."

"She thought of everything, didn't she?" she said wryly.

"I'm sure she and her legal counsel tried to cover every contingency."

"Did she have a plan if we decided not to raise her child?"

Cole's cautious optimism fell as Sara asked this same question for a second time, as if she wanted to be sure she had other options.

"As I said earlier, Ruth had hoped you wouldn't make that choice."

"Did she make a plan B?" Sara pressed on, as if through gritted teeth.

Cole sighed. "She did. Brody will become a ward of the state and will be eligible for adoption by another couple."

In that instant, he knew he was facing an untenable situation. Ruth had guessed correctly that he wouldn't be able to easily give up his son, but if Sara wasn't in favor of keeping him, he'd be forced to choose between his wife and a boy he'd just learned was his. Neither was a palatable option.

Still, he wanted to think positive…

She frowned. "Wouldn't you have to relinquish your rights if you're his father?"

He'd wondered if she would have realized that. While everything within him fought that idea, the letter Ruth had left for his eyes only had requested him to do just that if Sara wouldn't agree to her terms.

I know how difficult this would be for you, Ruth had written, *but you know far better than I how much harder Brody's life would be to live in a home where one parental figure didn't want him…*

He might not want to sign those documents, and his decision would haunt him if he did, but he'd do it, for Brody's sake. "Yes," he said simply, hating the mere notion of it. "I would."

And he'd regret it for the rest of his life.

She paused. The wrinkle between her eyebrows suggested she was weighing her options. "And if we take him?" she finally asked. "What then?"

A spark of optimism flared. "Then, starting tomorrow, he'll spend time with us. The Maitlands will stay in town for a few days to ease his transition but they can't stay longer because they have family commitments of their own."

"That's it? He just moves in?"

"More or less. There are several legal details to take care of during the next few days and weeks but, to be honest, I can't remember what Maitland told me they were. As soon as we come to an agreement, they'll arrange for the personal belongings to be shipped here."

"But all of this hinges on our decision."

As far as he was concerned, there wasn't a decision to make. The thought of committing himself to the responsibility of another human being who would depend upon him for years to come might send a cold shiver down his spine—a fact that Ruth had known full well—but he couldn't deny her request, not just because Brody was his own son but because it was time to face his fears.

Unfortunately, the decision wasn't completely his to make.

It was ironic to think that Sara would have jumped for joy at taking in Brody had someone else fathered him. Unfortunately, Brody's presence would not only be a visual and constant reminder of his error in judgment but also that she'd lost her own child. The only question was, could she look past those reminders or not?

"Yes," he answered simply, threading his fingers together in a white-knuckled grip. "Keep in mind he has nowhere else to go."

She met his gaze. "That's not fair, Cole. Don't play on my sympathies to get what you obviously want."

"I'm only stating a fact."

Slowly, she rose, leaving the photo on the table. "I won't apologize for needing time."

"Okay," he conceded, "but—"

She held up her hands. "I can't rush into a decision without thinking this through. The thing is, whatever we—I— decide to do about your son, our lives will never be the same."

As if he needed to be reminded... He was damned if he did, and damned if he didn't. Sara must have come to the same realization, too.

Suddenly, holding a person's life in his hands, medically speaking, seemed like less of a minefield than the situation looming ahead of him. Although he'd mentioned a twenty-four-hour deadline, somehow he sensed that announcing the Maitlands were expecting a decision by tomorrow morning wouldn't be well received.

He watched helplessly as she walked out of the room.

As he sat alone, he thought about how he'd enjoyed almost three years of blissful ignorance. Ruth should have told him and the fact she hadn't angered him. He had deserved to know, damn it!

Like Sara deserved to know? his little voice asked. *You wanted to protect your relationship with Sara, so maybe Ruth was doing the same for you...*

He sighed as he recognized the truth. Ruth's silence *had* provided a simpler solution to their dilemma. She'd known how crazily in love he'd been with Sara and breaking the news would have driven a wedge into his new marriage. Not only that, Ruth would have had to share Brody with him because as unprepared as he felt about fatherhood, he would have insisted on knowing his own son, even if he'd been a long-distance parent.

The idea that he might never have known about Brody if Ruth hadn't died didn't set well and was too close to his own situation for comfort. His only aunt and uncle hadn't bothered to make contact with him until he was eight, when circumstances had forced them to do so. While Brody's fate was still undecided, he certainly wouldn't ignore the boy in the meantime.

Idly, he wondered it this one subtle difference proved that his fears of repeating his relatives' dysfunctional behavior were unfounded. Of course, wanting to meet Brody was hardly enough evidence to make a case, but it was a difference that he could think about and consider. In the meantime, he had more pressing concerns...

The clock on the microwave showed six-thirty. Had only thirty minutes passed since he'd broken the news to Sara? Thirty minutes since he'd shattered his wife's faith in him?

He glanced at the sealed envelope on the table before focusing on the photo of his son. *His son*. A living, breathing product of his own DNA, a continuation of the Wittman family tree.

The same awed thoughts had bombarded him after Sara had announced her pregnancy but this time the feelings were a little different. Now he had a name and face whereas before the only tangible evidence of his child had been a number on her lab report. Before he'd had time to dream big dreams, to imagine a little boy or girl with Sara's beautiful eyes and his crooked smile, or to work through his reservations about being a parent, Sara had miscarried.

Brody, however, was here. In the flesh. Already walking and talking with a personality of his own.

Suddenly, the past two-plus years of ignorant bliss were far too long. He wanted to meet his son *tonight,* regardless of the hour or how cranky he might be. Waiting until tomorrow seemed like an eternity.

As he heard a loud thump coming from the direction

of their bedroom, however, his eagerness faded. Meeting a child he might never be able to claim as his own could easily be a prelude to heartache.

CHAPTER TWO

SARA stared at the suitcase she'd dumped unceremoniously on the floor and sat on the edge of the bed. Whether she unpacked or not, their trip was over. Done. Finished. If they took in Brody, they wouldn't go. And if they didn't, they still wouldn't go because these events had killed her romantic-weekend mood.

Oh, who was she kidding? Tonight's revelation had ruined more than the weekend. It had completely cracked the foundation of their marriage. Complete collapse was only a nudge away.

The question was, did she want to give their marriage that nudge, or not? Half of her was tempted beyond belief. The other half encouraged her to weather the storm.

She had to think. She had to decide what was the best option, which was the better course, but her emotions were far too raw to make a logical decision. Leaving meant the end of every hope and dream she'd nurtured.

Staying meant…meant what? That she'd already forgiven Cole? She hadn't. That she loved him? At the moment, it was questionable.

Whatever her choice, she had to make it for the right reasons. Right now, she felt as if she were balanced precariously on a wet log, struggling to maintain her footing while knowing it wouldn't take much for her to fall in either direction. With a decision this monumental looming over her, she needed time.

Not making a decision was making a decision.

Not true, she argued with herself. She wasn't choosing to stay or go. She was simply choosing to give herself time to come to terms with the fact that Cole had a son.

He had a son.

Without her.

Once again, much as it had when she'd first connected the dots, hurt and anger crashed over her in debilitating waves. She kicked the luggage defiantly, well aware it was a poor substitute for the man who deserved her wrath, but she still hoped that small act would ease her pain.

It didn't.

She hoisted the case back on the bed and unzipped the top. In spite of her rough treatment, the clothes inside were just as neat as when she'd placed them there. Once again, she was racked with indecision.

"Are you okay, Sara?" Cole asked from the doorway, a worried wrinkle on his forehead.

"I'm just peachy," she answered waspishly. "How do you *think* I am?"

He didn't answer, as if he knew the answer. "May I come in?"

"Suit yourself." She spied the edge of the black silk teddy she'd purchased specifically for this weekend and poked it underneath her jeans and sweatshirts to keep it out of sight.

"Are you unpacking?" he asked.

"Yes." She eyed the case and suddenly didn't feel inclined to empty it, especially when the urge to grab it and run away was far too strong. "No. I'm not sure."

"Maybe this will help. Packing means you're leaving. To stay, you have to *un*pack."

He sounded calm, as if he were simply helping her decide between wearing a pair of blue or green scrubs. "I realize that," she answered sharply. Then, realizing she sounded shrewish, she softened her tone. "I'm trying to decide. Unfortunately, I can't decide what is the right thing to do." She rubbed at the crease on her forehead.

"I know you're upset," he began as he crossed the threshold.

"Wow. Whatever gave you that idea? Why would I possibly be upset to hear that my husband…" Her voice cracked. "My husband had a child with another woman while we were separated? My God, Cole. It was only a week. *One lousy week.*"

"Actually, it was ten days," he corrected, "but, yes, those were lousy days on so many levels."

She brushed aside his comment. "One week, ten days, it's practically the same thing. All I know is that I didn't fall into bed with anyone during that time, even if I *technically…*" she made imaginary quotation marks in the air "…could have."

"It was a one-night error in judgment. It didn't mean a thing."

"Oh, that's wonderful, Cole. I'm sure Brody will be happy to hear his dad say that he was a mistake. An error in judgment."

"I only meant—"

"The point is," she continued, "I haven't forgotten why we split up or why we got back together."

"I haven't either," he said evenly.

She rubbed the back of her neck. "But now you're asking me to ignore what you did and welcome your son with open arms."

His expression grew grave. "I'm only trying to explain

what happened. While I know it's too soon to ask for forgiveness, I'd like you to understand—"

"I'm having trouble with that," she said flatly. "The Cole Wittman I knew prided himself on his control and for you to do something so obviously *out* of control...well, it makes me look at our life together in a different light, which is why I can't decide...about this." She motioned toward her suitcase.

"I knew the situation would be...tough to handle," he admitted. "If it's any consolation, I've dreaded telling you from the moment Maitland showed me Ruth's will. I expected the news would be hard for you to swallow."

At least he was cognizant enough of her feelings to guess at her reaction. "You were right."

"I'm sorry to have landed us in this predicament."

Predicament was such an insipid term for the situation they were in, she decided.

"Would you rather I'd kept this from you and told Maitland then and there that we weren't interested in taking Brody?"

It would have been so much easier, she thought with irritation, but she also knew that "easy" didn't always mean "better." Successful marriages were built on honesty, not secrets, and if Cole had kept this from her—even if part of her wished he had—they could be setting a dangerous precedent for their future relationship. What would stop him from withholding information from her again, especially if he deemed it was information she'd find uncomfortable?

"Why didn't you?" she asked, curious.

He shrugged. "The truth eventually comes out. Maybe not today or next month or next year, but sometime down the road it would surface again. Fate has a way of doing the unexpected," he said wryly, "and I figured that learning about Brody would be easier to handle now rather than in ten or twenty years.

"And," he continued tentatively, "knowing how badly you wanted a baby, I'd hoped…" His voice faded.

"That I'd overlook Brody's origins because he would satisfy my own need?" she asked icily.

He had the grace to wince. "Something like that."

"You were wrong. Yes, I want us to have a baby, but only because a child is a logical extension of our love for each other. While I'd be happy to adopt a child, too, the fact that Brody is yours and not a stranger's makes this situation unique. There's another layer of emotional baggage that has to be dealt with."

He nodded, his face lined with a combination of resignation and misery. "I know."

"You're placing me in a no-win situation," she pointed out. "You realize that, don't you?"

"It isn't a no-win," he insisted. "If we can't agree on Brody's future, then that's the end of it."

His even tone wasn't reassuring because in her gut she knew this wouldn't be the end. For the rest of their lives together, if she denied Ruth's request, the what-ifs would plague them.

On the other hand, if she walked away from Cole and the situation, she'd lose as much if not more.

"You want to bring him home, don't you?" That observation was irritating in itself. While she'd been eager to start the process of fertility testing, Cole had been content to bide their time, claiming he was happy with or without a baby. Now, though, he was almost falling over his own feet to welcome his secret child into their household.

In a distant corner of her heart she knew she was being unfair, but at this moment she was still too crushed by a multitude of emotions to be rational.

"I do, but not if we aren't in agreement. We're a team, Sara. We have to function like one. Besides, you're the one with the strong family background. Without your support, I can't be his father, or anyone else's," he said flatly.

The idea that he needed *her* to do this job mollified her to some degree. It also helped to hear that her husband—a brilliant, meticulous, caring physician who'd graduated in the top ten percent of his medical school class—suffered from a few feelings of inadequacy, too. Unfortunately, could she trust him again? She didn't realize she'd voiced her thought until he answered.

"We've had nearly three wonderful years together," he said simply. "And three before that. Have I given you any reason to doubt me during the time we've been together?"

"I presume 'together' is the operative word?"

Her barb had struck home because he fell silent. "I deserve that, I suppose, but I'm the same man I was yesterday, the day before, last week and last year. I love you more now than ever and I don't ever want to hurt you. Every decision I make is tested against that standard. Yes, on that one occasion, I let my fear overrule my good sense. Yes, I drank more than I should have and, yes, I made a bad choice that I'll regret for the rest of my days, but I don't want to lose you over this, Sara. I…I *can't.*"

The solution to this utterly devastating change in their circumstances was simple. Leave the past in the past and focus on the future. Unfortunately, that was easier said than done, especially when she would face the proof of his poor choice every day for the rest of her life.

Could she do it? Could she ignore how his son had been conceived? Could she let go of her anger and her sense of betrayal even if Cole had been a free agent at the time?

She had to, otherwise she might as well walk out now with her packed suitcase. As her mother had always cautioned her, "Don't do anything in the heat of the moment. You'll always live with your regrets." At this moment, her emotions were too raw to think rationally, so she cautioned herself to bide her time until she could approach the situation sensibly.

On the other hand, the difficulty she had went much deeper than the notion of having Cole's child underfoot. It was the reminder that Ruth had succeeded in one night with what she had failed to achieve for months. If that wasn't enough to howl at life's unfairness, she didn't know what would be.

"I'd do anything if I could turn back the clock," he said quietly, "but I can't."

He sounded sincere. She wanted to believe that he'd never done anything like this before or since, and part of her *did* believe, but her heart was still too bruised to forgive. Given enough time, she hoped she would, but at this moment she couldn't.

"I know you want me to smile and say everything's okay. That I'll unpack so we can bring Brody home and be one big happy family, but I can't say those things." She met his gaze. "I *can't*. Not yet."

He fell silent. "I can respect that, but while you're mulling over the situation, we need to meet him, Sara. I *need* to see him. Not just a photo, but *him*. Brody didn't arrive under ideal conditions, but he's my son."

She'd half anticipated his request. What man wouldn't be curious about his own flesh and blood? She, on the other hand, wasn't eager to meet the little person that he and another woman had produced so easily.

"If you're asking for permission, feel free to do whatever you want."

"I'd like you to go with me," he said.

She shook her head. "I can't. Not yet. Not tonight."

Expecting him to protest, she was surprised when he simply paused. "Okay," he said, weariness evident in those two syllables. "If you can't handle seeing him so soon, you can't. I'll call Maitland and decline his invitation."

As he rose and strolled toward the door, his usually squared shoulders slumped in defeat, she regretted being so petty. The thing was, she already guessed at how this situation would play out and she was simply trying to hold it at bay as long as she could, hoping another solution would present itself or, better yet, she'd wake up soon and discover this was only a nightmare.

As Cole had said, the boy's future had to be decided. How could she possibly make the right choice if she didn't face her demons? He was, after all, Cole's son no matter how, why or when he had been conceived. Being with Brody would be a painful experience whether she met him tonight, tomorrow or next week, so she had to handle it like one handled any adhesive bandage. Rip off the tape in one swift motion rather than by degrees. Besides, she'd always faced her problems head-on. Ignoring them, pretending they didn't exist, wasn't her way, even if she wanted to indulge herself.

"Cole, wait," she said as he reached the threshold.

He stopped and turned. "Yeah?"

"Would you really cancel and stay home tonight?"

"If that's what you wanted," he said simply. "I may not be the most sensitive fellow in the world, but I'm well aware that seeing the boy won't be easy for you. If giving you more time to adjust will help, then that's what we'll do."

It would have been so much easier if he'd been less thoughtful, less understanding, but he was being all those things and more, which meant she had to respond in kind.

"Unfortunately, I'm not sure there's enough time in the

world to do that," she said wryly. "So…" she drew a shaky breath "…we should put this first meeting behind us."

His gaze narrowed. "Are you sure?"

"No." Her smile wobbled. "But it won't be any easier tomorrow."

"Probably not.

"But after we visit, what happens if I decide I can't be his mother?" *Or your wife?* she mentally added.

He hesitated, his expression uncertain. "Let's take this one step at a time, shall we? When we come home, we'll talk. All I ask is for you to consider the possibilities."

She only hoped she could.

Sara walked with Cole toward the Maitlands' hotel room, lost in her thoughts. Cole had explained and apologized both profusely and sincerely, but until she came to terms with what had happened, talking about those long-ago events seemed futile. She'd never imagined their future would become as muddled as it was at this moment, but muddled it was. Now she steeled herself for what would come next.

"Come in, come in," a tall, white-haired Parker Maitland welcomed them far more warmly than Sara felt inside. "Eloise and I were just reading Brody a bedtime story."

Without looking at Cole—she still found it difficult to meet his gaze because if she did, she'd break down and now wasn't the time to fall apart—she crossed the threshold.

Inside, she found Eloise, a petite woman with salt-and-pepper hair, sitting against the pillows with a small, dark-headed boy wearing racecar flannel pajamas plastered against her.

Eloise smiled at her as she continued reading from her book about the exploits of a puppy. While she read, Sara watched the youngster's bright eyes follow the pictures, indicating how intent he was on the story. When Eloise said clearly, "The end," the youngster smiled, giggled, then flipped the book to the beginning and said plainly, "Again!"

"Not again," Eloise said firmly. "We have guests who want to say hello to you."

Taking their presence in obvious stride, Brody took the book, climbed off the bed and ran toward her. "Owie," he said, presenting his thumb to Sara.

She dutifully examined the nearly invisible scratch across the knuckle. "I see," she said as she crouched down for a better view. "Does it hurt?"

"Kiss?" he asked.

"Will that make your finger feel better?" she asked as the ice in her chest began to crack under his innocent friendliness.

He bobbed his head, so she kissed the spot, feeling his tiny bones in her hand as she smelled his bath-scented little-boy smell. His was a request guaranteed to enchant, and in spite of her reservations she was touched by his trust in an apparent stranger. It would have been so much easier if he'd run away from her and hid...but, no, he'd approached her with the assurance that, although she was a new face, she wouldn't reject him.

She wanted to, she really did. She wanted to walk out of the room and pretend the past few hours had never happened, but it was impossible. She held this child's future in her hands.

No, she held all three of their futures in her hands.

As sympathetic as she was to Brody's situation, she still had one question she couldn't answer. Was she strong enough to welcome Cole's son by another woman into her home when up until a few hours ago she'd always imagined it would be *her* son or daughter she carried across the threshold?

Happy with the attention his finger had received, Brody turned to Cole and presented him with his book. "Again," he repeated, this time with a lopsided grin resembling Cole's so closely that it was painful to see.

Master Brody was his father's son, from the cowlick in his dark hair to the cute dimple in his right cheek.

She'd secretly feared that once Cole met his son, he wouldn't be able to let him go. If the awe in his eyes, the benevolent smile on his face and the shaky hand as he gently stroked Brody's baby-fine hair were any indication, she was right.

Perhaps it might have been easier to watch the two together if she hadn't studied Brody closely enough to decide that his pointy chin and eyes were visible reminders of his mother.

Reminders that Cole had poured out his troubles to a woman he hadn't seen in years. Reminders that this same woman, after one night, had given Cole what she could not after all this time. Obviously, *she,* Sara Jean Wittman, was at fault for everything from her miscarriage to her failure to get pregnant.

She wanted to weep with frustration and disappointment and when she was finished, she wanted to hate the faceless Ruth for being so fertile while she was not. Shouldn't the love she felt for her husband carry some weight with cosmic fates? Obviously not.

As she watched Cole and Brody together, saw Brody's curiosity about this new man who was willing to read his story again, two choices lay before her in stark black and white.

She could be the bad guy and stop everything pertaining to Brody's guardianship, but if she did, Cole would never forgive her. Oh, he said he'd accept her decision, but that had been before he'd seen Brody and been exposed to his winsome ways. There would always be a hole inside him that she would never be able to fill.

On the other hand, could she be Brody's mother? Could she handle the constantly visible reminder of her failure to give him a child of *their* own—a child who represented *their* love and devotion? The little boy needed and deserved a mom who would nurture him as much as his had. Would she shortchange *him* if she wasn't completely sold on the idea?

Answers eluded her.

While Cole read the story one more time, Sara visited with the Maitlands, although admittedly she couldn't remember any part of their conversation afterward because she'd focused most of her attention on her husband and his son.

This time, when the end was declared and the book closed, Brody yawned and his eyelids drooped, but he simply snuggled against Cole as if he intended to fall asleep in his lap.

Sara was certain Cole would be more than happy to let him.

"We probably should go," Cole said, his tone wistful as he stared down at the little boy.

"We should," Sara agreed, more than ready for a chance to distance herself from the situation—and her impending decision. "Brody needs his rest."

"We're really glad you came by," Eloise told Sara with a smile. "I know you and your husband have a lot to discuss."

Sara glanced at Cole. His longing expression only sent her spirits into a deeper nosedive, but she pasted a smile on her face. "Yes, we do."

Her heart, however, insisted otherwise. They didn't have anything to discuss. Not one simple point had to be debated because in that instant she was reminded of her marriage vows... *For better, for worse...*

This definitely fell in the "for worse" category.

Regardless of how she classified their new circumstances, those vows made her path clear—the same path that was uneven and strewn with boulders of varying sizes, the same path that it would be easier *not* to travel on. In spite of her reluctance, in spite of her reservations, in spite of the small vindictive streak that demanded retribution, she couldn't deny Cole the opportunity to parent his own son. Neither could she deny Brody the opportunity to know his father.

Oh, she could, of course, but it would be the beginning of the end of their marriage and deep down she didn't believe she wanted that.

She simply *had* to welcome Brody into their home and learn how to deal with her jumbled emotions.

Normally, Sara snuggled against Cole when they climbed into bed but not tonight. For the first time ever, she remained on her side of the mattress, curled into a ball with her back toward him.

He sighed, wishing he knew the right words to break the silence as frigid as the great outdoors. He'd already apologized, but repeating himself wasn't breaking through the barrier between them.

He deserved her wrath, he supposed, but didn't six years of being together—minus one week—mean anything? He also knew he was asking a lot of her to raise his son when she so desperately wanted her own, but what else could he have done? Turning Brody over to someone else would rip open the scars on his heart that Sara hadn't realized she'd healed.

As the silence grew to unbearable proportions, he knew from her steady breathing and the occasional sniffly hiccup that she wasn't asleep. He wanted to reach out and draw her next to him in order to give as well as receive comfort but, given her mood, he might end up with a black eye. Still, the possibility was worth the risk.

He reached out and hauled her against him.

"What are you doing?" she asked, her body tense.

"Holding you."

"I don't want to be held," she said, although she didn't attempt to move away.

"Too bad."

"I'm not making love with you."

"I wasn't offering," he said with equanimity.

"In fact, if our second bedroom was furnished for guests, I'd be sleeping in there."

He didn't doubt it. From the moment he'd silently followed her into the house, he'd mentally prepared himself to watch her grab her still-packed suitcase and leave. As the evening had worn on and they'd gone through the motions of their normal routine of watching the ten o'clock news and weather broadcast before going to bed, he'd slowly grown more optimistic.

At the moment, though, he was grateful that the only other available room in their house was being used as their home office.

"So just because I'm sharing this bed with you doesn't mean you're off the proverbial hook," she added. "As far as I'm concerned, our relationship is on indefinite probation."

He had suspected as much when she hadn't unpacked

her clothes. Instead, she'd simply set the case near the wall, ready to grab at a moment's notice.

All he could do was take heart that she wasn't calling it quits. Probation, not to mention the suitcase standing in their bedroom rather than at the front door, meant he still had a chance...

"Indefinite?" he asked. "Seems like a long time, but we can debate that topic another day."

"I assume you have a different subject in mind?" she asked coolly. "Your son, perhaps?"

She knew him too well, he thought ruefully. He hated to press her for a decision about Brody, but as he'd told her before they'd left the house, they'd talk after they met the boy. Ever since they'd left the hotel, she hadn't said more than a few words. Now was as good a time as any for conversation. "Yeah. We should discuss—"

"Was she pretty?"

In spite of the conversational detour, he instinctively knew she was asking about Ruth. He paused, trying to remember the woman who'd only slightly resembled the same mousy, unassuming girl she'd once been. "She was nice-looking, yes. I never really noticed." He winced, realizing how horrible that made him sound, especially since they'd created a child together.

"Tell me about her."

"Don't do this," he begged.

"I need to know, Cole. If I'm going to make sense out of this—"

"You can't," he interrupted harshly. "You can't rationalize an irrational decision. God knows I've tried."

"Maybe I can't, but I need to know who she was, what she was like. Why she could help you sort out your problems but I couldn't."

Her quiet, almost defeated tone convinced him to dredge

up his memories in order to reassure her. "She didn't compare to you, in looks or temperament. She was...different from the other girls."

She flopped onto her back. "Different how?"

He sighed, sensing she wouldn't rest until he told her what she wanted to know—whatever that was. "She tended to be a spectator, a bystander if you will, rather than a participant, which meant she'd faded into the background. Ruth got shuffled from foster home to foster home, so she didn't trust many people. Only a few of us got to see the real Ruth—the Ruth who could crack jokes with a straight face, the Ruth who'd do anything for a friend if it was within her power. She'd helped me with my senior English project—we had to create a papier-mâché character from *Beowulf*—and I was all thumbs when it came to art. To repay her, I took her to the senior prom because I knew she was dying to go but no one had asked her."

Sara turned to face him, which was promising, in his opinion. "I didn't know you ever went to your prom."

"Yeah, well, it wasn't important enough to mention." Suddenly aware that he'd recited that same excuse throughout his entire life when anyone asked about his past, he winced.

"So what did you wear?"

She clearly wanted to know every detail. "After four months of saving my money, I rented a tux," he admitted. "Ruth found a bright pink dress that made her look like a bottle of stomach medicine, but it had all this glittery stuff on it and crinkled when she walked. She said that even though it came from a secondhand shop, she felt like a fairy-tale princess."

"What happened to her parents?"

"I'm not really sure," he said. "She'd mentioned living

with a grandmother and after she died, Ruth went into foster care."

"No aunts or uncles or siblings?"

"I don't think so, at least none that she ever talked about. I'm sure if there'd been a relative, social services would have located them."

She fell silent for a minute. "What happened after high school?"

"Our paths didn't cross. Occasionally, I'd hear what she was doing, but Ruth didn't stay in touch and I didn't expect her to. She'd wanted to forget her childhood and everything associated with it. I didn't blame her. We were both biding our time until we finished school and could leave and be on our own."

"Yet she came to your reunion."

"Yeah, it was the first one she'd ever attended. As I said before, I was surprised when I saw her."

For the longest time, he waited for her to speak again. When she didn't, even though he hated to break their uneasy truce, he had to.

"What did you think of Brody?" he asked.

She sighed. "He's a cute kid and obviously very intelligent, too. He looks a lot like you."

He pictured his son's face and felt an odd sense of male pride, which was quite amazing when he considered how a few short years ago he hadn't planned to get married, much less have a family. "Do you think so?"

"Oh, yes. Definitely. Were you as busy a fellow as he was?"

"I don't remember," he said honestly. Sadly enough, he had no one to ask, either. "I imagine I was, though."

He felt her nod. "That's how I pictured you, too. Speaking of pictures, do you have any of you as a child?"

Cole thought of the shoebox tucked away on the top

shelf of his closet, buried behind an odd collection of off-season clothing and Sara's handbags. "A few," he said.

"Will you show them to me?"

Somehow, it had always seemed safer to keep those photos—and the memories—locked away, but if Sara had her way, he'd eventually bring them into the open.

"Yeah, sure. Sometime," he said, because refusing wouldn't help his cause and if fate was kind, she'd forget she'd asked. Then, because the suspense was killing him, he asked, "Have you thought about Ruth's request?"

"Yes."

He allowed the pause to last for a full minute before he prompted her to continue. "And?"

"I saw the way you looked at him," she said simply. "You want him, don't you?"

He'd tried to hide his feelings—and his potential disappointment—but Sara clearly knew him too well. Although he felt completely inadequate to be a parent and hated the emotional cost she would pay for his past actions, he couldn't deny that he wanted the privilege of raising Brody.

"Did you think I wouldn't?" he asked instead.

She sighed. "No. I would have been worried if you didn't."

It occurred to him that his reaction could represent another difference between him and his relatives... Somehow, he felt as if he'd passed a test that he hadn't realized he'd been taking.

"And yet," she continued, "when we talked about having a baby of our own, you didn't seem as eager."

How could he explain that while he wanted to have a baby with Sara because he loved her, in the back of his mind his less-than-admirable role models had made him reluctant to embrace the idea with Sara's degree of enthusiasm?

"Just because I was happy to take things slow didn't mean I wasn't eager," he pointed out. "Besides, you can't compare us having our own baby to present circumstances. What we're facing now isn't the ideal way to start our family, but it's the situation we have to deal with."

Slowly, she nodded. For a few seconds they both lay in silence until she finally spoke with resignation in her voice.

"We don't have a choice, do we? He *is* your son, and as you said, he doesn't have anyone else."

"Yes, he's mine, but our decision can't be based on *obligation*. If that's how you feel, then this won't work," he finished flatly. As a child, he'd learned quickly how uncomfortable it was being treated as an "obligation" rather than a member of a family.

Her eyebrows drew together. "I don't feel obligated, but as your wife I suppose I feel a sense of responsibility, even if I'm not completely sold on the idea. At least not yet," she tacked on. "So if you're expecting me to jump up and down with excitement about bringing him into our home, you'll be sorely disappointed. However, I know that we're both too softhearted to live with the idea of giving him up."

He suspected as much and, in fact, her admission was more than he'd allowed himself to hope for. Somehow he sensed a smile wouldn't be appreciated, so he simply nodded to acknowledge her decision.

"Softhearted or not, I appreciate your willingness to welcome him here. I can't imagine trying to raise him without you."

For a man who'd learned to hide weakness and hated to reveal an insecurity, he was almost surprised he had. Sara, however, didn't seem to take his comment as a confession. Instead, it was as if she suspected he was only paying her a compliment to make this bitter pill more palatable to swallow.

"With or without me, I think you can do whatever you put your mind to doing," she told him evenly.

"Oh, Sara..." He leaned over and kissed her, noticing how she held herself stiffly under his caress.

"I know how difficult this is for you," he began contritely, "but everything will work out."

"I hope so, Cole."

Her packed suitcase and his probationary status indicated as much. The truth was, he wasn't confident at all. Brody's presence would remind her of the baby they'd lost and of the baby she was trying so hard to create, so she'd need time—and love—to recover.

"I'll do my best to convince you," he promised. "You won't regret doing this for Brody or for us, Sara."

She sighed. "I just don't want to compound one mistake with another."

He couldn't agree more. "As long as we pull together, we'll make it work."

CHAPTER THREE

WHEN Sara padded into the kitchen at seven-thirty the next morning, wearing her nightgown and robe, she found the coffee ready and Cole seated at the table. His mug was half-empty and the top page of a legal pad full of nearly illegible handwriting lay in front of him.

"Good morning," he said cautiously, as if he suspected from the way she'd tossed and turned all night that she wasn't disposed to doling out forgiveness just yet.

"Morning," she mumbled as she poured a mug for herself. "How long have you been awake?"

"A couple of hours," he admitted. "I couldn't sleep, thinking of everything we have to do today. So I got up and made a list."

She hadn't been able to sleep, either, although she couldn't claim the same excuse. Her thoughts had lingered along the lines of trying to work out how she was going to be the mother that Brody so obviously needed when the idea of inflicting a few medieval tortures on his father held immense appeal.

By 2:00 a.m., though, she'd gotten past her thirst for bodily harm and she'd started to look at her situation with a little more objectivity. The hurt was still there, as well as the disappointment over his one-night stand—even if it had occurred while they'd been separated—but, as Cole had said, their time together over the past six years had been good. He deserved credit for that.

A little credit, anyway.

And maybe, someday, she would be able to trust him again. At the moment, the man she'd thought she'd known seemed like a stranger.

As for Brody and the task she'd accepted, she simply had to think of him as a motherless little boy with no one to take him in. A motherless little boy who needed someone, namely her, to assume his mother's role.

Unfortunately, it wouldn't be easy because he resembled Cole in such a painfully obvious manner. She'd have to train her thoughts to not go down that fruitless path, just as she'd have to train herself not to wonder if he was still unable to share his fears with her and if he had any other secrets that would eventually haunt them.

Idly, she wondered how long it would take before those thoughts of Brody became second nature because right now they were not. In any case, Cole was studying her with cautious optimism as if hoping she'd already forgiven and forgotten, which meant it was time to begin that painful process.

She forced herself to sit beside him at the table when she'd rather take her coffee into the other room to drink in peace. "What's on your to-do list?"

"First was to cancel our plane tickets and our hotel reservation, which I've already done."

Although she'd known it had been inevitable, a fresh pang of disappointment struck. "That was fast," she commented before she, without thinking, sipped on her hot coffee and burned the roof of her mouth in the process.

"I'm sorry about this weekend, but I promise we'll go another time."

But it won't be the same, she wanted to cry, before she

realized that given these events and her shattered feelings, celebrating their anniversary as if their lives hadn't taken a right turn seemed hypocritical.

"Yeah, sure. Another time," she echoed, wondering if another anniversary was actually *in* their future.

"I mean it," he insisted, as if he sensed her doubts. "I'll make it up to you."

"Fine." Then, because she wanted to push that subject aside before she embarrassed herself with tears, she asked, "What else is on the list?"

He shoved the pad closer to her. "Childproof the house, which means we have to put away all the things he might destroy, like your figurines. Then we need to install latches on the drawers and cupboard doors that we don't want him to open, which means a trip to the hardware store. The unused electrical outlets need plugs, too, which is something else we have to buy."

She perused the list, impressed by his thoroughness. Then again, he'd been at this for hours. "You've given this a lot of thought."

He shrugged. "I tried, but I'm hoping you'll notice something I've missed."

"It looks rather complete to me."

He glanced at the clock. "It's nearly eight. I thought I'd call the Maitlands while you're getting dressed and then we'll run to the store before they arrive."

"Slow down a minute," she said. "I know how eager you are, but they might be sleeping in. Absolutely do *not* call them before nine."

He frowned, then his expression turned sheepish. "You're right. Nine o'clock is early enough. Do you think we can drive to the hardware store and back before then?"

"Is that a hint I should hurry and get dressed?" she asked wryly.

He chuckled. "It is."

While she showered and dressed, hurrying because his impatience was so obvious, she reminded herself not to look on the situation with dread but with anticipation. Even though the child she'd been hoping, praying and waiting for wasn't coming in the way she'd envisioned, one was coming nonetheless. The only way they could make this work was to pull together, as Cole had said last night.

As it turned out, Cole didn't phone the Maitlands until almost nine-thirty. After that, they worked feverishly to accomplish as many projects on Cole's list as possible before their guests arrived at eleven.

After Cole had dropped a screw several times while he was trying to install a latch on a cabinet door, Sara smiled at her husband's uncharacteristic clumsiness, wishing for an instant that the anxiety—and suppressed excitement—she'd seen all morning had been for *her* child, and not Ruth's. Unfortunately, it didn't accomplish anything for her thoughts to dwell there, so she pushed them aside.

It was a sad day when every thought had to be discarded...

"Nervous?" she asked.

He looked up at her and grinned sheepishly. "Does it show?"

"A little," she admitted.

He sat back on his heels. "This all seems so surreal. As a physician, I'm used to juggling responsibilities for my patients, from making a diagnosis to choosing the best treatment option, and yet the idea of being responsible for one little boy is..." He shrugged, as if unable to find the right word.

"Overwhelming? Daunting? Frightening?" she supplied.

"All that and more," he answered. "None of that hit me until I started looking at all the possible ways a child could hurt himself around here." He glanced around the kitchen, his expression rueful. "I'd always preached safety to parents and felt rather smug about it, but now that *I'm* standing on the other side, knowing *I'm* the one who has to have eyes in the back of my head and practice what I've always preached, it's a different story."

"We'll definitely have a steep learning curve," she said.

He studied her for a moment. "What about you? Are you nervous?"

She paused to consider. "A little," she finally answered. "As you said, this is a huge responsibility. Normally we'd have nine months to get used to the idea of being parents and to physically prepare. Instead, we've gotten twenty-four hours. Less than that, actually."

He nodded, then met her gaze. "Have you told your parents?"

"Heavens, no. Not yet." She'd thought about phoning them, but hadn't arrived at a way to explain the situation without making Cole look bad. Another wife facing these circumstances might not care, but for reasons she couldn't pinpoint, *she* did. Suggesting to her parents that she hadn't known Cole as well as she'd thought she had didn't slide down well at all.

"If you don't mind, when you're ready, *I'll* break the news to them," he declared.

His offer took her by surprise before she realized it required both guts and a strong dose of humility to face his in-laws and admit to actions that didn't show him in the best light.

Silently, she added several points into his plus column. If he could brave the wrath of her mother and father, then he was obviously willing to accept whatever penance they doled out.

But penance or not, the fact remained that he'd kept so

much of his life hidden, even from her, and she begged to know why. It wasn't for lack of asking, because she had. The most he'd told her was that he'd moved in with his aunt and uncle after his parents had died, and that those times had not been happy ones. Because he'd treated those questions with easy nonchalance, she'd assumed his life had been filled with the usual teenage problems and angst with nothing remarkable to note.

Now she suspected otherwise. Now she suspected that those days had been so traumatic that he refused to revisit them. It would certainly explain why she'd never met any of his relatives, even at their wedding.

But, she vowed to herself, the time for secrets was over. She wanted to know *precisely* what experiences had shaped Cole into the man he was. Dredging up bad memories wouldn't be pleasant, but it was necessary. While this particular minute wasn't the appropriate time to ask those questions, those days would be discussed.

Soon.

She shook her head. "We'll tell my parents together. Knowing my mother, she'll be thrilled to have a grand-baby, especially this close to Christmas. My dad will be happy, too, *after* he delivers his famous right hook. And after my brothers throw a few punches of their own."

A ghost of a smile appeared on his face. "I figured as much." He met her gaze. "What about you? How are you holding up?"

Like I'm being held together with a wad of used-up chewing gum, she wanted to say. Instead, she answered, "Fine."

His gaze landed on her arms crossed protectively over her chest and she dropped them to her sides. "Really?" he asked.

"Yes," she said more firmly than she felt. It was pointless to belabor how her biggest problem came when she thought of how Brody was more Cole's than hers. While Cole only saw Brody's arrival as the beginning of a wonderful future with his own flesh and blood, she saw it as the beginning of an extremely difficult emotional journey.

"If I could relive that weekend, I would. I wish I'd never gone," he added fiercely.

"Don't apologize again, Cole. I know you're sorry and, as you said, technically we were both free to…see…other people during that time."

She wished she hadn't been so delighted to see him when he'd appeared on her doorstep after their ten-day separation. In fact, she'd been so thrilled by his declaration that he'd been miserable without her that she hadn't bothered to ask questions. Instead, she'd assumed he'd been sitting at home every night, alone and lonely, just as she had been.

That was the problem with assuming.

However, she couldn't correct that mistake now.

"I'm still trying to sort out everything," she continued honestly. "One day, I hope I'll be as thrilled with Brody as you are, but it won't be today."

He nodded, as if he accepted her terms. "I don't want him to pay for my mistake."

"Regardless of what you've done, I wouldn't make a child become your scapegoat," she chided, suddenly realizing that Cole had his own trust issues to work on.

He shrugged. "One never knows how another person will react when the chips are down."

Part of her wondered what had happened during his childhood and the other part was irritated that after a six-year relationship, he still questioned her character.

She poked him in the chest. "You can take what I said

to the bank," she said fervently. "I haven't broken a vow to you yet, have I?"

"No," he said slowly.

"Then consider what I just said to be a new vow. I won't hold Brody accountable for your actions. He's an innocent little boy and it isn't his fault how he came to exist."

He nodded, as if satisfied she meant what she'd said. "Okay."

The doorbell chimes sounded and she exchanged a glance with him. "They're here," she said inanely, feeling her heart skip a beat.

As she met Cole's gaze in that instant, the realization of what she'd agreed to came crashing down. A combination of dread and excitement caused her to take Cole's hand. They still had a lot of personal issues to deal with, but they were in this new venture of raising Brody together.

Cole squeezed Sara's hand, grateful that in spite of the problems in their relationship, she had reached out to him in this moment.

That alone gave him hope that they'd eventually be able to repair the damage. Working on that restoration, however, would have to wait for another time. Right now, they had the more immediate task of welcoming the Maitlands inside.

"Brr, it's gotten cold early this year," Parker said, stamping his feet. "I'm thinking we'll have a white Christmas."

While he and Cole discussed Parker's prediction and a long-term weather forecast, Cole's gaze never left his son. He watched as young Brody ripped his stocking hat off his head and his mittens off his hands. His coat was closed with snaps and in a flash he ripped them apart and his royal-blue parka had landed on the floor.

Eloise stared at him fondly as she handed her own knee-length leather coat to Sara. "That boy," she said with a trace of exasperation. "Before you know it, his shoes will be off, too."

She'd hardly finished speaking when Brody plopped onto the floor, twisted off his shoes and stared at the grown-ups, looking pleased at his accomplishment.

Eloise shook her head. "Just like his mother."

Like a sudden, noxious fume, her words hung in the air and Cole hated seeing Sara's response. For an instant, a stricken expression crossed her features, which made Cole wish he had the ability to erase Eloise's thoughtless remark. Fortunately, Eloise took matters into her own hands.

"I'm sorry, dear," the woman said softly, her face pink with obvious embarrassment. "My observation just slipped out. It's just that Ruth was like our own daughter. I still can't believe she's gone."

"Don't give it another thought," Sara said magnanimously, but Cole saw her brittle smile, knew how much her gesture cost and felt a now-familiar ache of regret and sorrow lodge in his chest.

"Naturally, he'll have some of her traits," Sara continued. "Ignoring them doesn't change the facts. I'm sure you have a lot of things to tell us, so please sit down."

"Yes, please do," Cole echoed, once again mentally telegraphing his apologies to his wife.

"Brody?" Eloise chided as she did. "Please pick up your coat and give it to your daddy."

Daddy. The sound of his new title came as a blow to his solar plexus. Was this how his own father had felt when *he* had been born? Had he been as overwhelmed by the responsibility as *he* now was? But as the little boy shyly glanced at Cole, that panicky feeling slowly transformed into a firm resolve to handle the job to the best of his ability.

Brody clearly didn't have the same conflicting emotions to sort through because he simply smiled before he thrust his coat into Cole's hands. Without hesitation and clearly without dwelling on the ramifications that having a father would mean for him, Brody brushed past Sara and grabbed the oversize bag that Eloise had carried inside. With a herculean effort on his part, he hauled the sack to Cole and dumped it at his feet. "Toys."

Realizing his son had taken the news in his stride, Cole laughed with some relief that the little boy didn't sense his new father's insecurities. "Are you asking me to play?"

Immediately Brody bobbed his head and began pulling out cars and trucks, a container of blocks and an assortment of other colorful items.

"We brought his favorites," Parker said as he sat on the sofa beside his wife.

"Including his teddy bear," Eloise said. "A word of warning—do not lose that bear. It's his bedtime buddy."

"That's good to know."

Suddenly, Brody tugged on Cole's fingers. "Daddy, play," he demanded. "Box."

As the child grabbed the drawstring bag containing his blocks, Cole sat on the floor beside him, overjoyed to hear that one word coming from his son's mouth. "Okay," he said agreeably, "we'll stack blocks."

As Sara watched the two build a tower that eventually leaned, then crashed to Brody's delight, the sight of the two dark heads together was a bittersweet moment.

He should have been their *son.*

The fact that he wasn't bothered her more than anything else. She still wasn't happy about so many things but being around his child only emphasized how after a miscarriage and subsequent months of trying to get pregnant again, nothing had happened on that front. Although

Cole had suggested waiting for Josh's recommended year to pass before going ahead for fertility tests, she had suddenly become too impatient. If there was truly a problem of some sort, she wanted to know now, rather than later. After all, what difference would a few months make?

Of course, to get pregnant, she couldn't keep to her side of the bed every night and she wasn't ready to cross the center line. Her emotions were too raw and her faith too crushed to entertain the idea, which meant her wish for a special Christmas present wouldn't happen. She wanted to howl out her grief for that setback, too, but now wasn't the time or the place.

For the next ten minutes, Cole played with his son while Sara stoically listened to the information that Eloise and Parker freely shared. She really should write their tips down, she decided, because at the moment, her brain felt like a sieve.

Finally, the youngster rose from his kneeling position and hurried over to Eloise.

"Dwink," he demanded.

"Ask your Mama Sara," Eloise encouraged.

He cocked his head and his face grew thoughtful. "Mama?"

Eloise pointed to Sara. "Sara is your new mama," she told him. "Ask her. Ask Mama Sara."

He stared at Sara, the wrinkle between his little eyebrows revealing that he didn't understand how this was possible. "No." He shook his head before glancing around the room. "Want *my* mama."

As he looked back at Sara, his face wrinkled with unhappiness and he burst into tears. "Mama," he cried, crawling into Eloise's lap.

Although Sara hadn't expected Brody to accept her easily, his rejection bothered her more than she'd thought it might. "Please don't push the issue," she said.

"I'm so sorry, dear," Eloise apologized as she cuddled Brody. "I'm not doing a very good job with this transition, am I? It was thoughtless of me and I should have known... I've been trying to tell him that you're his new mother, and I thought that by tacking on your name, he'd accept the change, but he doesn't seem to understand."

"I'm sure he doesn't," Sara said, feeling sorry for the child who was faithfully waiting for the most important person in his young life to reappear. The ironic thing was that she'd been worried about how *she'd* accept being his mother when she should have been more concerned about Brody accepting *her*.

"He knows what he called his mother," she pointed out, "and adding another name is probably confusing him. All things considered, he should probably think of me as Sara for now. It'll be less stressful."

"You're probably right, dear," Eloise said as she kissed Brody's forehead and smoothed his hair.

Wondering how long it would take for Brody to turn to *her* for comfort instead of seeing her as the enemy, Sara rose. Perhaps if she left the room, Brody would calm down. "I'll get him a cup of juice," she mentioned to no one in particular. "And coffee for the rest of us."

As Brody's wails increased in volume, she fled to the kitchen and began preparing a tray.

"Need help?" Cole asked a few minutes later.

She brushed past him to remove the creamer from the refrigerator, refusing to meet his gaze and see the pity in his eyes. "No, thanks. I can manage."

He grabbed her arm and tethered her in place. "He doesn't understand, Sara."

She wasn't ready to accept his comfort and she stiffened. "Don't you think I know that?" she asked.

To her surprise, as if he'd decided he wouldn't be rejected so easily, he didn't release his grip. "He'll come around."

"Sure he will," she dutifully agreed. *Maybe when he's eighteen.*

"He will," he insisted. "He'll soon learn what I've known for a long time…that you're a kind and loving person who has a heart big enough to let him in, no matter what."

"Stop trying to flatter me."

"This isn't flattery. It's the truth. I may not be a psychiatrist, but this isn't a rejection of you. He's frustrated because his life has crumbled around him and he doesn't understand why or know how to repair it."

Boy, could she relate to that!

She sighed. Young Brody had to learn how to make the best of an uncomfortable situation just as she did. She might not share a blood bond with the child, but they certainly shared this emotional one.

"I know," she agreed. "As Parker told us last night, the adjustment won't happen overnight."

Slowly, Cole's hold became more of a caress than a leash, making her realize how much she'd missed the closeness of their physical contact and she'd only done without for less than twenty-four hours. Yet, she wasn't quite ready to forgive him, even if he was being thoughtful and supportive.

"Dwink," she heard a plaintive voice demand loudly in the other room.

Brody's request broke the mood of the moment and she tugged free of Cole's hand. "Would you mind carrying in Brody's juice? I'll bring the coffee in a minute."

He nodded, then left with the plastic cup she'd poured.

As Sara lifted the tray and prepared to follow him, the incident painfully reminded her that she wasn't Brody's mother. She knew it and the sad thing was that little Brody knew it, too.

CHAPTER FOUR

THE time with the Maitlands went all too quickly and before Cole knew it, he and Sara were on their own. Fortunately, both of them had received short-term compassionate leave so Brody wouldn't have to attend day care just yet, but Cole knew those two weeks would flash by.

After only three days of being a parent, Cole had decided that a hectic day at the hospital was less exhausting than following this little whirlwind of energy. At the same time, though, these new experiences were energizing. They also reminded him of all the usual milestones he'd missed—first steps, first smiles, first words. He hated that those were memories he could never recover, but he was also grateful that he'd stand nearby for the subsequent ones.

At the moment, though, the tense moments were balancing out the good ones. He'd caught himself on several occasions thoughtlessly commenting on Brody's habits that were so characteristic of his mother, like kicking off his shoes whenever he could.

As if Sara had needed a reminder that Brody wasn't hers, he'd scolded himself. Although she had nodded and gone about her business, Cole had seen the bleakness in her eyes in spite of the smile she'd pasted on her face. Gut-wrenching guilt had swept over him for his insensitivity and the urge to fall back into old habits and look for a means of escape sounded more and more attractive. He'd been tempted to call the Maitlands on more than one occasion and announce that they'd changed their minds—that having Brody around was as painful as probing an open wound, that he simply couldn't subject his wife to such misery—but he never acted on those thoughts. For one thing, it was cowardly to use Sara as his excuse when she hadn't uttered one word of complaint.

Neither was he the ten-year-old boy who'd clung to the only hope he'd had—the hope that one day his life would no longer be subject to the whims of others. He'd grown up with one goal in mind—to endure as best he could, while vowing to never be placed in a similar situation.

Sadly, that mindset had nearly cost him Sara. It seemed as if his present circumstances were another test that the fates had decided to give in order to see if he was willing to face a few more of his deep-seated fears. While escape seemed attractive at times, it really wasn't an option—not if he wanted to keep any measure of self-respect.

Then there were the moments when Brody's mannerisms mirrored his and he saw himself in the youngster's features. How could he possibly give up the privilege of raising his own son?

Those feelings were reinforced whenever Brody came to him without hesitation or fear. Without any muss or fuss, Brody had accepted him as his father and their relationship was already growing by leaps and bounds, probably because he was still trying to sort out what role a father played in his young life when he'd never had one before.

Unfortunately, Sara wasn't faring as well. Although she'd said several times that she wasn't taking Brody's rejection to heart, Cole suspected the little boy's wariness troubled her. Normally, children gravitated to her, but ever since Eloise had referred to her as "Mama," Brody had stared at her with suspicion and only went to her when no one else was available.

Cole had tried to stand in the gap, but he suspected he wasn't doing a stellar job. While he told the youngster that Sara hadn't been responsible for his mother's disappearance, he wasn't sure that Brody understood. Somehow, he had to figure out a way to persuade the little boy that Sara hadn't created this sudden gaping hole in his short life, but so far he'd drawn a blank.

It wasn't the only blank he was drawing, either. Their anniversary was coming up soon and he still didn't know how they could celebrate the occasion. Dinner at the fanciest restaurant in town ranked high on his list, but he couldn't figure out the logistics. He might still be finding his way when it came to juggling the roles of parent and husband, but he instinctively knew that bringing Brody with them defeated the purpose of giving his wife his full and undivided attention. One of his colleagues had mentioned how he and his wife had kept a date night to keep their romance fresh after the kids had started to arrive, and he couldn't think of a better time to start the habit than with their anniversary. Unfortunately, hiring a sitter for the evening was out of the question. Brody didn't need another stranger introduced into his life so soon after moving in with a couple he'd only known a few weeks.

Of course they could always postpone their celebration until their life with Brody settled into a routine, but that could take months. Sara would probably understand if their special day passed without their usual fanfare, but Cole didn't *want* her to have to understand. He wanted her to know that she was still number one in his life. He simply needed to be creative. Luckily, he still had about ten days to dream up the perfect celebration.

As he mentally considered his options and scanned the newspaper's business ads, Brody climbed onto his lap as he clutched one of his cars. "Daddy, wet."

"That's nice," Cole murmured idly, his thoughts still focused on creating the perfect anniversary celebration.

Brody babbled something that Cole couldn't understand, but as he dropped the newspaper to listen, he suddenly became aware of a dampness seeping into his jeans.

"Are you wet, Brody?" he asked.

"Wet," the little boy echoed as he enthusiastically bobbed his head.

Suddenly, Cole realized that he'd never dealt with Brody's basic needs since he'd come to live with them. While he was willing to do his share, he also realized that he'd never changed a diaper before in his life. He didn't have the first idea of how to go about it.

"Okay, bud," he said as he rose and took Brody's hand. "Shall we see if Sara will help us out this time?"

He led Brody to the kitchen, where Sara was drying dishes. She paused, tea towel in hand. "If you're here to beg for more cookies, the answer is no. We just had lunch."

He grinned. "As wonderful as another cookie sounds, we're not here for that. Brody needs his britches changed."

Sara met his gaze. "Then change him. You can take off his clothes and put on a fresh diaper as well as I can."

"But I've never diapered before," he protested.

"There's no time like the present to learn," she said smartly.

"I've never even *seen* it done." He hoped that would sway the argument in his favor. "Can you show me? For Brody's sake?"

For a minute, she looked as if she might refuse, but then her shoulders slumped in an obvious sign of capitulation. She tossed the towel onto the counter and shooed them ahead of her to Brody's bedroom where she proceeded to stand back and supervise while Cole pulled off Brody's pants.

"All you have to do is pay attention when you remove the wet one," she said as he ripped off the tapes holding the soggy diaper around Brody's waist. "Then put the new one on."

Cole followed her instructions as she watched, feeling as clumsy as the first time he'd sutured a gash under the critical eye of his professor.

"Shouldn't he be toilet trained by now?" he asked, desperately hoping this stage would soon fall behind them.

"Eloise said that Ruth had started to work with him, but she hadn't gotten very far."

"Then maybe we should make that a priority."

"You're welcome to try," she answered cheerfully, "but until he adjusts to his new circumstances, I think it best if we wait awhile. Even if we started immediately, it won't fix Brody's immediate problem. So resign yourself to changing a few diapers. Just be glad he's only wet."

Now, *that* was a scenario Cole hoped he'd never have to face by himself.

In the end, the entire process was far less stressful than Cole had expected.

"Will you two be okay by yourselves while I run a few errands this afternoon?" she asked.

It would be the first time Cole had been completely alone with Brody without Sara for backup. While he knew that day had to come, he wasn't ready to face it just yet, which was an odd thing for a man who'd gone through medical school and an internal medicine residency to fear, he thought wryly.

"Why don't we go with you?" he asked instead.

Sara paused. "It's really cold to be taking him outside unnecessarily," she began.

"We're driving, not walking," he pointed out. "And we'll warm the car before we go. He'll be fine. Besides, it'll be fun."

"Fun?" She stared at him as if he'd grown another nose. "You clearly haven't shopped with a toddler before."

"I haven't," he admitted, "but how hard can it be with both of us?"

An hour later, Cole's words of *how hard can it be?* came back to haunt him. He could explain in vivid detail of how difficult it was to keep one active, curious toddler occupied while taking care of the business of shopping.

Fortunately, Sara didn't say "I told you so." Instead, she simply smiled and suggested that he concentrate on his son while she filled the cart with the essentials.

So Cole obliged. At first it wasn't too difficult to entertain the little boy as he sat in the cart, but that soon grew boring.

"At the risk of making a huge mistake," Cole said as Brody kicked his legs and arched his back to try and escape his seat, "maybe he'd be less noisy if I let him walk."

"Do you really think you can hold on to him?" Sara asked. "If he darts away…"

"I'll hold his hand," he said as he lifted the youngster out of the cart.

"You'd better," she said darkly.

Freed from his constraints, Brody clung to Cole's hand until he suddenly jumped up and down with obvious delight. "Toys!" he squealed, before slipping out of Cole's grasp and racing toward every child's favorite section of a store.

Fear struck Cole's gut. Although he was never more than two steps behind his son, the idea that his little boy was quicker than he was gave him new sympathy for parents whose children darted into harm's way while under their watchful eye. By the time he'd toyed with the idea of tethering Brody to him until he was at least sixteen, he'd caught up to him.

Brody, with reflexes as quick as any pickpocket's, had snatched a stuffed lion off the shelf and wrapped both arms around it. He talked to the lion as if it were his long-lost pal.

"What did you find, Brody?" Cole asked.

"Grr," Brody said. "Wions grr."

Like all parents, Cole was impressed with his son's obvious knowledge. "Yes, lions growl."

The little boy nodded. "Grr."

Cole glanced at Sara, who'd finally caught up with them. "Smart kid," he said proudly. "Who would have thought a stuffed lion would catch his eye?"

"Who would have thought," she echoed, looking both relieved and exasperated. "Unfortunately, as much fun as it is to stay and play, I have everything on my list."

Cole spoke to Brody. "Okay, son. Put down the lion. It's time to leave."

Brody shook his head and clutched the toy to his chest. "No."

"Yes," he said firmly.

"No-o-o-o," the toddler yelled as Cole reached for the toy. "Mine."

"It's not yours," Cole said patiently.

Brody frowned. "Mine."

"Brody," Cole said sternly. "We have to leave the lion."

Brody's lower lip quivered and a huge tear slid down his cheek as he continued to hug the lion. "Mine," he sniffled. "My wion."

Although Cole knew that giving in to tears didn't bode

well for the future, Brody's obvious distress tugged at his sympathies. Unsure of what to do, he glanced at Sara and shrugged helplessly, hoping she'd give him some direction on how to handle Brody's tantrum.

Sara saw Cole's indecisiveness and knew he wanted her to intervene. The resentful, still hurting side of her insisted that she let him deal with the situation on his own—after all, he'd wanted to be a parent and she was struggling with her own feelings of inadequacy, so why shouldn't he?—but one thought after another popped into her head and made her repent.

I can't do this without you, Sara.

Brody is yours, too.

She'd stepped into Ruth's shoes, albeit reluctantly, but an agreement was an agreement. She needed to fulfill her part of this bargain and if the truth were known, she wasn't immune to Brody's obvious distress, either. However, before she could offer a suggestion, Cole crouched beside the youngster, held out his hand and spoke softly, yet firmly.

"Brody, give me the toy."

"Daddy, *mine*," Brody wailed. "Warry is my wion."

"This lion isn't yours," Cole explained with surprising patience.

Suddenly, Sara understood what was happening. She placed a hand on Cole's shoulder. "You don't suppose he has a stuffed lion like this one, do you? It would explain why he thinks this is his."

Cole stared up at her. "He could just be throwing the usual two-year-old temper tantrum."

Sara glanced at Brody and watched as he buried his nose in the lion's neck. "He might," she admitted, "but I don't think he is. He called the lion Larry. What child his age names a toy in less than five minutes?"

Cole hesitated as he obviously mulled over Sara's comment.

"Even if he is acting like a normal toddler who wants what catches his eye," Sara continued, "after all the adjustments he's been forced to cope with lately, do you really want to deny him this one small thing just to prove a point or establish that you're the boss?"

The little boy's soulful gaze would have melted Sara's heart even if she hadn't connected the dots about the lion and it obviously had the same effect on Cole because a look of relief spread across his face, which suggested that he hadn't wanted to disappoint the little boy but had thought he'd had to.

He rose, plucking Brody and his lion off the floor in one smooth motion. "Okay, sprout. Let's take Larry the lion home."

This time, Brody didn't fuss as Cole settled him back in the cart. Instead, he bestowed such a huge smile on his father—a smile of gratefulness that was only more powerful because of the tears glimmering in his eyes—that Sara sensed she'd read the situation correctly.

Over the next few hours, Sara watched Brody shower attention on his lion. She'd obviously done something right for the boy, which made her rethink her ability to act as his mother. Granted, what she'd done was minor in the grand scheme of things, but it pleased her to know that she'd been able to put her personal issues aside—for a short time, at least to focus on Brody. Maybe, given enough time, she *could* be the mother he needed her to be.

Now she had to focus on trying to be the wife that she still was... It wasn't easy. The hurt was still there and it showed in their stilted conversations—conversations that centered around Brody to the exclusion of all else.

It would take more time than had passed so far for her

to return to their former easiness but, strained relations or not, she was still observant. And she'd observed that her husband, who wasn't a talkative man on any given day, seemed more introspective than usual.

She sensed it had to do with their trip to the store—maybe he was still fighting the same heart-stopping fear that she had when Brody bolted out of reach—but she waited for him to speak.

As the late-afternoon shadows began to lengthen, she decided enough was enough. While there were still many topics that she considered off-limits, they had to start communicating about *something*. Discussing Cole's current feelings seemed like a good place to start.

As she watched Brody drive his lion across the living room floor in his largest dump truck, she was certain the right moment had arrived when Cole finally joined them.

"I just phoned the Maitlands," he said offhandedly before she could broach the subject on her mind.

"What for?"

"To satisfy my curiosity. It seems Brody *does* have a stuffed lion but Eloise said he didn't play with it very often, so she didn't bring it with him. It's boxed with the rest of his things that should arrive any day now."

Sara smiled, inordinately pleased by his announcement. "I wonder what he'll say when he realizes he now has *two* Larrys."

"Yeah, I wonder." He fell silent for a few seconds. "How did you know it was so important to him?" he asked.

She shrugged. "I didn't. I watched, listened and had a hunch. That's all."

"Yeah, well, your hunch seems fairly accurate. Obviously the conclusion I drew was way off base."

She heard the disgust in his voice. From personal experience, she recognized his suffering as a bout of perceived failure and while part of her wanted him to stew over it, she simply couldn't let it happen. Not because she was feeling particularly benevolent but because he was her husband, and she still hated to see him hurting.

"Don't be so hard on yourself," she told him. "You were only trying to do what any parent would do under the circumstances."

"Maybe, but you were obviously more attuned to the situation than I was. I didn't hear him call the toy by name, but you did."

"Only because I was the objective bystander and you weren't."

"Maybe, but what happens next time, especially if I'm by myself and don't have your powers of observation? This is exactly—"

He stopped short and Sara waited for him to continue. "Exactly what?" she prompted.

He hesitated.

"This is exactly *what,* Cole?" she repeated.

"It's what I was afraid of," he burst out. "Being inadequate. Maybe I'm not cut out to be a father."

"You aren't the only one who suffers from doubts," she pointed out. "My dad always said that anyone who isn't daunted by the responsibility of parenthood has an over-inflated view of himself. The question is, do you still *want* to be a father?"

He nodded.

"Then stop worrying about making a mistake. If there's a repeat of today's incident at the store, you'll make the best decision based on the circumstances at the time," she said simply. "Sometimes we'll get it right, like we did today, and sometimes we won't. Parenthood isn't a perfect science."

His chuckle was weak. "No kidding."

"The point is, the more we get to know Brody, the easier it'll be to tell the difference between a tantrum and when he's truly upset about something."

He nodded slowly before his gaze grew speculative. "Thanks for the pep talk."

Given that their relationship was still broken and that she hadn't been able to dole out any forgiveness yet, his gratitude made her a little uncomfortable. "It was nothing," she said, dismissing him with a breezy wave of her hands.

"Thanks also for not saying 'I told you so.' Shopping with a toddler isn't as easy as it sounds," he added ruefully.

"It isn't," she agreed. Then, because she was curious, she asked, "Would you have felt better if I had?"

"No, but you would have had the satisfaction. It was a perfect opportunity for you to point out how inexperienced and unqualified I am."

"It would have been," she admitted, "but all first-time parents are inexperienced until time solves that problem. Besides, what purpose would it have served?"

"You'd have felt vindicated."

"Maybe, but, again, how would that have helped either of us?" she asked, fully aware that the urge to do just that hadn't completely left her. She'd simply been able to take the moral high ground today but who knew what she'd do tomorrow? "As attractive as the idea is, being resentful and throwing recriminations at each other won't make life easier. As you've already pointed out, we're in this together."

As soon as she finished speaking, she felt his gaze grow intent. "Did I say something wrong?" she asked, uncomfortable under his piercing stare.

He shook his head. "You said everything right. I was just thinking how lucky I am to have you," he said soberly.

His kind words, coupled with her roller-coaster emotions of the past few days, threatened to bring on tears that she couldn't explain. Intent on holding them at bay, she swallowed hard and forced a smile.

"Hold that thought for when you have to change Brody's pants again," she said lightly.

The next two weeks passed quickly and they settled into a routine of sorts, although the day came when the responsibilities of their respective jobs couldn't be ignored. On Monday, because Cole didn't report to work until eight and Sara's shift began at six, he was automatically elected to take Brody to the hospital's day care. Not that he'd minded, of course. Knowing Sara was still struggling with the situation to varying degrees depending on the day, he was doing everything possible to make life easier on her. It was the least he could do because they wouldn't be in this situation if not for him.

While he would have preferred that Sara quit her job to look after Brody, her decision to cut her hours from full-time to part-time came as a relief.

In a way, he felt guilty over Sara being the one to disrupt her schedule and career for Brody, but she'd suggested it herself as being the logical solution. Another woman might not have been as accommodating, but he wasn't fooling himself. Her willingness to act as Brody's mother wasn't a guarantee that their marriage would return to its same open and unguarded status. He had a lot of bridges to build and instinctively he knew that if he didn't construct them properly, he and Brody could easily end up on their own.

Fortunately, as soon as he'd dropped Brody off to join the rest of the children, a toy fire truck had caught his son's eye and their parting had occurred without incident. If Cole's schedule permitted, he hoped to sneak away throughout the day so Brody could see his dad's familiar face and know he hadn't been deserted.

Now he only hoped the events he had planned for their anniversary celebration tonight would help Sara realize that she hadn't been deserted, either…

Sara's first day back at the hospital was stressful, not only because she had to add Brody to her early-morning routine but also because she'd been running at full speed ever since she'd clocked in to work. As of this morning, nearly every patient bed was filled because of a sudden influx of influenza cases. The poor respiratory-therapy staff looked frazzled as they struggled to keep pace with the demand for their services. According to the charge nurse for Sara's medical unit, the new patient she would soon receive would add to that workload.

She was on her way back to the nurses' station after silencing another IV fluid alarm when the ward clerk waved to her. "What's up, Georgia?" she asked.

"Delivery for you."

"What?"

Georgia, a forty-year-old black woman who wore a perpetual smile on her face, handed her a large mug emblazoned with the local coffeehouse logo. "This is for you."

Sara recognized the aroma wafting out of the cup and knew it was her favorite espresso flavor, skinny caramel macchiato. "Who brought this?" she asked.

Georgia shrugged. "Some kid. Didn't leave his name or ask for a tip. I asked who'd sent him and he just said you'd know."

Which meant Cole had done it. Her favorite coffee shop had been across the street from the hospital where they'd first met and Cole would often bring espressos or lattes to share when they'd had a free minute. For him to do so now, when the nearest coffee bar was across town, showed he'd put some thought into today's surprise.

Our relationship is on indefinite probation.

As she held the still-warm cup in one hand, she understood what the drink represented. He was trying to court her again.

Suddenly, her friend Millie fell beside her. "You lucky dog," she breathed. "Where did you get that?"

"A secret admirer," Georgia supplied.

"Cole sent it," Sara explained.

"Ooh," Millie gushed in obvious envy. "Must mean you had a fantastic trip." Millie turned to Georgia. "We're taking five so she can drink that while it's still warm."

Before Sara could protest, Millie herded her to the ward kitchenette. "I've been dying to hear about your weekend for the past two weeks. Imagining the fun you two were having was the only thing that kept me going when I was at home, dealing with kids and a husband with stomach flu." She shook her head. "Why is it that none of them could come down with it at the same time? Anyway, I want to know if you did any sightseeing, or if Cole didn't let you out of your hotel room."

"We didn't go."

"Didn't go?" Millie's mouth formed a surprised O. "What happened?"

"A family emergency."

"Oh, my gosh. What happened?"

She sipped her drink, reveling in the familiar flavor. She didn't want Cole's thoughtfulness to soften her attitude toward him, but it was working quite successfully. "We became parents instead."

Millie's smile instantly spread across her face. "You're parents? Wow, Sara. I had no idea you were trying to adopt. I knew you wanted a baby for the longest time—"

As if she suddenly realized that Sara's response wasn't typical of a new mother, she cut herself off. Her smile faded and her gaze became intent. "You don't seem as excited as I would have guessed. This is a good thing, isn't it?"

"It is," she agreed obediently.

"So how old is he? What's his name? Is it a boy or a girl? Did you get a phone call or wake up one morning and find him on your doorstep? *What?*"

Sara smiled at Millie's rapid-fire questions. "Brody James is his name and we learned about him when I got home from work on the Wednesday night before we were going to leave. The lawyer representing the mother of Cole's son broke the news to us."

Millie's eyes widened. "Whoa, back up a minute. Cole has a son?"

"Yes." She paused. "We were just as surprised as you are."

"Oh, Sara." Her expression became sympathetic. "No wonder you look stressed. He must be fairly old by now, though. You've known Cole for a long time."

"Brody is almost three."

Millie's eyes widened. "Almost three?" she echoed. "But you and Cole have been a couple for…"

Sara filled in the blank. "Six years."

Millie's eyes narrowed. "Do you mean to tell me that he *cheated* on you?"

Sara closed the door. "Could you please lower your voice?" she muttered. "I'd really rather this doesn't end up as fodder for the hospital grapevine." The rumors would begin soon enough, especially after people saw father and son together.

"But, Sara, people can add two and two. When they do, they'll come up with four."

"Cole didn't cheat on me," she defended. "Not really. Not technically."

Her defense sounded lame to her own ears because the situation involved more than a mere technicality.

Millie looked skeptical. "Sorry, but according to my math, he had to have something going on the side if he has a two-year-old and you've been together for six."

"You may not remember, but before Cole proposed, we'd had a huge argument and we broke up. It wasn't for long, but we'd gone our separate ways. During that time, Cole met a high school friend and…Brody is the result."

"Oh, Sara." Millie's face registered distress, or perhaps it was concern, but Sara didn't bother to classify it.

"All they need to know," Sara said firmly, "is that the boy's mother was an old friend of Cole's and when she was killed, she'd granted custody to us."

"Killed?"

"Did you read about a medical helicopter crash a few weeks ago? One of the nurses on the flight was Brody's mother."

"Oh, Sara. How awful."

Millie's pitying expression was more than Sara could handle, although she knew she'd see it often in the coming days. People would speculate all they liked but, as far as she was concerned, Brody's parentage was none of their business.

"I'd appreciate it if you give the edited version to anyone who asks," she said.

Millie nodded. "Of course. But, Sara, how are you handling this? It can't be easy for you."

Not being easy was an understatement. "We're managing," she said instead. "Brody seems to have accepted Cole as his daddy and I do okay with him as long as no one refers to me in his hearing as 'mama.'"

Millie shook her head. "You're a good woman, Sara Wittman. I don't think I could be as gracious as you are under the circumstances."

"I don't always feel gracious," she admitted. "I have my days, but on the whole it's getting better." Seeing Brody's and Cole's similarities was a bittersweet reminder of so many things that had gone wrong, beginning with the secrets she'd allowed Cole to keep and ending with her failure to conceive. Some days she wanted to scream with frustration and throw things, like Brody did when life seemed to be too much to handle, but she didn't. Flying out of control would only cause Cole to suggest either a counseling visit or a prescription for an antidepressant. She didn't need or want either.

However, all things considered, as much as she wanted a baby of her own, getting pregnant right now wasn't a good idea. Bringing another child into the mix while she and Cole were sorting out their trust issues wouldn't be a wise move.

"Then why are you here at work?" Millie asked bluntly. "You should be taking maternity leave."

"I've had the past two weeks as compassionate leave," she replied. "Now I'm on part-time status for a few months. After that, we'll see how things are working out both here and at home before we decide what to do next."

Sara had been happy to accept a temporary option of part-time work because going to the hospital, even two or three days a week, allowed her to feel as if her life hadn't totally spun out of control.

A brisk knock interrupted. "Your new patient is on her way, Sara," the ward clerk announced before she disappeared again.

"Thanks, Georgia." Sara took another long swallow of

her drink, savoring the taste before she set the mug in an out-of-the-way spot on the counter. "Catch you later, Mil."

Interruptions were commonplace, so she didn't worry that her friend and colleague would take offense at their abrupt parting. She reached the nurses' station in time to greet the emergency nurse who was delivering a woman in her sixties, Dorothy VanMeter, courtesy of a wheelchair.

"Caught flu?" she commiserated as she guided the pair to an empty room.

Dorothy's answer was a deep, harsh and productive cough. Sara handed her a box of tissues and set the trash can nearby for her use. When Dorothy's episode had ended, her facial color held a bluish tinge and she was holding her ribs. "I caught something," she rasped. "If this is flu, then it's something I've never had in my life. I'm so exhausted, sometimes I wonder if I can draw my next breath."

"We'll do everything we can to make you feel better," Sara said kindly. "First, though, we'll make you comfortable so you can rest."

The next twenty minutes passed quickly as Sara listened to the nurse's update, helped Dorothy into bed and brought two blankets from the warmer to cover her. As she started her IV, Sara asked about her family.

"I have three children," Dorothy rasped. "Stepchildren, actually, but they don't...we aren't close."

Sara had heard similar stories before. Estrangements in families were more common than one might imagine. "Sometimes people react differently when an illness is involved," she offered. "I'll be happy to call them for you, to let them know you're in the hospital."

"Won't matter," the older woman said tiredly. "They have their own lives now." She closed her eyes and Sara took it as a signal that she either couldn't or wouldn't continue this particular conversation thread.

Fortunately, the IV fluid was dripping steadily as Cole arrived.

Her pulse jumped as it always did when she saw him looking so handsome and authoritative in his white coat, and she wondered how she could respond to him as easily as she always had. Events of the past few days should have doused the sparks quite effectively, but clearly they had not.

Sara lingered in the room while he introduced himself to Dorothy and discussed his treatment plan for her while she took mental notes. As soon as he'd finished, she washed her hands and followed him into the hallway.

"Do you really suspect whooping cough?" she asked.

"I do," he said. "According to the E.R. docs, there have been two confirmed cases in town over the weekend and her symptoms fit."

"But that's a childhood disease. We vaccinate everyone for it."

"We try," he corrected, "but the incidence has been increasing among children who haven't completed the full course and among adolescents and adults whose immunity has faded. Before you ask, though, pertussis *is* included with the tetanus booster that's recommended every ten years, but not everyone stays on top of their immunization schedules."

"I suppose not. To be honest, I'm not certain when I got my last booster shot," she confessed.

"We'd better find out," he advised, "especially with a toddler in the house."

The thought of carrying the germ home to Brody horrified her. "You're right. I'll look into it."

"Good. Meanwhile, we'll give Mrs. VanMeter supportive care and start her on an IV antibiotic. Be sure everyone uses their personal protective equipment, including a mask, when they go into her room. Hand-washing is a must, but I don't have to tell you that."

"I'll take care of it," she said, already planning to place a cart outside the room with the necessary items and post the appropriate signs on the door.

"Check with the lab. If they haven't received a sputum specimen for a *Bordetella* culture, then collect one."

"I will," she promised. "Anything else?"

"No. Er, wait, there is one more thing," he said.

While she waited expectantly, he met her gaze. "I've made plans for this evening, so don't fix dinner."

"Plans? What for?"

His dark eyes suddenly sparkled. "Tsk, tsk, Sara. Don't tell me you've forgotten what day this is?"

"It's Monday."

"Monday. Our anniversary," he reminded her.

Her face instantly warmed. "I guess I did forget."

"Well, I didn't and so I've planned our evening."

"You planned...? But what about Brody? We can't leave him with a sitter after he's been with one all day."

"We aren't leaving him," he announced.

"Then how—?"

"I have everything under control, at least if the timing works out," he said ruefully. "I would have surprised you, but I was afraid you'd throw a tuna casserole in the oven before I got home."

Clearly, he knew her well enough to know that when she was irked at him, she served tuna casserole—his least favorite meal. No doubt with today being their anniversary, he'd been afraid she'd make him pay for their lost weekend.

"It's your lucky day," she said lightly, "because I'm out of canned tuna. I had hamburger in mind."

"Tonight calls for something a bit more special than ground beef, don't you think?"

She really didn't feel like celebrating, anniversary or not. Physical exhaustion after working a full day aside, she was still struggling to keep her emotions in check. It was ironic to realize she'd been worried at one time that he'd forget their anniversary date and yet she was the one who'd forgotten. More than likely, she'd blocked it out of her mind, she thought wryly.

"Why are you going to this much effort?" she asked bluntly. "It isn't as if you have to worry I'll send Brody back, like a refused package."

"This is about us, not Brody," he said. "You put me on probation, remember? I planned this because I know how much our anniversary weekends mean to you. Although what I arranged doesn't compare to the trip we would have taken, the occasion deserves to be marked, don't you think?"

"Oh." For the past few weeks their entire lives had revolved around one small boy to the exclusion of all else, but apparently Cole had taken time to look at the calendar. "I don't know what to say."

"Then it's a date?"

Why not? she asked herself. A quiet evening wouldn't make her feel less lacking as his wife, but it might give her an opportunity to finally establish why Cole hadn't ever been able to share his deepest secrets with her. Maybe their anniversary wasn't the best night for a soul-baring conversation, but emotionally, she hadn't been up to tackling that touchy subject before now. The shock had finally worn off and they were trying to give their relationship a solid footing again, so dinner might be the perfect opportunity to ask those hard questions.

She nodded slowly. "Yeah. Dinner sounds nice. But I don't see how—"

"Leave the details to me," he said with a smile. "Just feed Brody like usual."

"Okay. By the way, thanks for the espresso. It was really good, at least what I drank of it."

His smile lit up his face. "I'm glad."

"It must have cost you a fortune to have it delivered."

He shrugged. "Worth every penny." Immediately, he leaned down and kissed her before he strode away.

For a moment, she simply stared at his retreating back, still feeling the impression of his lips against hers. For the first time in weeks, she actually found herself anticipating an evening alone with her husband.

Brody had been eager to leave the day-care facility and his little face had brightened as soon as he saw her—which had made Sara hope she'd turned the corner and he no longer thought of her as "the lady who wasn't his mother no matter what everyone called her"—but as soon as they were back at home, he alternated between throwing his toys and yelling "No" to whatever she suggested.

Frustration became the emotion of the day but that faded to sympathy when she saw him crawl onto the sofa, scrunch the sheer curtain in his hand and peer out the window, clearly watching for someone. Occasionally, she'd hear him babble, but one word was always recognizable. Mama.

He was waiting for someone who would never come.

She'd studied enough grief counseling to know that Brody was caught between the denial and anger stages of loss. She recognized the signs and could certainly relate.

Oddly enough, though, she'd assumed she'd dealt with the psychological issues of losing their baby, but Brody's presence seemed to prove otherwise. Her grief wasn't far beneath the surface and it reared its head more often than she'd like.

However, while she couldn't sit at the window and wait for her baby to return, analyzing every abdominal ache and pain each month and hoping she'd miss her period was very similar to his faithful action of standing lookout for his mother. Like Brody, each day of unrealized hopes only made her feel the loss again and again.

In essence, they were both waiting for a miracle. Sadly, Brody didn't have a chance at getting his, but she did, provided that she and Cole repaired their trust issues. The possibility was the only thing that kept her going.

CHAPTER FIVE

BEING late had definitely tightened Cole's schedule for the evening considerably, but as he walked into the kitchen and saw his son with macaroni and cheese woven through his hair and ground into his clothes, those concerns faded.

"Brody!" he exclaimed with a hearty chuckle. "Are you eating dinner or wearing it?"

"What he isn't wearing, I am," Sara muttered.

"Daddy," Brody yelled as he held out his arms and offered a gamin smile.

Cole tickled a spot under Brody's chin as he leaned over to kiss Sara's cheek. Her stiffness bothered him, but she clearly wasn't in a loving mood, considering how frazzled she looked and how he was an hour late. He hoped she'd feel a little more charitable as the night wore on.

"So I see," he said. "Mmm, cheese."

"Among other things," she said darkly.

He pulled a strand of macaroni out of Sara's hair. "Does this mean he hated your cooking or loved it?"

"Who knows?" She reached for the wet washrag and began scrubbing Brody's face and hands. "Okay, bud. Dinner is officially over."

Brody ran off to the living room and a few minutes later Cole heard the distinctive sound of toys being thrown against the wall.

Cole moved to the doorway to check on the youngster, aware that Sara had followed him. No blood and nothing broken was a good state of affairs.

Sara sighed. "I'm not sure if watching his anger is better than having him stand on the sofa and stare out the window looking for Ruth."

Cole watched Brody grab a plastic car and begin driving it in circles. He hated the thought of the little boy struggling to understand how and why his life had changed so drastically because he'd *been* that child at one time in his life, too. Granted, he'd been older—eight—but age didn't insulate one from grief and loss.

"I did the same thing," he murmured.

"Throw things or stare out the window?"

"Both. How did he handle day care?"

"According to the staff, he definitely wasn't a model child."

"Oh?"

"He had a hard time sharing the toys and got into a couple of tugging matches. Eloise had said he's such a happy-go-lucky fellow so I'm hoping he's simply expressing his frustration rather than revealing his true personality."

"He's feeling insecure and will settle down when he realizes this is his new life."

"Let's hope so," she answered fervently. "How long did it take you to adjust?"

"A while," he answered. "For me, it wasn't so much acceptance as tolerance. Then again, my situation was different."

"How so?" she asked.

He brushed aside her question. "It's too long to explain now. We have an anniversary to celebrate."

She pointedly glanced at his hands. "Celebrate with what? I didn't cook and it's obvious you didn't bring dinner."

"Nope," he said cheerfully. "I thought you deserved something more classy than food in a take-out bag."

"Ah," she said in a knowing voice. "You're having something delivered, I assume. What kind of pizza did you order this time?"

He wasn't surprised by her guess. "It's better than pizza."

"Better than pizza?" Another crash sounded in the other room and she visibly winced. "I can't imagine."

"Pizza isn't special enough for our anniversary," he insisted.

She slowly shook her head. "Whatever it is, we should save your plans for another day. The kitchen is a mess. Brody needs his bath, I'm bushed and—"

"And I have our evening all arranged," he informed her. "I'll take care of Brody and get him ready for bed while you work your magic in here." He motioned around the room. "And when everything is spick-and-span, like it always is, I want you to enjoy a nice long, relaxing soak."

"In the tub?"

He grinned. "Where else?"

Longing flared in her eyes. "I shouldn't. We have stories to read and—"

"You can have the honors tomorrow night," he said. "Tonight, I'm letting you off the hook so you can pamper yourself. I only have two requests, though."

"Only two?"

He nodded. "Wear your little black dress and no matter what you might hear in the rest of the house, don't leave the bedroom until I call you."

Her smile slowly spread. "Sounds interesting. Okay,

I'll stay put, but if you find me asleep in the tub, don't be surprised."

"If I do, I'll wake you," he promised.

Brody's bath became a challenging endeavor, but Cole learned that his son responded quite well to the authority in his deep voice. Soon Brody was wearing his pajamas and ready for his bedtime story, which Cole happily supplied. By the time Cole turned the last page, the little boy's eyelids were drooping. Clearly he'd worn himself out from his stressful day.

Although timing was of the essence this evening, he allowed himself a few minutes to simply hold his son and enjoy the feeling of closeness and trust between them. He'd never experienced this depth of emotion before and it filled him with awe.

The idea of potentially losing this precious little boy pierced his chest with an intensity so powerful he could hardly breathe.

This, he realized, was what Sara had felt after her miscarriage.

She'd lost a future little person she could love, cherish and raise to adulthood.

Intellectually, he'd understood that the child within her was gone. Without close family ties, without the experience of seeing baby brothers and sisters, nieces and nephews, he'd treated the incident as a minor event in the grand scheme of life and moved on.

However, holding Brody in his lap with his head resting against his chest, he finally realized the full depth of their loss. *Their* son would never sit on his lap, listen to a story or drool on his shoulder. It was *their* loss, not just Sara's.

While he'd known Brody would be a difficult reminder, this moment was the first time he actually felt the same pain. He truly *hadn't* known what he was asking of her and now he could only hope that Brody's presence would eventually soften the blow.

Carefully, Cole placed him in his bed, then tiptoed from the nursery. From the delicious smells coming from the kitchen, his catering company had obviously come in through the garage door Cole had left open and made themselves at home.

He found two of the Chefs-to-Go catering staff hard at work. The owner, a woman in her mid-forties, was busy with the food while her assistant was in charge of creating the ambience. After receiving last-minute instructions from both, he went to the master bedroom.

"No peeking into the other room while I take a quick shower," he ordered as he watched her put on the finishing touches to her makeup.

"You know the suspense is killing me." Her good-natured complaint sounded so much like the old Sara—the one before Brody had arrived—that he felt as if he'd stepped back in time.

"Suffer through a few more minutes," he told her. "I promise I won't be long."

He wasn't. He showered, shaved and put on the tux he'd dug out of a dusty garment bag. Satisfied with his appearance, he approached Sara, looking beautiful in the black dress he'd requested her to wear. The fabric clung to her curves and made him wish they were walking *into* the bedroom instead of walking *out* of it.

"You look fantastic," he said, regretting that he couldn't show her off at a fancy restaurant, although having her to himself came with its own benefits.

She smiled. "Thanks. You clean up nicely, too, although I hadn't expected a tux."

"As I said, it's a special night." At least, he hoped the

evening would be a success. "And you're wearing my favorite perfume."

She shrugged. "It goes with the dress."

He didn't follow the logic, so he chose to believe she'd fallen into the spirit of things, which was a promising sign.

He crooked his arm. "May I escort you to dinner?"

"I'd like that very much."

As he led her into the hallway, she inhaled sharply and froze in her tracks. "Something smells fabulous. What did you do, Cole Wittman?"

"I arranged for an intimate dinner," he said, guiding her through the house toward the cozy breakfast nook where the round table had been covered with a white linen tablecloth and set for two. A single red rose floated in a rose bowl beside a white tapered candle, which flickered in the subdued light. A freestanding silver ice bucket stood beside the table, the bottle of wine he'd requested chilling inside. He flicked a switch and a romantic soundtrack began playing softly.

Sara stopped short, her jaw slack from her surprise. "Oh, my," she said, sounding surprised and a little dazed.

"Have a seat." He pulled out a chair and seated her. "I chose a special menu for tonight. I hope you'll like it."

"I'm sure I will."

"Relax while I serve the first course."

Cole quickly referred to the sheet of paper left on the counter and served the tossed salad with Italian dressing.

"This is…phenomenal," she praised as she placed her linen napkin on her lap. "I'm totally impressed."

"I'm glad," he said. "But before you dig in, I have one rule about this evening."

"Which is?"

"This night is for us and us alone."

"But what if Brody—?"

"If he wakes up, we'll deal with him, but unless he does, it's just you and me—like it would have been if we'd flown to Arizona."

She blinked in surprise and, darn it, he thought he saw her eyes shimmer. "Okay," she whispered before she repeated herself with a stronger voice. "Okay."

He pulled the bottle out of the ice and deftly removed the cork with the tool lying on the table. "Would you like some?"

"Please."

After pouring two glasses, he held his aloft. "To us and many more anniversaries."

At first, she hesitated, which gave him a moment of concern, but then she smiled and chinked her glass against his. "To us," she echoed, before she took a sip.

Relieved and feeling as if he'd done something right with this dinner, he began to enjoy the meal, noting how Sara appeared to do the same.

"How was your day?" he asked.

"At the hospital, it was busy, but you already know that," she said. "I heard two peds patients were admitted with a preliminary diagnosis of whooping cough."

He nodded. "A six-month-old and an eighteen-month-old."

"From the same family?"

"The same day care."

"Then the disease is spreading."

"Afraid so," he said ruefully. "I hope we can nip this before the town ends up in a full-blown epidemic. Did the infection control team come to your floor?"

"Right before I left. Of course, they didn't tell us anything we didn't already know, but it never hurts to be reminded. By the way, I got my new work schedule. I'm off duty until Thursday."

"How does your weekend look?" he asked.

"It's free. Why?"

"Your parents want to visit on Sunday."

"Sunday?" Her chocolate-brown eyes widened. "Did you tell them about Brody?"

"I did."

She sat back in her chair. "Oh, dear."

"We can't keep him a secret forever," he pointed out. "Unless you don't want to see your folks for the next twenty years or so, someone had to tell them they're grandparents."

She sighed. "I know, but what…what did they say?"

"After her initial shock, your mom squealed in my ear until I thought I'd go deaf," he said wryly.

"And Dad?"

"He had a few choice words, which I won't repeat, but after he got those out of his system, he sounded excited, too."

"Did they wonder why we waited to mention Brody?"

"They did, but I told them we didn't want to raise anyone's hopes until we had squared away all the legal issues." He'd been half-surprised she hadn't called them with their announcement several weeks ago, but she'd obviously needed time to accept the situation. As much as he liked his in-laws, he had been glad of the reprieve because it had allowed the two of them to settle into the situation without well-meant outside interference.

"Good idea."

"They wanted to call you right away," he added, "but I convinced them to wait until you were at home tomorrow. So be prepared."

"I will. If they're coming on Sunday, I'll plan dinner. Did they say when they were coming?"

"As excited as they sounded, I suspect they'll arrive

early and stay all day," he said, "but you'll have to ask them yourself. In any case, because Sunday will be busy with family, we should pick up our Christmas tree on Saturday."

"We don't have to get a live one," she began. "An artificial might be more practical."

"We've always had a real tree. I don't want to break our tradition, do you?"

"No, but…" Her gaze grew speculative. "I didn't realize this until now, but we've always incorporated my family traditions into our holiday celebrations, never yours. What kind of tree did your family have?"

Without thinking, he gave his standard answer. "I don't remember."

She leaned back and stroked the stem of her glass. "I don't believe you. You were eight when your parents died. That's old enough to recall your Christmases. Unless, of course, you don't trust me enough to share those stories."

He couldn't believe what he was hearing. "You think *I* have trust issues?" he asked in a tone he reserved for staff members who hadn't done their jobs to his satisfaction.

She met his gaze without flinching. "Don't you?"

"Of course I don't," he snapped.

She raised an eyebrow in response. "If you didn't have trust issues, you would have come to me with your fears instead of going to Ruth."

Back to that again! He clenched his jaw, frustrated that everything circled around to those two fateful days. "I didn't *go* to Ruth. She just happened to be in the same place that I was. And for the record, any trust issues that I had I'd resolved before we got married, remember?"

"I believe you," she said softly, "but I'm only using her as the most obvious example. Whenever I've asked about your growing-up years, you've always brushed off my questions. If not for Brody showing up on our doorstep, I would never have learned that she had been a close friend."

"Is that what this is about? You want a play-by-play account of my childhood friends?" He was incredulous. "Fine. If you'd like a list, I'll go through my yearbook and give you one."

She shook her head. "You're missing the point, Cole. There's a whole side of you I've never learned about. A side that these people knew, but I don't."

"If you're accusing me of keeping more secrets from you—"

"It isn't about secrets, as such. I want to know what makes you tick."

"We've been together for six years and you still don't know?" he asked wryly.

He'd expected her to back down, but she didn't. "You've never been open about your past. Yes, you've told me the basics, but I want more than the bare minimum facts."

He knew what she wanted—for him to spill his guts and talk about his feelings—but he couldn't give it to her. "Why do you need to hear every little detail about my youth? None of it matters. Events can't be changed."

"No, but all I'm asking is for you to share some of those stories with me. Whether they were good or bad, I really don't care. I just want to hear them so I can see how they shaped the man you are."

He'd tried to block out most of those experiences because the memories had left a bad taste in his mouth. He'd done remarkably well, too. His life had become what he'd made of it. Now Sara was asking him to reminisce about the days he'd rather forget.

Damn, but he *knew* going to his reunion had been a mistake. He should have stayed home and guzzled those margaritas in the privacy of his apartment. When the twenty-year reunion invitation arrived in two years, he'd toss it in the trash, unopened, and save himself a ton of grief.

"You said tonight was about us," she reminded him. "Which, to me, translates to a date night. And like anyone on a date, the idea is to discover new things about each other. I want to learn things about my husband that I never knew."

This wasn't how he'd planned his evening. Somehow he'd lost control and they were only on the first course.

"What I'm asking won't be easy for you," she said kindly. "I suspect you never shared those things for a reason—"

"What was the point?" he asked wearily.

"But," she continued, "we can use them to help Brody adjust to his life-changing loss in a healthy manner. You don't want him to suffer through what you did."

Could she be onto something? Would baring his soul help Brody in any way? Because the idea of his son experiencing what he did turned him cold.

"He won't," Cole said fiercely. "I won't allow it."

"Can you be sure?"

"Of course I can," he snapped. "You and my aunt are as different as night and day."

"I hope so, but unless I know what she did, what happened to you, I can't avoid her same mistakes, can I?"

While he knew in his heart that Sara's loving nature would never allow her to do the things his aunt had done— even in her hurt and anger the past few weeks, she hadn't come close to his aunt's vindictiveness. However, Sara obviously had her own fears in that regard—fears that wouldn't disappear just because he'd discounted them.

"Whatever you say won't make me think less of you," she added softly.

Logically, he supposed that was right. No one knew him as well as she did, except perhaps for Ruth, and she'd only known because she'd lived in foster care and they'd compared experiences quite often. After he'd graduated, he'd started a new life for himself—a life that had come with a carefully edited past because he hadn't wanted anyone's pity or scorn.

He definitely didn't want his own wife's, so he'd avoided the risk completely.

She reached out and touched his hand. "Let's start with your Christmases. I really want to know what they were like."

Drawing a deep, resigned breath, he forced himself to remember. "The Wittman family tradition included a real tree, but after the fire, my aunt and uncle always used artificial."

"Fire? There was a fire?"

He nodded. "It was my second Christmas in their home. Apparently no one filled the stand with water and the tree dried out, although no one knew it. I was told to light the scented candle in the living room and my older cousin, who took pride in making my life miserable, started playing with the lighter. The next thing I knew, the tree was blazing." After twenty-five years, he still hadn't forgotten the scene, or the horror he'd felt.

"I'll bet his parents were furious at him."

"No," he said calmly. "He said I did it and, of course, they believed his story, not mine. The fire chief gave us both a severe lecture on fire safety, although I think he knew from my cousin's actions and cocky attitude that I was telling the truth. Anyway, after that my aunt and uncle always used an artificial tree." They'd never let him forget the incident, either.

"And your parents?" she asked softly. "What did you do when they were alive?"

He eyed his glass with its token splash of wine, reluctant to share the few precious memories he had. He'd only allowed himself to replay them when he felt strong enough to deal with his loss, but if Sara could face her demons, then he could do no less.

"We went to a nearby tree farm to cut our own. It was always so much fun, traipsing through the rows in search of the perfect pine. After we sawed down ours, we drank hot apple cider and ate sugar cookies my mom had baked for the occasion while we listened to Christmas carols. It was the one time of year when she added red and green sprinkles to the frosting." Amazingly enough, he hadn't recalled that detail until just now...

"Sounds like fun," she said.

"It was. I always thought a day couldn't be more perfect."

"Did you have a similar tradition with your aunt and uncle's artificial tree?"

If he hadn't sworn off alcohol two years ago, he might have refilled his glass and drained it dry. Instead, he simply rotated the glass and watched the liquid swirl around inside.

"I really can't say. I usually wasn't around when everyone decorated it."

"You weren't? Where were you?"

"At a friend's house. Or the movies. Or the library. In high school, they usually chose a Saturday when I was out of town at a swim meet."

Sara's face registered her confusion. "Why would they exclude you?"

He watched the wine swirl faster, hardly aware that he was causing it to slosh like storm-tossed seas. "My aunt insisted on creating traditions with her own kids," he said evenly, relying on the nonchalant tone he'd perfected over the years. "I wasn't part of that group."

"How awful." Her face registered dismay. "Did they go to your school events?"

"Only if one of my cousins was also involved, which wasn't often. They weren't in the same classes or didn't have the same interests I had."

"Cole, that's terrible!" she protested.

He shrugged. "It was the way things were."

She leaned across the table and placed her hand over his. "I'm sorry."

"Why?" he asked bluntly. "It wasn't your fault."

"No, but your story explains a lot. Thank you for sharing," she said softly.

A response didn't seem indicated, so he nodded. Then, eager to change the topic, especially to one on a lighter note, he eyed her empty salad plate. "Are you ready for the main course? It's stuffed chicken breast with a sun-dried tomato pesto. And be sure to save room for dessert. Red velvet cheesecake."

That had been the menu on the night he'd proposed and he'd chosen it again for tonight to make a statement. Honestly, he couldn't say why he'd remembered those details, but he had…probably because the meal had been a prelude to a future he'd wanted but had always considered out of his reach.

Her gaze flew to meet his and she blinked in obvious surprise. "You remembered," she said, clearly awed.

"It was the most important night of my life," he said simply. "How could I forget?"

Even in the dim light, he could tell her eyes grew misty. Although he knew he wouldn't redeem himself with one special meal, it obviously wasn't hurting his cause. "Sit tight. I'll be right back."

He left the table and thanks to the instructions he'd been given, he soon returned with two steaming plates of gourmet-quality food—even if his presentation didn't quite look like the photo   and a basket of garlic Parmesan bread.

"You... I... This is more than I'd ever imagined," she managed to say. "What a wonderful surprise."

"I'm glad you think so."

She began eating. "Did you plan all this or did you talk some poor ward clerk into organizing it for you?"

"This might come as a surprise, but I even dialed the phone number myself."

She chuckled. "Now I really am impressed."

"And you should be," he teased. "So dig in before it gets cold."

As the dinner progressed, Cole noticed how Sara's wariness of late seemed to fade. He hoped that what he'd planned next would banish it for good.

CHAPTER SIX

SARA carefully placed her silverware across her dessert plate and leaned back, feeling remarkably mellow after two glasses of wine and a melt-in-your-mouth meal. "That was wonderful," she told him.

"I'm glad you liked it."

"The wine was delicious, too." As he attempted to fill her glass again, she covered it with her hand and shook her head. "No more or I'll be snoozing under the table." Then, because she'd noticed he'd never emptied or refilled his own glass, she asked, "Aren't you going to finish yours?"

"The hospital might call me."

"You aren't on call, are you?"

"No, but I had a couple of dicey patients today. One never knows what will happen."

Her theory suddenly seemed less like conjecture and more like fact. "You don't drink alcohol of any kind anymore, do you?"

He blinked, clearly startled by her remark. "Not really, no."

"You stopped after that weekend," she guessed.

He shrugged. "It seemed the right thing to do."

Although she'd suspected she was right, having it confirmed stunned her. "You really *did* regret your actions that evening."

"I told you I did."

She warmed under his gentle rebuke. "Hearing someone say so doesn't mean as much as when he actually modifies his behavior as a result," she defended.

"Then you believe me now?"

"I think I always did," she said slowly, "but it helps knowing you weren't merely paying lip service." Then, because she didn't know what else to say, she changed the subject.

"Thanks again for the great meal and the wonderful evening," she told him. "I'll help with the dishes—"

He rose and pulled her to her feet. "Oh, but the evening isn't over yet."

"It isn't?"

"No." Using the remote control, he selected a different playlist and music suitable for slow dancing drifted out of the speakers. He pulled her against him and because she could either follow his lead or lose her footing, she fell into step.

"What are we doing?" she asked as they moved to the song's rhythm.

"Isn't it obvious?" His breath brushed against her temple. "We're dancing."

"Yes, but—"

"Shh. You're ruining the mood," he teased.

Suddenly, being in his arms seemed like the best place to be. "Can't have that," she murmured as she allowed him to draw her close enough that she could feel his heart beat.

His hand engulfed hers and being in his embrace gave her the sense of being both protected and cherished.

For several minutes, she didn't say a word. After the stress of the last few days, it was far too easy to pretend that someone had turned back the clock and everything was as wonderful as it once had been.

"Now I know how Cinderella felt," she mused aloud.

"How so?"

"At the moment, everything is perfect, but at midnight everything changes. The coach and six white horses will become a pumpkin and a few mice. Her gown disappears into rags and—"

"And the prince eventually finds her because of the glass slipper," he said. "Did you ever wonder why her shoe didn't disappear, like everything else?"

She looked up at him. "Honestly? No. Have you?"

"Oddly enough, I have, because it didn't make sense."

Spoken like a man who looked for logic in everything. "Of course not. It's a fairy tale. You have, though, so what did you decide?"

"Well," he began slowly, "other than the author took liberties with the plot to create a happy ending, I like to think it meant that those two created enough magic during their time together that it *couldn't* disappear completely, even after they were separated at midnight. Granted, the magic was only strong enough to affect her shoes, but that small amount was able to bring them back together again."

She'd never thought of the story in those terms before and the parallel to her present circumstances didn't escape her notice. "Since when did you become a philosopher and literary critic?"

"Hey, you're the one who mentioned Cinderella."

She had. She simply hadn't expected him to draw this lesson out of it.

"It's these magical moments that make life bearable when troubles come," he continued. "They give us something to hold on to—they bring hope for happier times. That's why we have to enjoy them when they come along."

She thought of his stories about his childhood and suddenly understood her husband a little better. Granted, he'd only shared a minuscule amount, but it was a very good start.

His determination to steer clear of his few remaining family members had never made sense until now. While he'd only shared one small Christmas experience, if his aunt could treat him so poorly during the most generous, happy season of the year, what must she have done throughout the other eleven months?

Was it any wonder why he was worried about how she'd accept Brody into their lives? He'd clearly wanted to include Brody in their family, but he obviously didn't want his son to endure the constant rejection he'd had. Given his stories, she certainly couldn't blame him.

She imagined a younger Cole trying to please his aunt in order to win her approval and her love, and getting rebuffed time and again. It nearly broke her heart to imagine his disappointment and hurt until he'd finally walled off any and all expectations. At one time, he'd used the word "tolerance" instead of "acceptance" when he'd mentioned his only relatives and she understood why.

She also understood why he'd been so introspective after the lion incident. "Are you afraid of following in your aunt and uncle's footsteps? Of perpetuating their mistakes?"

"Would you blame me if I were?" he asked instead.

"No, but I don't think you have anything to worry about. You've always shown a remarkable amount of patience with Brody—far more than it sounds as if you'd received."

"I appreciate the vote of confidence."

She smiled. "You're welcome."

A distinctive wail interrupted the moment.

Sara bit back her sigh. "Our midnight has arrived," she murmured, more to herself than to Cole.

"Sooner than I'd thought, too." His voice held the same disappointed note that hers did.

"I'd better check on him," she said, but Cole didn't let go.

"I want to have more nights like this, Sara."

Considering how she'd learned a lot about her husband, it had been quite productive, not to mention thought-provoking. She'd been so certain they'd been ready to have a baby, but now she wasn't so sure. In fact, in light of Cole's personal issues, she wondered if they were truly ready to be Brody's parents, but if not for Brody's untimely arrival, she'd still be operating under her old assumptions that everything was fine. All things happened for a reason, she supposed, and helping Cole deal with his past was clearly long overdue.

Regardless, thanks to the magical evening, she felt less like she was lacking and more like a woman who could conquer any challenge, including the ones facing her.

"Yes," she said. "I'd like that, too."

Cole had just finished making his rounds on Sara's floor when he saw her approach the nurses' station. He tapped his patient notes into the computer as she sat beside him and began entering her own information.

"How's it going today?" he asked.

"Busy, as usual. Any change to Mr. Harvey's orders?"

George Harvey was a spry fellow in his seventies who'd just had a hip replaced and now seemed to be suffering an infection in the joint.

"Not really. Continue the gentamicin and send an order to the lab for an ASAP creatinine level. And page me if the results are abnormal," he said.

"Will do."

"One more thing." He logged off the computer, aware

that she'd paused to listen. "Do you mind if we buy our tree tonight instead of this weekend?"

"Tonight? It'll be dark."

"So? The tree lot has lights."

"You can't wait until Saturday?"

He shrugged and grinned. "No."

"I don't know, Cole. I hate to take Brody out when it's so cold."

"It won't be any warmer this weekend," he told her. "Besides, we're painting his room, remember? That'll take most of the day by itself."

After weeks of waiting, his son's furniture had finally arrived yesterday and they'd spent all evening organizing his belongings, trying to create a space similar to that the boy had enjoyed in his old home. Thanks to the pictures Eloise had emailed, they had been fairly successful, but until they painted the walls sky blue and included the same woodland-creature wallpaper, they wouldn't achieve the result they wanted—to make Brody feel as if he were at home.

To that end, Sara had spent last night poring over the sample books from several home-decorating stores and they'd planned to begin the room's transformation bright and early on Saturday. With any luck, they'd finish before Sara's parents arrived and if not, he was sure they'd welcome the opportunity to help.

"I'd almost forgotten. Weekends just don't seem to be long enough, do they?" she said wryly.

They didn't, and this particular weekend would seem even shorter to her if she knew of the plans Cole had tucked away in his proverbial lab coat. Sally Thompson, their neighbor, had agreed to slip over on Friday evening after Brody had gone to bed so he could take Sara on another date. Granted, it would be a short night out, two hours, max, and he still didn't know for certain what they'd do— Christmas shop, perhaps?—but it would be two hours spent together, without any interruptions.

With any luck, they'd come home and spend the rest of the night setting the sheets on fire. The nights of loving each other hadn't yet resumed, but she'd stopped staring at him with those sad puppy-dog eyes and seemed more like the old Sara. Their anniversary had been a turning point of sorts and while their relationship wasn't completely back to normal, it had settled into an even—and amicable—keel.

His coffee deliveries on the days she worked hadn't hurt either.

"Two days go fast," he said. "And speaking of going fast, the day's half-over. Would you care to join me for lunch?"

His hopeful note reminded her that they hadn't coordinated their meal breaks since Brody had arrived. Granted, she'd only worked two shifts since then, but she'd purposely been too busy to join him.

"They're serving your favorite ham-and-cheese pockets in the cafeteria today," he added, as if trying to entice her. "If we don't go soon, there won't be any left."

Sara laughed at his warning, quite aware that even if the menu had included all the foods she disliked, being in Cole's company wasn't as difficult as it once had been. In fact, as much as she hated to admit it, during her days at home with Brody she missed sharing that half hour with her husband.

"Okay, I'll do my best to meet you, *after* I take care of Harvey's orders. His doctor is a real stickler for promptness, you know. In fact, it wouldn't surprise me if he calls and hounds me for the results in about thirty minutes." She grinned to soften her complaint.

He winked. "What can I say? Some physicians are real bears to work with."

"They are. Now go…" she gave him a gentle nudge "…so I can tend to my patient."

Sara hofted Brody on her lip as she followed Cole around what once had been an empty lot but was now filled with every size, shape and color of Christmas tree. Lights were strung along the perimeter and throughout the enclosure to add a festive touch. The scent of freshly cut pine was strong and intermingled with the wood smoke from the bonfire in the center. Several tall patio heaters were strategically located so that shoppers didn't feel the cold while they selected their perfect holiday decoration.

In fact, it was warm enough that Sara struggled to keep Brody's stocking cap on his head.

"Aren't the lights pretty?" she asked him, pointing overhead.

He clapped his hands and grinned.

"Which tree do you like?" Cole asked her, standing between two blue spruce that dwarfed his six-foot frame. "The skinnier or the wider?"

"How about something smaller?" she suggested. "I don't think either of yours will fit in our living room. What about those over there?" She pointed to a grouping on the left.

"Too small," Cole said. "Those are barely three feet tall."

"Too 'mall," Brody echoed. "Down."

He squirmed to the point Sara would drop him if she didn't let go, so she lowered him to the ground and he raced over to Cole. "Up," he demanded.

"You're supposed to let Sara hold you," he scolded lightly.

Brody shook his head as he clung to Cole like a leech. "Daddy hold me. Not 'ara."

Cole glanced at Sara and she shrugged. "Be my guest. He's starting to weigh more than I can handle."

Before long, Cole had perched Brody on his shoulders and the three of them wandered around the lot. By the time they'd found a tree they could live with—a five-foot Douglas fir—hauled it home and set it in the garage in a bucket of water, it was nearly Brody's bedtime.

Because Brody was so keyed up from their excursion, Sara had expected a fight about his bath and she got one. Finally, he was dressed in his footed fleece pajamas and ran into the living room with his puppy book in hand.

"Daddy, read me."

"Sara will read your story."

"No. Daddy read." The little boy's lip lowered into a pout.

"Brody," Cole warned. "You know this is how we do things. Sara reads this story."

From the beginning, they'd opted for Sara to read his puppy book because Ruth had always read it. The hope had been for him to subconsciously associate Sara with the things his mother had done, but after nearly a month it didn't seem as if they were making progress. Brody simply wasn't ready for Sara to take over the more precious routines in his memory. Tonight Sara was too exhausted to fight him.

"Read the story, Cole," she said, resigned. "He needs to go to bed."

"But—"

"Please, Cole. His bedtime should be a pleasant experience rather than a traumatic one and if listening to you will do the trick tonight, that's the price we'll pay."

He frowned and before he could protest again she sank

onto her easy chair and opened the newspaper to signal an end to the discussion.

"Daddy!" came an insistent voice.

"Okay, but kiss Sara good-night," he instructed.

Obediently, Brody rushed over to her, bussed her on the cheek with an openmouthed kiss, then latched on to Cole's side.

"Only one story tonight, peewee," Cole said as he headed down the hall. "Then it's lights-out."

Sara lowered the newspaper and closed her eyes as she touched her face where Brody's sloppy kiss lingered. To Brody, this small nighttime ritual was probably a necessary evil, but to her, it was another bittersweet moment among many. If not for her miscarriage, she might have been feeling *her* child kiss her good-night, not because he'd been coaxed but because he loved her as his mother.

The rumble of her husband's deep voice and Brody's childish giggles carried down the hall. Wanting to be a part of their circle, even if only from the sidelines, she tiptoed to the bedroom door and watched.

Cole was sitting on the padded rocking chair with Brody on his lap as the two gazed intently at the colorful pages of his picture book. Her husband changed the tone of his voice to match the characters, which clearly tickled his son's funny bone. Occasionally, Cole would glance at his son and hug him. Brody smiled, clearly feeling secure in his father's love.

At one time, Cole had claimed he needed her help to be Brody's father, but ever since that day at the store and the incident with Larry the lion, as far as she could tell, he was doing just fine on his own. As for Brody, the little boy seemed to thrive under his dad's attention, which only confirmed that, regardless of how difficult her decision had been, she'd made the right one for the two of them.

The ironic thing was that Cole had been afraid of being an inadequate father, but she was the one who felt completely inadequate for the task of raising *this* child. No matter what she did, Brody still hadn't warmed to her and she wondered if he had sensed her reservations about bringing him home from the very beginning. Then again, the dynamics of her relationship with Brody were different than what she'd have with her own child. Brody had to sort through his grief and his anger over being told that Sara was taking his mother's place. While a child inherently trusted his or her parents, she had to *earn* Brody's.

Just like she was trying to earn his father's.

Their heart-to-heart conversations so far had been great. She'd learned so much about her husband that she hadn't known before. His focus on excellence had begun long before he'd entered medical school, she'd discovered, in order to gain his family's approval. When he'd accepted that they were ambivalent about his achievements, he'd worked even harder because of the personal satisfaction. In some respects, she felt as if they'd done things backward by sharing these things after they'd married rather than before, but, regardless of the timing, she wanted to believe the seeds of trust were beginning to take root, in both of them.

If they were getting to know each other all over again, wasn't it time she stopped keeping him at arm's length? She'd declared their relationship on probation while waiting to reach a nebulous milestone, but wasn't she, in essence, acting like his aunt, who'd withheld her love and affection as a way to control him?

It seemed ironic that Brody's presence had caused the cracks in their armor to finally be revealed. It would be even more ironic if Brody helped to repair them.

* * *

Cole left Brody's room and went in search of his wife. Although he was more than happy to read Brody his bedtime stories, he refused to do so at Sara's expense. The boy would never learn to depend on her if they catered to his every whim.

He found her in the kitchen. "We need to talk," he began firmly.

Sara turned away from the stove and handed him a mug. "I already know what you're going to say."

"You do?" He eyed the steaming cup in his hand and inhaled the spicy apple fragrance. "What's this?"

"Hot cider. If it wouldn't be so late, I'd whip up a batch of sugar cookies so we could continue your Christmas tree tradition, but I had to create a plan B. We're having the cider now and I'll have the cookies ready for when we decorate on Saturday."

He wouldn't have been more surprised if she'd handed him an early Christmas present. Then again, perhaps she had...

"I can't believe you went to the trouble," he said.

"It's no trouble." She blew across the top of her drink in an obvious effort to cool it to a drinkable temperature. "Correction. It will be when I'm trying to make cookies tomorrow with Brody trying to help, but there's another generation of Wittmans, so it's time we reestablish the Wittman family traditions, don't you think?"

He stared at her, taking in her tousled hair, her gentle smile and the soft expression in her eyes. After working all day, coming home to prepare dinner and then going on a shopping excursion, she was the most beautiful thing he could possibly hope to see.

Hope that she'd finally forgiven him flared. He wanted to believe she had but didn't dare in case he was mistaken.

Maybe he was dreaming. The hot mug in his hand indicated otherwise.

"Yeah," he said, speechless. "Thank you."

"So let this be a lesson to you for next year," she scolded without heat. "We have to plan our tree purchase in advance so I'm not caught unprepared, like I am now."

She was talking about *next Christmas*.

"Then you're planning to stick around?" he asked, wanting confirmation.

For a second, she seemed taken aback by his question. Then her expression became speculative as if she realized she'd spoken of the future in a general way rather than with any real plans. "Did you think I wouldn't?"

He shrugged. "Your suitcase is still packed."

"My suitcase?" She sounded as puzzled as she looked, but in the next instant her expression became sheepish. "It is, isn't it? I hadn't realized…"

He didn't see how she could overlook that detail. He saw the bulging piece of luggage every time he walked in and out of their bedroom. Having lived his entire life with an escape plan in place, he recognized it for what it was. Oddly enough, now he understood how the concept had troubled Sara because it bothered him to see her do the same.

"I'll take care of it," she said.

He pressed on. "I've also seen the way you sometimes look at Brody."

"Oh? And what way is that?"

"Like you're sad and ready to cry. He reminds me of the baby we lost, too."

She stared at him, incredulous. "He does? You've never said."

"I should have," he said. "I should say a lot of things, but I don't."

"Because you don't want anyone to discover your weak spots."

He'd never considered his reticence in those terms. He'd learned to hold his feelings and thoughts close to his chest because some things were just too personal to share while others—his mind froze as he suddenly realized how accurate she was—made him vulnerable. If there was one thing he'd learned, it was to avoid being vulnerable.

But if he couldn't be open and honest with his wife, then who *could* he be open and honest with?

He nodded, surprised by her perception. "When I think about losing the baby," he began slowly, "*our* baby, it hurts."

"Really? You never acted as if you cared."

He thought back to those days and realized she was partially correct. "I didn't have time to get used to the idea before he…was gone."

"I really didn't either," she admitted. "And that almost makes losing him worse. Maybe if I'd suspected sooner, I would have done something different. I'd have skipped my aerobics class or wouldn't have helped lift a patient—"

"No, don't go there. Don't blame yourself. It was merely nature's way."

She nodded. "Yeah. Survival of the fittest and all that." Her smile seemed weak. "Unfortunately, when you want something so badly you ache from the wanting, blaming it on Mother Nature doesn't always help. And sometimes when I'm around Brody…" Her voice died.

"It only emphasizes what we lost," he finished for her. "I discovered that, too. It wasn't just a mass of tissue or a few cells, but a little boy or girl who'd grind macaroni into his hair, suck his thumb or bring a book and say, 'Daddy, read me.'"

"Then you really do understand."

He met her surprised gaze and nodded. "Which is why I wouldn't have been shocked if you'd decided to walk away, although I hoped and prayed you wouldn't."

"The idea seemed attractive at times," she admitted, "but we promised to stick together through good *and* bad times. As I want our marriage to last and our family to grow, then—"

"After Brody's tantrum tonight, do you really want more children?" he asked, incredulous.

"I do," she said with a soft smile. "Maybe not immediately but soon. If you recall, we'd talked about having four."

He hadn't forgotten. Running after Brody kept him busy enough; he couldn't imagine keeping tabs on four at once and he said so.

She laughed. "It's a matter of organization. The important thing is that there will be four individuals who need us to look after them and guide them into adulthood."

"It's the years between babyhood and adulthood that are daunting," he said dryly. All that aside, though, the one thing he wouldn't mind would be *creating* them. It seemed like such a long time since he'd made love with his wife...

"As you brought up his tantrum," she continued, "you're going to tell me to be more firm with him, aren't you?"

He leaned against the counter and cradled his mug in his hands when he'd rather cradle the woman a few feet away. "We can't cater to his whims, not if we ever want him to accept you as his mother."

"I'm beginning to doubt if we ever will," she murmured.

"What makes you say that?"

She paused, her expression downcast. "When Brody's with you, he acts as if the sun rises and sets in his daddy while I'm merely someone to tolerate. I feel like a third wheel—handy to have around in a pinch but useless the rest of the time."

"You're imagining things."

"I'm not, Cole. You might think he's more accepting of me when you aren't around, but he isn't. Rather than follow me around the house, he sits by the door like he's waiting for Ruth to walk in at any minute. It breaks my heart to know he's hurting and I want to minimize that as much as I can, but he won't let me."

Unable and unwilling to stop himself, he set his mug on the counter and drew her into his arms. "He will. It's only been a few weeks. Of course he's hurting, but he can't avoid the truth. One day, he'll wake up and the hole in his chest won't feel quite so big because we—*you*—will be filling up the space."

Having her against him had never felt so good. He ran a finger along her jawline, marveling at her soft skin. "Just like you filled my empty spaces."

He lowered his head and brushed his mouth against hers. As her lips parted in invitation, he continued his gentle assault, uncertain of where this might lead.

"I've missed this," he murmured between his kisses. "I've missed having you next to me."

"I have, too," she answered, "but—"

"No buts," he responded as he nuzzled the spot on her neck that had always made her melt. "I want to make love with my wife. Tonight. *Now.*"

"Oh, my," she breathed. "I want it, too."

He ran his hand under her shirt. "Then what are we waiting for?"

"To finish our conversation?"

"Later," he promised. "Much later."

Eager to enjoy the comfort of his own bed, he pulled away and began flicking off the lights.

"What are you doing?" she asked.

"Being discreet. We have a two-year-old in the house."

She giggled, sounding like the girl he'd married. "I'd forgotten."

It gave him immense satisfaction to know that she had, because it meant he hadn't lost his ability to drive his rational-thinking wife into a mindless state. "I haven't."

He tugged her toward the door, but she stopped. "The stove," she reminded him.

"Oh, yeah."

After a two-second detour to turn off the burner, Sara found herself swept along to their bedroom where Cole closed the door with a quiet snick.

She stripped off her sweatshirt and stepped out of her jeans, aware of Cole doing the same, but before she could dive under the comforter, he stopped her.

"I want to see you," he said hoarsely. "Like the first time."

"The first time wasn't in the dead of winter," she returned.

His grin turned feral. "You won't be cold for long."

Under his heated gaze and reverent hands, the chill in the air no longer affected her and she reached out to conduct her own exploration.

She'd seen him naked before and knew his body almost as well as she knew her own. His shoulders were broad, his muscles defined from the hours spent on his weight bench in the basement, and the crisp dark hair on his chest that arrowed down to below his waist was soft against her skin.

"Tell me you want this as much as I do," he said.

"I want this."

"Then far be it from me to withhold Cinderella's wish."

His fingers found her nipples and toyed with them until she ached.

"Oh, Cole," she whimpered, and she whimpered again when his mouth took over and his hands ventured into other territory with such skill that she found herself standing on the brink.

She gripped his shoulders and whimpered again, this time more loudly.

"Shh," he said, his voice as soft as his caress. "We can't wake Brody."

"Mmm," she murmured as his hands drove her wild.

Lost in her sensation of fireworks, she only vaguely noticed when they landed against the sheets. "Oh, don't stop. Please."

"I love it when you beg," he teased, "but don't worry. I'm not stopping. Not now, not ever."

Impatient, she tugged him onto her and welcomed him into her body. Slowly, he moved, until she thought she'd die from impatience. His hands roamed again, locating the responsive areas he'd mapped earlier. Sensation after sensation rocked her, demanding release, but she forced herself to hold back until he was ready.

Finally, just when she couldn't bear it any longer, his shudders drove her off the edge. They soared together until the tremors stopped and she slowly drifted into the most peaceful state she'd ever experienced.

Sara snuggled against Cole's back, grateful for his warmth and remarkably content for the first time in weeks. She'd missed this closeness and was glad they'd finally found their way back to each other again.

She smiled, thinking of how intense their lovemaking had been. It was as if digging into Cole's past, encouraging him to face his fears, as well as forgiving and forgetting previous mistakes, made a powerful combination.

As she lay there, she decided her first order of business that morning would be to unpack her suitcase. For all she knew, Brody had picked up on her subconscious symbol of escape, which was why he still resisted her attempts to get close to him. With any luck, he'd sense the change in her attitude and respond accordingly.

Pleased with her decision, she slowly drifted off, but an odd sound startled her awake. She listened, but just as she dismissed it as nothing, she heard it again.

A child's whimper.

"Cole." She nudged him. "Brody's crying."

"Hmm," he mumbled, unmoving.

She touched his warm shoulder. "You have to see what's wrong."

"Okay," he murmured sleepily. "I'll go."

A subsequent soft snore indicated her request hadn't registered.

"Cole," she urged again.

"Uh-huh…going," he muttered.

When he didn't move, Sara knew she had to take matters into her own hands. After all, if she didn't sleep well tonight, she could nap tomorrow when Brody did. Cole didn't have that luxury. Still, uncertain of what she might do to console the boy, she slipped out of her warm cocoon, blindly slipped on her nightgown and fuzzy robe, then padded into Brody's room.

He wasn't there.

Panic-stricken into full wakefulness, she wondered what had happened to him. News stories of children abducted out of their beds flooded her mind. She was ready to throw on the lights and yell for Cole when she heard the whimper again.

She followed the sound and found Brody curled in a ball on the sofa, with his teddy bear and blanket. He was asleep, but the hall night-light was strong enough for her to see the wet glimmer on his cheeks.

"Oh, sweetheart," she said, sad that he was clearly acting out his dreams. "Let's go to bed."

She tried to pick him up, but he protested. "No-o-o."

"Brody, you'll sleep so much better in your own bed," she coaxed.

His eyes remained closed, but his objection was plain. "No."

Sara debated waking Cole, then decided she had to resolve this on her own. This time she picked him up and cradled his weight against her. And when he mumbled "No," she simply rocked him.

Eventually, he melted against her and she leisurely strolled back to his room where she changed his wet diaper and settled him in his bed. "Good night, sweet prince," she said as she kissed his chubby little cheek.

Minutes later, she'd just started to doze when she heard the same sound.

Once again, she found Brody on the sofa, crying softly in his sleep.

Certain they'd both spend the night traipsing back and forth, which meant no one would sleep well if at all, she pulled a spare comforter out of the linen closet and returned to the living room. Ignoring his weak protests, she tucked the blanket around them and settled down for the rest of the night with Brody cradled in her arms.

"Good night, young man," she murmured against his tear-dampened hair. "Sleep tight."

He let out a deep sigh and nestled against her, as if he'd either finally found the comfort he'd been searching for or he was too exhausted to fight her. Yet, as his shuddering sobs slowly evened into peaceful breathing, she felt satisfied to have been the person who'd seen him through his nightmare.

In his half-asleep state, he probably didn't realize she'd been the one providing comfort, but she didn't mind. He might reject her nurturing while he was awake, but he obviously was content with it while he was asleep.

This certainly wasn't the way she'd envisioned motherhood would be, but for now it was better than nothing.

CHAPTER SEVEN

"OH, COLE, how could you?" Sara wailed on Sunday as soon as she walked into the kitchen where he and Brody were snacking on her homemade chocolate-chip cookies.

"How could I what?" he asked, popping the last bit of evidence into his mouth.

"Eat cookies right before lunch. I was saving those for this afternoon."

"We only took two and, besides, please note." He pointed to the artfully arranged tray she'd prepared. "I moved the rest around so no one will ever notice a few are missing."

"I'm not worried about the numbers or how the platter looks," she groused. "Brody's the one with chocolate smeared from ear to ear."

He glanced at his son, who stared back at him with wide-eyed innocence as if to ask, What's wrong? As Sara had said, chocolate and cookie crumbs were all over his face and the hands clutching the cookie were grubby as well. To make matters worse, a dark smear ran across the appliqué of Rudolph on Brody's red pullover sweater.

"He'll wash."

"Yes, but my parents will be here any minute and I don't have time to change his clothes again. You were *supposed* to keep him clean while I got ready," she said sternly. "We're trying to make a good impression."

He smiled at her distress. "Your parents are going to be too excited to notice he's wearing a few crumbs and stained with chocolate. If they do, they'll understand. They had four kids of their own, remember?"

She shot him an exasperated glare. "That's not the point, Cole. I wanted everything to be perfect—"

The doorbell rang and her exasperation turned to shock. "Oh, dear. They're here." She glanced at the clock. "They're *early!*" she wailed.

For an instant he wanted to wail with her. In spite of his assurances that Sara's parents could arrive when they wished and stay as long as they liked, in spite of his easygoing manner and the smile on his face, his gut churned. He'd spent most of his childhood being on the receiving end of thinly veiled hostility and he braced himself for more of the same today. As a teen, he'd sworn he'd never allow himself to be put in the same situation, and yet here he was, about to endure it again.

The only difference was, as a kid, he hadn't deserved such treatment. Fortunately, he'd usually been able to escape to his room or a friend's house, or even his school books, but that luxury wouldn't be granted him today. Today, he *deserved* his in-laws' wrath and he'd bear it with grace because deep down he knew they were only acting out of love for their daughter.

He hoped she realized how lucky she was.

"Take a deep breath," he ordered with undisguised humor. As soon as she obeyed, he added, "Now, let your parents inside before they freeze on the front porch."

While Sara flew out of the room, Cole bent down to brush off the worst of the crumbs on his son's clothing. "Shall we meet your grandparents?" he asked.

Brody babbled something that Cole took to mean agreement.

As the sound of Greg and Marcia Adams's voices drifted in his direction, Cole hoisted Brody into his arms and held him like a talisman as he went to greet Sara's parents.

Greg was a few inches shorter than Cole, gray-haired and, thanks to his job as a mechanic and his weekend job as a woodcutter, extremely fit for a man his age. As he noticed Cole and Brody hanging in the background, his normal smile spread widely and his eyes softened.

"There's my grandson," he said, sounding like a proud grandfather. "He's a fine-looking boy, isn't he, Marcia?"

Marcia, an older version of Sara, nodded with her eyes suspiciously bright. "Oh, my, yes. I'm so glad our appointment for a family photo isn't for another two weeks. Now he'll be included. What do you think about everyone wearing red and—?"

"Enough about the annual photo," Greg chided his wife good-naturedly. "Brody and I have more serious things to discuss than what to wear. Like what's in my box of goodies."

He picked up the large box at the door and carried it to a draft-free spot in front of the Christmas tree. After a bit of coaxing, Brody joined him in the game of pulling out all sizes and shapes of brand-new cars and trucks.

Cole watched the two hard at work, pleased that his son had such a kind and forgiving grandfather. Yet how could he not? Sara was a reflection of those traits. As his gaze landed on her, he silently thanked the fates for bringing her into his life. As far as he was concerned, she was his saving grace.

Suddenly, Brody ran out of the room and returned with more toy cars in his arms.

"Goodness!" Marcia exclaimed. "I do believe he has as many vehicles to play with as you had dolls, Sara."

Cole's ears perked. "How many did you have? You never told me you had a *collection*," he teased his wife.

"Because I didn't *collect* them," she informed him grandly.

"Yes, you did," Marcia corrected her. "Maybe not in the sense of acquiring them just to look at, but somehow they always managed to come home with you." She addressed Cole. "Whenever we passed a thrift shop, we had to go in so she could see if anyone had dropped off a doll. If one was there, we had to buy it."

Cole eyed his wife, surprised to hear this story. And yet he wasn't. "Why haven't I heard this before?"

"Because I'd forgotten myself until now," Sara answered. "For the record, though, we didn't buy *every* doll we came across."

"Maybe not, but you came close," Greg added from his spot on the floor. "I built enough miniature bunk beds that I could make them in my sleep. Thank goodness we had enough bedrooms for her and her sister to each have their own, because no one could walk around in hers."

"You made seven beds," she defended. "I only kept fifteen dolls and one always slept with me."

"Fifteen?" Cole asked.

She shrugged. "It wasn't so many, really. I took the dolls that I didn't think anyone else would buy so I could give them a home."

"You *rescued* dolls?" Cole asked.

Sara grinned. "Sure, why not? Someone had to."

"But *dolls?* Why not cats or dogs?"

"We didn't have room for pets," she said. "The expense of feeding them would have been horrific and dolls didn't have to go to the vet."

"What made you start in the first place?" Cole asked.

"I can answer that," Marcia interjected. "Sara always complained that because she was the baby of the family, no one needed her for anything. So I told her to find something she could call her own. She always loved dolls and one day—"

Sara picked up the story. "One day, I was at a friend's house and she had a doll that she didn't want anymore because its clothes were torn and her brother had cut off one pigtail. Because I knew my dad could fix anything…" she cast a benevolent glance at her father "…I brought her home and the rest, as they say, is history."

"And, boy, was she right," Greg added affectionately. "She dragged home dolls that had more problems than you can imagine. Missing eyes, hair, arms, legs, you name it. Her mother and I became good enough at repairing them that we could have opened a side business."

"Don't forget that once they were restored, I found them new homes," she pointed out.

"True," her father admitted. "She only *kept* fifteen, but I'll bet we had hundreds over the years."

Sara laughed. "Now, Dad, I'm sure you're exaggerating."

"Want to bet?" he retorted without heat. "So, Cole, be prepared for Brody to follow in her shoes. With all these cars and trucks, you could end up adding master mechanic skills to your medical degree."

"I'll keep it in mind," Cole answered. "But, Sara, with fifteen dolls, how did you ever play with them all?"

"I had a system," she began.

"I'll say," her mother interrupted. "I can't tell you how many times we had to wait on Sara because she was feeding or changing or bathing one of them."

Clearly, Sara's mothering gene had been activated early

in her life. In light of the doll story, she probably felt she was limiting herself to her dream of four. No wonder she was so impatient to start their family.

Cole listened to their good-natured banter, knowing that this was the sort of home life he wanted Brody to experience. He wanted him to feel loved enough to say and do what he wanted without fear, secure in the support of his parents.

As the stories continued, oddly enough his own insecurities inched their way to the surface. Had Sara reconciled so quickly with him because she loved him, or because he was only a means to the end she wanted?

"Our ward is taking on the overflow from Peds," Beverly McCarter announced during an impromptu early-morning ward staff meeting on Monday. Beverly was the medical-surgical unit supervisor and the strain of handling the increased patient census with a shortage of staff showed on the forty-eight-year-old's face. However, she wasn't the only nurse who sported dark circles under her eyes. To varying degrees, everyone was working overtime.

Except for Sara, of course. When she considered her lack of progress with Brody, she'd glumly thought her time would be better served if she worked more hours to take care of people who really needed her, but, as her mother had reminded her yesterday during their visit, she and Brody would never form a bond if they didn't spend time together.

"We're getting peds patients?" someone asked. As glances were exchanged, plainly most of the nurses were feeling out of their element when it came to caring for the younger set.

"Don't panic," Bev ordered. "They're only sending us the older kids, ten and up. We decided it would be in everyone's best interests if the experienced peds nurses looked after the littlest."

"That's a relief," another nurse remarked.

"Age aside, we have six very sick kids with us now," Bev reported. "They range from age ten to fourteen and the doctors are warning we might get more."

"Do they all have whooping cough?" Sara asked.

"With complications," Bev told her. "Two have had seizures and four have secondary bacterial pneumonia. I might remind you that pneumonia is the most common cause of pertussis-related deaths, so don't take their conditions lightly. These are very sick children."

"Shouldn't they be in ICU?" Millie asked.

"ICU is also bursting at the seams," Bev said wearily. "Once again, I want to remind everyone that transmission of this disease is through direct contact with respiratory secretions. I don't want to see anyone without proper protective equipment, including a mask. Granted, once these kids have finished their five-day erythromycin regime, they aren't considered contagious, but in the meantime they are."

"So who's the doctor in charge?" another nurse asked. "Do we call Dr. Wittman, or one of the pediatricians?"

"Dr. Wittman is our first contact as usual, but he's working closely with the pediatricians and the family physicians. Unless he tells you otherwise, run everything you see, do or suspect by him. Any questions?"

The group dispersed with each outgoing nurse giving specifics about her patients to those who were relieving them. In addition to her other patients, Sara had been assigned siblings Mica and Mandy Berton, who had pneumonia.

Normally, pertussis patients were isolated but because these two came from the same household, they were allowed to share one of the larger rooms so their mother could stay with them.

After donning her protective gear, including a mask, Sara found the woman dozing in a recliner between the two beds. Knowing how exhausted she must be, Sara quietly began to replace Mica's bag of IV fluid.

Mrs. Berton stirred. "Is it morning already?" she murmured.

"Afraid so. Feel free to go back to sleep. I'm only going to check their vitals. After the night they had, I suspect they won't even know I'm here."

"They both had a rough time," Mrs. Berton admitted. "If one wasn't coughing, the other was. In between that, the respiratory therapist was here giving breathing treatments. I was beginning to think we were at a bus stop from all the people coming and going."

Sara smiled as she noted blood pressures and pulse rates. "It seems that way at times, doesn't it?"

As she finished her tasks, their mother asked, "How are they?"

Sara wasn't inclined to speak as bluntly as the night nurse had to her. *No real improvement. Persistent mild fever with intermittent spikes. Coughing spells often result in cyanosis.*

"From what the night staff told me," she said instead, "no real change."

Mrs. Berton's sigh said it all. "I'd hoped we'd see some improvement by now."

Sara would have liked that, too.

"How much longer can they go like this?"

Another question Sara couldn't—and wouldn't—answer. "I wish I could give you an exact timetable, but so much depends on staying ahead of any secondary problems."

"Like their pneumonia."

"Like the pneumonia," Sara agreed. "We're doing everything we can to help them kick this. Unfortunately, recovery takes time."

Mrs. Berton nodded, but the bleakness in her eyes said that she wasn't particularly comforted by Sara's remark.

"I know this is rough on you," Sara added, "but sometimes a little thing like a break to run home and shower can change our perspective. Maybe you'd like to do that when the RT comes in?"

According to the nursing reports, the children's mother hadn't left the hospital since they'd arrived two days ago.

"My husband is coming in after he takes our youngest boy to school. Until then, I have to stay. I *need* to stay." She gave a mirthless chuckle. "It sounds crazy, but I feel like as long as I'm here, they're going to be all right."

Sara understood what she meant. "A lot of parents have told me that," she said kindly.

"Mica always drove me crazy when he asked, 'What's to eat, Mom?' before I'd cleaned the kitchen from the last meal. Now it would be music to my ears." She glanced at Sara. "I won't ever complain again about that boy's bottomless stomach."

"When he's past the worst of this, he'll be hungry again. You'll see."

Mrs. Berton sighed. "I hope so. I'd be devastated if the worst happened..."

"Of course you would be," Sara murmured. "But, as I said earlier, they're holding their own." Her pager went off and she checked the display. Today would definitely be one of those days that would go down in the annals of nursing infamy... "I have to go, but I'll be back as soon as I can. Meanwhile, you know where the call button is. Let me know if you sense a change of any kind."

Sara checked in another new patient—thankfully, this

one was a thirty-year-old woman with a complicated leg fracture as a result of a car accident rather than another whooping-cough case—before continuing on her rounds. Then she had to make a quick trip to the blood bank to pick up a unit of blood for a severely anemic patient. On the way back, she stepped into the elevator to find Dr. Eller, her ob-gyn.

"Congratulations," the fifty-four-year-old specialist told her with a smile. "Cole told me your good news. You're looking well for being a new mother."

She smiled, tamping down the lingering disappointment that motherhood hadn't come in the manner she'd expected. While all of her energies were focused on Brody, she still had unanswered questions about her own health—questions that she hoped Dr. Eller could answer in order to ease her mind.

"Thanks," she answered politely. Then, because the elevator was empty and there was no time like the present, she pressed on. "I'd like to set up an appointment to see you, though."

"Feeling tired, eh?" He grinned. "I haven't met a woman yet who has a two-year-old and isn't tired."

"This isn't about feeling tired or stressed," she corrected him carefully, hating to go into detail in an elevator, even if they were the only people on board. "While now probably isn't the best time for me to get pregnant, I'd like a reassurance that when we *are* ready, I *can* have a baby."

His bushy eyebrows drew together. "You miscarried about, what, six months ago?"

"Nine," she corrected.

Dr. Eller stared thoughtfully at her before he spoke. "How long has it been since you had a thorough physical?"

She shrugged. "I have no idea."

He nodded. "Then we'll start with that, just to rule out any of the obvious health issues."

"Perfect," she said, relieved he was willing to be proactive.

His gaze grew intent. "I talked to Cole the other day and he didn't mention you were concerned."

Not long ago, she *had* been concerned because not having a child made her feel as if an important part of her was missing. Brody's presence had helped, but while she could accept him as part of their family, Cole's son didn't fulfill her personal dream of having a baby of her own. Granted, getting pregnant had dropped its top-priority status in relation to the other events in her life but, regardless of those events, she still had questions that demanded answers.

"I'm more curious than concerned," she explained.

He smiled. "Understandable. In any case, a physical is always the best place to begin. Call my office for an appointment and meanwhile I'll have my nurse phone in lab orders."

Her knees shook with relief. "Thank you."

"After I see those results—it may take a week or so to get them—we'll talk. How does that sound?"

"Marvelous. You don't know what this means to me, Dr. Eller."

The door slid open and he stepped out. "I haven't done anything yet," he said cheerfully, before he disappeared around the corner.

Sara leaned weakly against the rail as the door closed. Perhaps she should have talked this over with Cole before she talked to Josh, but when the opportunity had presented itself, she'd seized it. Cole surely couldn't fault her for that, could he?

However, the answer to that question never came because as soon as she arrived at her floor, she immediately started her patient's blood transfusion. By the time she returned to the Bertons' room, where the respiratory therapy technician was finishing up the children's treatments, nearly an hour had passed.

"What do you think?" she asked the woman after she followed her into the hall.

"To be honest, I'd expected them to be better by now. Has Dr. Wittman come by to see them this morning?"

"Not yet."

"See if he can come sooner rather than later," the therapist advised. "Mica's lung function seems to be dropping. I don't know if a different antibiotic might be helpful, but see what he thinks. Page me if he wants me to come more often."

"Will do."

She returned to find Mica coughing and clutching his abdomen. "Hurts," he murmured.

"What's wrong now?" his mother asked, obviously worried.

"It could be something as simple as sore muscles." Sara frowned. "But I'll be sure to point it out to the doctor." She punched in a text message to Cole's phone. "He's running later than usual, but don't worry. He'll stop by soon, I'm sure."

Sara returned to her station to record her nursing notes. Then, hearing an alarm which seemed to originate in the Berton children's room, she gowned again and went inside.

This time, the children's father was in the room, talking in a loud whisper to his wife. A big, burly man wearing jeans and a plaid flannel shirt under the paper hospital gown, he was the sort one didn't want to meet in a dark alley. The glare he shot her above his mask when she walked into the room only reinforced her opinion.

"Tom," his wife said, "this is Sara, and she's their nurse today."

"I don't care who she is," he retorted hotly. "I want to talk to the doctor."

Sara identified the source of the alarm— kinked tubing—and silenced the offending noise, using those few seconds' delay to modulate her tone in the face of the man's hostility.

"And you will," Sara promised once the only noise in the room was the whoosh of the humidifier. "I've paged Dr. Wittman and he should be arriving shortly. He's always happy to talk to family members."

"My kids aren't getting better."

"We're doing everything we can—"

"It isn't enough," the man insisted. "They should be in ICU or have constant nursing care or something."

"We're giving fluids and antibiotics, and the breathing treatments are delivering medicine into their lungs," she explained. "We simply have to wait for our measures to get ahead of the infection."

He approached her, his face grim. "That's the best you got? To tell me that we have to *wait?*"

"Tom," his wife chided. "Yelling at the nurse won't help. She's—"

"You aren't hearing me," he growled at Sara, ignoring his wife's plea. "My kids are not getting better." With each carefully enunciated word he poked a finger into her shoulder hard enough to throw her off balance.

Sara had dealt with belligerent patients before but this guy had caught her off guard. The call button seemed a million miles away, but even if she reached it, she had no guarantee that anyone would answer it soon enough to help her defuse the situation.

"And I want to know what you're going to do about it," he continued grimly.

"I know you're concerned and upset," Sara said evenly in spite of her racing heart, "but getting angry won't help them or you."

"Tom," his wife urged again. "Calm down."

"I will *not* calm down," he rasped. "I want to know why my kids aren't getting better and what you so-called medical *experts* are doing about it."

This time, as he reached out to poke her again, Sara found herself being unceremoniously moved out of the way.

"I will tell you *exactly* what we're doing, Mr. Berton." Cole's eyes glittered with fury. "*We're* all going to take a deep breath while *you* put your hands in your pockets. And if I see you touching my wife or any of the staff again, *for any reason,* I will ask Security to escort you from the building. Do I make myself clear?"

Although he spoke pleasantly, Sara heard the steel in his voice. Obviously Tom did, too, because he shuffled back a few steps.

"Didn't mean to push her," he mumbled as he avoided Sara's eyes. "I was just trying to get some answers."

"Answers come easier when the questions are asked in a civil tone and the help isn't threatened," Cole answered coldly. "Can we continue this conversation like adults or not?"

As Tom focused on a point near the ceiling, his eyes suspiciously as red as his wife's, Sara took pity on them. "No harm done," she said softly. "Tom was just concerned about his kids."

While Tom nodded, his eyes expressing his gratitude, Cole frowned. He shot her a glance that promised the discussion was merely postponed and not over, but she simply smiled at him.

"Tom, why don't you and your wife step outside while Dr. Wittman examines Mica and Mandy?" she suggested. "The waiting room at the end of the hall has a pot of coffee. Have a cup and when we're finished, we'll find you."

Mrs. Berton nodded. "I think that's a wonderful idea. Tom, shall we go and let the doctor work?"

Tom hesitated, as if he was uncertain about leaving, but between Sara's encouraging smile and his wife tugging on his arm, he strode from the room.

"What in the world were you doing?" Cole muttered. "Why didn't you—?"

"Cole, please. Not now. We have two sick kids and two worried parents." She immediately went into nurse mode, repeating everything the respiratory therapy technician had reported, as well as adding her own observations.

He examined Mica first. "Do we have his sputum culture results?"

"They were posted an hour ago," she replied, pulling up the document on the computer screen.

He studied the report. "According to this, the drug we're using is only marginally effective, so I'm going to switch to a higher-powered antibiotic. Continue with everything else."

After noting his orders in the computer, she joined him at Mandy's bedside.

"Hi, hon," Cole said softly. "How're you doing today?"

"Not…not so good."

"I'm not surprised," he said. "But you'll be up and around soon."

The nine-year-old smiled. "Okay." After Cole finished listening to her lungs, she coughed. "I'm sorry about my dad. Sometimes he can be scary, but he's not. Really."

Sara patted her arm. "I know. He was just worried about you."

"You'll let him keep coming to see us, won't you?"

Sara raised her eyebrow at Cole and immediately saw resignation in his eyes. "As long as he behaves, no one will stop him from visiting," Cole answered, his gaze meeting Sara's.

"Promise?" Mandy asked.

"I promise."

"We're finished, so you can rest," Sara told her. "Meanwhile, we'll send in your parents, okay?"

Mandy nodded as she closed her eyes. "Okay."

Outside the room, Cole stripped off his protective wear. "Hell," he muttered.

"What's wrong?"

"I was looking forward to watching Security escort him from the premises."

Her husband wore a distinctly disgruntled expression, much like a little boy who'd plotted some misdeed only to have his plan thwarted at the last minute. "But now you can't," she reminded him. "If you do, you'll have one upset nine-year-old."

He ran a hand through his hair. "I know. Do you have any idea how worried I was?"

She smiled. "I think so, but I had the situation under control."

He snorted. "Yeah, right. Guys like that usually have trouble with their tempers, which means that I may get to see Security in action after all. His presence in the hospital *is* contingent on good behavior."

"Cut him some slack, Cole. The man's worried about his kids. If you were in his shoes—if Brody were lying in that bed—wouldn't you take on the world for him?"

He frowned. "I guess so. When I saw him threaten you—"

"He didn't hurt me," she assured him.

"Well, I'd feel better if you didn't go into that room alone when he's there."

"Trust me, Cole. He'll be on his best behavior. His wife will see to it. Besides, he loves his kids and if he knows— which he does now—that if he steps out of line, he won't be able to see them, he'll be motivated to stay calm."

"Let's hope so."

She grinned at him. "Now go and be nice to the Bertons while I phone the pharmacy with your new drug orders."

"You don't want to join me to make sure *I* behave?"

"I could, but we want to show Tom that we're attacking Mica's medical condition aggressively. That means the sooner we start the new antibiotic, the better."

"Okay, but just so you know, I plan to stick around this ward as much as I can. To keep an eye on things," he muttered darkly.

She smiled at his protective streak, deciding this wasn't a good time to point out she'd encountered far more antagonistic patients than Tom Berton and had lived to tell the tale. "As much as I appreciate your coming to my rescue…" she rested her hand on his arm and noticed the tension underneath the layers of clothing "…we—I—will be fine, so don't do it on my account," she said.

He met her gaze and spoke in a serious tone. "Of course I'm doing it for you."

"Oh, Cole," she said, surprised by his blatant protective streak, "were you really worried?"

"Why wouldn't I be? A fellow twice the size of my wife was pushing her around. I had no idea what he'd do next. For all I knew, he intended to throw you through the window."

"He wasn't *that* far out of control."

He raised an eyebrow. "Are you sure?"

In spite of wanting to believe that her calm attitude would have activated Tom's common sense, she wasn't sure.

"I'm sticking around as much as possible," he said in no uncertain terms, "and I'm doing it as much for me as I am for you. Now, we'd both better get to work before Tom gets too impatient and comes looking for us."

For the rest of the afternoon, Sara was certain she walked around her ward with a goofy expression of surprise, but it wasn't because Cole was true to his word and had a very visible presence so she'd feel safe. Neither was she surprised by his obvious concern. As he'd pointed out, Tom wasn't a featherweight and an angry male could be a dangerous force to be reckoned with.

No, what had surprised her the most was that he'd *admitted* to being worried. Had this incident happened a few weeks ago, he would have been just as protective, but he'd never have confessed to needing peace of mind for himself.

There was hope for him yet.

CHAPTER EIGHT

IF COLE lived to be a hundred, he'd never forget Sara's expression after he'd announced his reasons for not letting her out of his proverbial sight. If he'd been thinking more clearly at the time, he would have simply called Security and asked them to patrol the ward, but he hadn't.

He also could have hung around under the guise of monitoring the Berton children, but he hadn't done that either. Instead, he'd blurted out what he'd really been feeling.

To his own surprise, the sky hadn't fallen, the earth hadn't trembled, his tongue hadn't snapped off its rollers and Sara hadn't made fun of him. Instead, she had looked as happy as she had on the day he'd finally proposed, and that happiness seemed to carry her for the next week.

Did he really hold that much of himself back, especially from his own wife? If so, he truly needed to make a few personal changes, especially if the rewards would be so great.

However, a few days later, when Sara had tentatively announced her upcoming doctor's appointment, his own response made it obvious that he'd been changing and hadn't realized it...

"I know we'd talked about waiting before we pursued fertility tests," she began, almost apologetically, "but the opportunity presented itself and I just couldn't pass it up.

And it isn't like we're going gangbusters on this. It's only a physical, Cole. When life with Brody has settled down and he's adjusted, we'll do something, but until then... please don't be angry—"

Cole interrupted her breathy explanation with a short kiss. While he was a little disappointed that she'd taken this step on her own, he understood about seizing opportunities. And now that Brody had enriched their lives, he discovered he wasn't as reluctant to eventually add to their household as he once had been.

"It's okay," he told her. "You don't have to explain. I'm not angry."

"Truly?" she asked, the worry in her eyes lessening.

"Truly. If a physical will give you peace of mind, then that's what we should do," he said firmly, certain a doctor's report would chase away her doubts and restore some badly needed confidence in this area of her life. Considering everything she'd done for him, this seemed like the least he could do for her.

However, as they sat in Josh Eller's office a few days later, she was anything but peaceful...

"Nervous?" Cole asked as she thumbed through her third magazine in less than five minutes.

She flashed him a half smile. "Silly of me, isn't it?"

"No, but worrying won't change anything."

"I know." Her chuckle was weak. "It's just that I'm torn between hoping he found something abnormal and hoping that he didn't."

"Don't look for trouble," he advised. "Chances are everything is fine and you're worrying for nothing."

"Let's hope so."

"Mrs. Wittman?"

As soon as the nurse called her name, Sara exhaled

once, smiled at him tremulously, then rose. "You're coming, aren't you?" she turned back to ask him.

His wife was obviously giving him permission to sit in on her exam, so he jumped to his feet. "Of course."

For the next thirty minutes, he chatted with Josh as the ob-gyn checked Sara from the top of her head to the soles of her feet. As soon as he'd finished, he ushered Cole into his office where they talked of inconsequential things until Sara rejoined them.

"Your physical exam was unremarkable," Eller told them. "I didn't expect it to be otherwise. Your basic lab results were also within the established reference ranges."

"That's good, isn't it?" she asked.

"It is. However..." he shuffled a few papers on his desk "...we also ran a few hormone assays and one result stood out." He placed the page in front of them so they could both review it.

The FSH result was in bold-faced print with an *H* beside it, indicating it was higher than normal.

"As you can see," Eller continued, "the level of FSH, or follicle-stimulating hormone, is elevated."

Sara glanced at Cole and he steeled his face into impassive lines to hide his dismay. "Which means what?" she asked.

"As Cole can tell you, FSH does what its name implies—it stimulates the growth of immature ovarian follicles."

"But that's good, isn't it?"

"If the level is high in the first days of a woman's cycle, yes. But then, as a follicle grows, other hormones kick in to stimulate maturation and then these in turn suppress the FSH. Based on what Sara told me, high levels of FSH at this time in her cycle indicate that this restricting feedback mechanism is either absent or impaired."

"Are you saying that Sara is menopausal?" Cole asked.

Menopausal? Fear struck Sara's heart. That couldn't be. It just couldn't...

"I'm not saying anything," Josh said. "While premature menopause is a possibility, at her age it could also indicate she has poor ovarian reserve, which is a fancy term to describe a woman's chance for conceiving. Because women are born with all the eggs they're going to have, we have to assess if the elevated FSH level is due to a decreased number of eggs or some other hormonal condition that is interfering with the normal feedback mechanism."

"Would IVF be a solution for us?" Cole asked.

"It might be," he admitted, "and it might not. So much depends on properly diagnosing the cause of your infertility. However, the fact that she'd been pregnant before suggests that structurally there isn't a problem. Because the FSH is elevated and is the most obvious issue, we'll focus our attention down that path."

Then she still had hope... "If in vitro fertilization is the answer, then how did I get pregnant the first time?"

Eller smiled. "What can I say? The conditions must have been just right. In any case, IVF would simply increase your chances of achieving pregnancy, but before we rush you to an IVF facility, we'll run a lot more tests, including a sperm count on you, Cole."

"More tests?" Sara asked, trying to remember what she'd learned during her nursing-school days.

"We'll start with the clomiphene citrate challenge test. This procedure will indicate how well you'll respond to induced ovulation and is the best predictor of ovarian reserve that we have at the moment."

"What's involved?" she asked.

"On day two or three of your next menstrual cycle, we'll draw a blood sample for another baseline FSH level and perform a transvaginal ultrasound. On day five, you'll begin taking the clomiphene citrate tablets and continue for five days through day nine. Then on day ten or eleven, we'll draw blood for another FSH level."

Sara glanced at Cole. "Sounds simple enough."

"And this will give us the answers we need," Cole stated, as if asking for confirmation.

"Yes and no. This test is merely a predictor. If the results are abnormal, a very poor chance of pregnancy is predicted. Studies have shown that these women respond poorly to injectable fertility drugs, have fewer eggs retrieved for IVF, lower pregnancy and higher miscarriage rates, and an increased risk for chromosomally abnormal embryos. Which is why many fertility programs use this test to screen prospective IVF patients to eliminate those with odds against their success."

"And if the results are normal?" Sara asked, her tone hopeful.

"Unfortunately, normal FSH levels during this challenge test don't tell us anything. A normal result doesn't *prove* your ovaries are working well and therefore the test won't predict that you *will* get pregnant. This is confusing, I know."

"Then why run the test?"

"Because predicting what *won't* work saves a lot of stress and heartache on everyone, especially the couple, for the reasons I mentioned earlier. And if you can screen out those who don't have good odds, you can save them a huge financial burden as well."

"In other words, an abnormal result identifies patients with poor ovarian reserve," Cole clarified.

"Exactly. Then these couples can pursue other options. But before we debate the predictive value and your candidacy in an IVF program, let's see what the test reveals. No sense in getting ahead of ourselves."

Eller addressed Sara. "You're close to your next period, aren't you?" At her nod, he added, "Then we can either arrange to perform this test at your next cycle, or we can wait until next month, after the holidays are over. Or we can wait to continue until you're both ready to add to your family."

Sara exchanged a glance with Cole, uncertain about what to do next.

"Can we have a few minutes to discuss this?" Cole asked Josh.

"Of course."

As soon as Josh closed the door behind him, Cole faced Sara. "What do you want to do?"

Her smile was weak and she plucked at some imaginary lint on her pants. "Logically, we should wait. Brody is still adapting and we've just recently ironed out our own differences. Maybe we should just be satisfied with the three of us as a family."

"But you'd still like to know for certain."

She met his gaze. "Yes, I would."

"Then it's settled." As he rose to summon Josh into the room, she stopped him.

"I don't want you to feel pressured."

He bent down and kissed her forehead. "I don't. In fact, the idea of giving Brody a brother or a sister isn't as frightening as it once was, thanks to you."

She searched his face for the truth. "Really?"

He smiled. "Really."

Six months, even six weeks ago, Sara would have taken his words at face value and blithely continued on, believing Cole's reticence was because he was a man of few words.

Then Brody had come along and his presence had forced

her see her husband in a new light. While she'd demanded that Cole change and bring more openness and honesty to their relationship—and he was making progress—she had changed, too. She'd become more cognizant of when his mood didn't quite match his remarks, and less inclined to take situations and comments at face value. And right now his smile didn't quite reach his eyes, which suggested he had a few worries.

"But you have reservations," she continued.

He paused, brow furrowed, as if weighing his words. "I suppose I do," he finally admitted. "Not because we don't love each other enough to handle another baby but because couples can get so caught up with trying to get pregnant that it interferes with the rest of their family life."

His concern suddenly seemed so obvious she didn't know why she hadn't seen it before.

"This won't detract from our first Christmas with Brody," she assured him. "He won't miss any of the usual holiday festivities and I won't deprive him of any of our family traditions. We'll do everything we'd normally do at this time of year and more."

She made her promise with sincere determination, but at the same time she hoped and prayed for a breakthrough with the little boy who didn't want her to be his mother.

Although Cole didn't mention it, he was relieved to see that Sara had followed through on her promise to make Brody's first Christmas in their home special. He watched as she decorated the house, baked cookies and made candy. They took him to ride the holiday train at the mall where a pretty young elf snapped his picture as he sat on Santa's lap. When the first snowfall came, as the weatherman had predicted, Sara ushered Brody outside so he could catch snowflakes for the first time.

The little boy's wide eyes clearly showed his wonderment as he took in these new sights and experiences but, in spite of Sara's efforts, he still treated her with wariness.

"I know I should be patient," she revealed during one particularly trying afternoon when Brody refused to let her change his wet diaper. "He tolerates me doing things for him if he and I are alone, but if anyone else is here, especially you, then he won't have anything to do with me."

Cole studied his son, wishing the little boy would give Sara a chance to be the mother she so desperately wanted to be. If only he didn't feel so powerless. "Maybe he's just experiencing the normal terrible twos."

She shook her head. "I don't think so. It's more deep-seated than that. It's like he's focusing his anger at the world on me and I don't know how I can help him channel it in another direction. I think we need professional help."

"Okay," he said slowly, "if that's what you think, we can certainly pursue that idea. And maybe it's a matter of you expecting too much from him too soon."

"He doesn't have a problem with you," she pointed out.

"No, but in his mind I wasn't replacing his mother. You are."

She heaved a great sigh. "I guess. I only want…" Her voice died.

"Want what?" he coaxed.

"I want him to need me," she said simply.

He stared at her, incredulous. "Of course he needs you. He's only two, going on three."

"I'm not talking about caregiving. I'm talking about *emotionally* needing me. When he's upset or tired, he goes off by himself, even though I'm right *here*."

"He will. Give him time." He pulled her against him. "You'll see."

Her smile wobbled. "I suppose. It's just that I feel like

I'm failing at the most important job I could ever have—
the job that Ruth should have had. And if I can't do my
job with Brody, what makes me think I could be a mother
to anyone else, even my own baby? Maybe we should just
forget the test Josh suggested."

"It's my turn to give the pep talk," he told her kindly.
"You aren't failing at anything. This is only a rough patch."

"Yeah, right. A rough patch."

He sensed she didn't believe him. "As for your lab test,
you don't want to give up so soon, do you?"

She rubbed the back of her neck. "Not really, no."

"Then just be patient." Then, because she didn't seem to
welcome his advice, he asked, "Have you ever read Ruth's
letter?"

"No."

"Why not? You might gain an entirely new perspective
on what makes Brody tick."

"Maybe," she said, her tone noncommittal.

"Then you'll read it?" he coaxed.

She nodded. "Someday. When I'm ready."

"Don't wait too long," he cautioned. "For all you know,
she had a few tips to make his adjustment easier." Then,
sensing he wouldn't help his cause by pushing too hard,
he traced her mouth with his thumb. "You know what you
need at this very moment?"

"A kiss?" she asked hopefully.

He grinned before he planted a long, lingering one on
her mouth. "Besides that."

"I can't imagine."

"You," he said as he tugged her to the mud room directly off the kitchen, "need some fresh air."

She laughed, sounding like a schoolgirl. "It's freezing
outside."

"It's thirty-one," he said, "which makes it perfect snow-man-building weather."

"You've got to be kidding."

"I'm not. You can't build snowmen if it's warm enough for shirtsleeves. There won't be any of the white stuff."

"Yes, but—"

"No arguments. I'll get Brody while you find things to make their faces and accessorize."

"Faces?" she asked. "As in plural? I thought we were only making one snowman."

He shrugged. "One, three, who's counting? We'll see how many we can create before our noses and toes get cold."

"But I have so much to do—" she began.

"It can wait," he informed her. "Making the first Wittman snow family can't."

"Is he asleep already?" Sara asked as Cole dropped onto his easy chair later that evening.

"Oh, yeah. After you finished his story and left the room, I only read as far as the third page of his second book before he closed his eyes. He had a busy day today."

"I'll say," she said. "Building a snow family is hard work." She thought of the trio they'd created. The biggest was Papa Snowman, as Cole had called him, and he sported a disreputable baseball cap on his round head. Mama Snowman was smaller, with a long strip of fabric around her neck to act as a muffler. Baby Snowman was Brody-size and without adornment until Brody had shaken his head and demanded a cap "like Daddy's."

Fortunately, when Cole had named the family—Daddy, Mama and Baby—Brody hadn't objected. He'd posed happily beside *his* snowman for one of the many photos that Sara had taken.

To Sara's further delight, he'd joined her in making snow angels and had even gone so far as to grab her hand and tell her "More" when he wanted her to help him cover the yard with them.

Maybe she *was* making progress...

"Did you get any good pictures?" he asked.

"More than enough," she answered, mentally reviewing the digital images of Brody giggling, his little cheeks rosy from the cold as he played in the snow. His red stocking hat drooped over his eyes and his matching mittens were caked with snow, but his smile stretched from ear to ear and his eyes sparkled with excitement.

And, of course, there was Cole, looking at his son with a benevolent air as he rolled a giant snowball and explained the finer points of his technique to a little boy who was more hindrance than help.

To think that Cole had been afraid he wasn't father material... As far as Sara was concerned, Brody could have none better.

An image of the one very special garment she hadn't ever worn popped into her head. Suddenly feeling rejuvenated, she dropped her magazine on the coffee table and rose.

"I'm going to take a shower," she said, "and go to bed."

Concern crossed his face. "This early?"

She smiled her best come-hither smile. "I didn't say anything about *sleeping,* did I? Unless, of course, you're too tired?" She raised an eyebrow.

His eyes sparkled with enthusiasm. "Me? Tired? Not a chance."

Sara tiptoed down the hall to their bedroom and after digging through a drawer and turning the contents into a jumbled mess she pulled out the teddy in a flurry of silk and lace. Then she hurried into the bathroom with her lingerie and her plans to make this an evening to remember

When she came out of the bathroom twenty minutes later, Cole was lounging on top of the bed, obviously waiting for her.

A slow, feral grin spread across his face as he rose with the same grace as a jungle cat and approached her. "You look…fantastic."

"Thanks," she answered, pleased by his obvious delight "but it seems to me you're overdressed."

"Not for long," he answered as he reached for her. "Not for long."

Cole woke up early the next morning blissfully content. As he reached instinctively for Sara, he was surprised to find her missing. Not only that, her side of the bed was cold, as if she'd been gone for hours. After the night of loving they'd had, he couldn't believe she'd left their cozy nest.

He was disappointed, too, because he would have loved to start their morning in a very special way…

Curious, he slipped on his bathrobe and padded out of the room to find her.

The last of his mental cobwebs disappeared as soon as he discovered Brody's empty room.

Thanks to the streetlight's glow streaming through the window, he found Sara on the sofa, spooned protectively around his son.

The sight made him smile.

Sara would wake up stiff and sore from her cramped position, he was certain. He debated the wisdom of carrying Brody to his own bed, but they seemed so comfortable together that he hated to disturb either of them. If he'd needed proof that Brody was on the verge of accepting Sara, this was it.

Seeing one of her feet had escaped the comforter, he tucked it around her toes and covered them with an extra afghan for good measure.

She stirred. "What time is it?" she whispered.

"Four-thirty," he told her. "Do you want me to put him in his own bed?"

"No," she murmured. "We'll end up back here anyway. He'll wake soon enough."

She talked as if this had happened often enough to establish a pattern. He was surprised he hadn't realized what had been happening under his own nose, but now that he did, he intended to grill her for details. At a decent hour, of course.

"Good night," she added sleepily.

Feeling oddly left out, he returned to his own cold bed. Although the sensation of being on the outside looking in wasn't new to him—his childhood had been full of those moments—this was the first time he'd experienced it with Brody.

As he lay there, he thought about the woman who'd wanted to be needed since she was a little girl. No wonder Sara struggled with the little boy's rejection, and no wonder she savored these nighttime moments when Brody's subconscious allowed him to accept her mothering. While he was glad their relationship was improving, even if only on such an elemental level, at this moment only one thought bounced around his head.

He was jealous of his own son.

"How long have you two been sleeping on the sofa?" Cole asked Sara the next morning over coffee.

Sara smiled as she liberally poured in sweetener and creamer. She'd anticipated this conversation from the moment she'd woken up and put Brody back in his own bed.

"I'm not sure. A week. Ten days, maybe," she answered. "It began one night when I heard him crying and found him in the living room. Every time I put him back in his bed, he'd eventually gravitate back to the sofa. I could have left him alone out there, but it didn't seem right." She sipped her coffee, hoping the warm drink would ease the familiar achy feeling in her abdomen.

"So you stayed with him."

"It seemed the only way either of us would get any sleep," she said simply.

"You could have brought him to bed with us."

"I could have," she admitted, "but he always gravitates to the sofa, so I thought it best to share it with him."

"We need to think of a different solution," he said. "Neither of you are getting a good night's sleep."

She flexed her arms and moved her head to ease the kinks in her neck. "Tell me about it," she said dryly. "But what choice do we have?"

"We should have retired his toddler bed and gotten a regular bed when he moved in," he said.

"If you recall, we wanted to surround him with as many familiar things as possible," she reminded him. "New furniture could wait, you said."

"That was before we had this problem. Now we're going to sell him on the idea of having a big-boy bed, like his mommy and daddy have."

"I'm not sure he's ready for that sort of change," she began slowly.

"We have to do something," he pointed out. "Continuing like this isn't an option."

He sounded so forceful that Sara smiled. "What happened? Did you miss me?"

"Always," he growled as he hugged her. "Then it's settled. We'll shop for a new bed and if he needs company because he's afraid or had a nightmare, we can join him there instead of on the sofa."

"A little behavior modification."

"Precisely." He smiled. "It's what you're already practicing on him so it should be easy to take matters a step further."

She stifled a yawn. "It's worth a try.

As it turned out, Brody began to wander into their room during his sleepwalking episodes. They took turns carrying him back to his room where they spent what remained of the night in his bed. Sometimes they simply allowed him to climb between them.

However, no matter what they did, he'd heave a sigh—of relief, perhaps, or maybe it was contentment—as she cuddled him close. Idly, she wondered if he'd ever climbed into bed with his mother, but that was something else she'd never know.

Immediately the letter Ruth had written came to mind, but she couldn't bring herself to read it. Not because she didn't want to potentially gain insights into Brody's first two years of life, but because she didn't want to risk reading that Ruth had been in love with her husband all this time or that his version of events wasn't quite as he'd explained. She was certain they had been—at least from Cole's point of view—but why dwell on the past and introduce unnecessary doubts?

So Sara continued to do what she always did and left the letter on top of their dresser, unopened.

A few days later, Sara began her clomiphene citrate challenge test with a combination of disappointment and relief—disappointment that she hadn't gotten pregnant on her own and relief that they were taking matters into their own hands. However, by the time the ten-day protocol ended, cautious optimism had taken hold. She also suffered from moments of dread, but she swiftly pushed those out of her head. Not knowing the truth was worse than knowing, she'd decided, and she was eager for answers.

"Are you ready for Christmas?" Eller's nurse asked her as she drew Sara's final blood sample during Sara's lunch hour.

"I think so," Sara answered. "Goodies are made, presents are under the tree and the house is ready for guests. The only problem I have now is keeping everyone healthy. Our son—" she still found it difficult to refer to Brody as such "—developed the sniffles and I'm hoping he'll fight off his cold before the holidays are upon us."

"At this time of year, it's tough," the nurse commiserated. "Unfortunately, we seem to be passing our germs back and forth at my house and winter has only begun. Spring can't come soon enough for me." She taped a cotton ball over the puncture site on Sara's arm. "That's it for now. We'll see you in five days for your follow-up appointment."

Offering her thanks, Sara left, taking a detour to the hospital cafeteria for a carton of yogurt before returning to her ward.

Georgia, the ward clerk, immediately stopped her. "Your husband signed out the Berton kids while you were gone."

"He did? That's great." The two children had made remarkable progress over the past few days. The change she'd seen from the last shift she'd worked until today had been phenomenal, thanks to the miracle of antibiotics. "Did he say anything about Mrs. VanMeter?"

Dorothy had been off-color that morning, although Sara couldn't point to anything concrete that would account for it. Her vital signs were good, she wasn't having trouble breathing or had any unusual pain, but something wasn't quite right. She'd hoped Cole would see what she was missing.

Georgia shook her head. "Not to me. You might ask one of the other nurses, though."

"I will. First, though, I'll see about sending the Bertons home. As busy as this place is, it won't take long to fill an empty bed."

As expected, Mica and Mandy were delighted to be leaving the hospital. Although they weren't completely recovered, they were definitely on the road to recovery.

As soon as she took care of all the paperwork and discussed the list of dos and don'ts, she accompanied them to their car and waved goodbye. Afterward, she went directly to Dorothy's room.

"How are you feeling?" Noting that her patient's coloring was still off, she automatically took her pulse.

"Oddly enough, not good," Dorothy admitted. "My chest and my back feel strange."

This was the first time the woman had mentioned a specific symptom. "Did you tell Dr. Wittman about this?"

"No, because I just started feeling like this a few minutes ago."

Sara immediately dug her phone out of her pocket and texted Cole, smiling all the while so as not to let Dorothy see her concern. "I'm sure it's nothing, but let's get the doctor back in here, shall we?"

Dorothy nodded. "Okay. By the way, I've been thinking. Would you mind calling my kids for me?"

Remembering how Dorothy had mentioned her kids were actually her stepchildren and her contact with them was minimal, Sara was half-surprised by the request. "I'd be happy to," she said. "Do we have their phone numbers?"

"I gave them to the lady when I checked in at the front desk."

"Then they're probably in your computer records. I'll look and if the numbers aren't there, I'll come back."

"Okay," Dorothy said. "My address book is in my handbag if you need it."

"Is there anything specific you'd like me to tell them?" Sara asked kindly.

"No, just that I'm still in the hospital. And that I'm sorry—" Suddenly, Dorothy clutched her chest and her head rolled limply to one side.

Sara immediately ran around the bed to grab the phone and punch 0 for the operator. After a terse and well-rehearsed message, she hung up. Without hesitation and only a few seconds later, she lowered the head of the bed and began cardiac compressions just as the disembodied voice came over the hospital loudspeaker.

"Code blue, room 412."

CHAPTER NINE

AFTER receiving his text summons to room 412, Cole was on his way when the announcement blared out of the speakers. Muttering a curse, he raced down the hall, up the stairs and burst into the room, not surprised that Sara and two other nurses were already at work.

"Status?" he barked.

Someone called out the most recent blood-pressure reading while another nurse was forcing air into Dorothy's lungs via an Ambu bag. Sara, meanwhile, was performing chest compressions with enough vigor to produce a sheen on her forehead.

"Still no pulse," a voice supplied.

"Okay, Sara," he said, "step aside. We'll defibrillate."

Another pair of hands slapped the paddles into his and as soon as he yelled "Clear," a jolt of electricity surged into Dorothy's body. The heart monitor, which had previously shown a flat line, now showed the characteristic blip they'd wanted to achieve.

"BP is one-ten over seventy and rising."

"Let's get labs and move her into CCU," he added. "Good job, everyone."

As soon as Dorothy was wheeled away, with an oxygen mask covering her face, Cole stopped Sara. "I presume you were here at the time of her MI?"

She nodded. "I'd come in to check on her because I didn't like the way she looked, which was why I'd texted you."

"I was on my way when the code blue was announced."

"Anyway, we were talking and she asked me to contact her kids. She's never asked me to do that before and as far as I know, none of them have ever come to see her. Regardless, she'd asked me to give them a message and then she collapsed. I immediately called the code and began chest compressions."

"You probably saved her life," he said. "If she was going to have a coronary, she had excellent timing to have one while you were in the room."

She smiled, clearly pleased by his praise. "Well, thanks. Let's hope her family feels the same way."

"Do you want me to call them?"

She thought a moment. "As tempting as it is, I'll do it. If they want more information, then you can call them later, after you see her settled in CCU."

"Okay." He hesitated. "How did the blood test go this morning?"

She rubbed the bend of her elbow and felt the wad of cotton underneath her long-sleeved shirt. "Like any blood test," she said. "One prick and it was over. All that's left now is the waiting."

He grinned. "Then that's what we'll do." Although he'd made light of it, he also knew that waiting was often the most difficult part.

Sara entered the house after work, exhausted from the day's hectic pace. She was pleased, however, to find Cole feeding Brody, although she wasn't happy with his choice.

"Fast food?" She raised an eyebrow. "I had our dinner in the refrigerator. All you had to do was heat it."

He chucked Brody under his chin as the little boy shoved four French fries into his mouth at once and grinned. "Ah, but this sounded so much better to our tummies, didn't it, my man?"

Brody wrinkled his nose and tried to shove another fry into his still-full mouth. His little cheeks resembled a chipmunk's from all the food he was trying to chew.

"Cole," she scolded. "He's going to choke. Brody, spit it out."

The little boy shook his head. "Umph."

"Spit it out," she said firmly.

Once again, he shook his head and tried to swallow. "No."

She heaved a deep sigh, but before she could say a word, Cole broke in, his voice stern. "You heard your mother. Empty your mouth before you eat any more."

Brody complied by spitting most of his food onto the floor.

It was a blatant act of defiance and Sara clenched her hands in her pockets, determined not to lose this battle of wills. "Brody," she said calmly, "you will not spit on the floor again or you will not get ice cream for dessert."

As it was his favorite, she expected him to comply. However, he pursed his lips as if he intended to spew more onto the floor, but before he could, Cole put a finger to Brody's mouth.

"No," he said firmly in a tone that meant business. "No spitting. Do you understand?"

Brody answered with a grin. "Okay," he said with good humor.

"Are you finished eating?" At the little boy's nod, Cole wiped his mouth and freed him from his booster seat.

"Play?" Brody asked.

"Yes, you can play," he answered.

As Brody ran off to do just that, suppressed fury made Sara's voice shake. "Did you see that?"

"Yeah. He definitely has an ornery streak."

"Yes, and you just rewarded him for it by letting him play."

He raised an eyebrow. "What would you have him do? Sit in the corner for an hour? Write 'I shall not spit' a hundred times?"

"Of course not," she snapped.

"This isn't like you to get upset over something this minor," he said evenly. "Have a seat and tell me what's *really* bothering you."

"That," she said, pointing to the booster seat, "is what is bothering me. Didn't you see what he did, *after* I told him not to?"

"He's testing you, that's all."

"That's all? That's *all?*" She raised her voice, irritated that Cole dismissed her concerns so easily.

"I've been doing some thinking about the situation and I came up with an idea that seems to fit. In his eyes, his mother left and never returned and now there's a new person in his life who's supposed to take her place. He's pushing you to see if you'll disappear, too."

"And why doesn't he treat you with the same mistrust?"

"Because he never had a dad before. I'm an extra, not a replacement."

"That's rather high-level thinking for a child his age, isn't it?"

He shrugged. "He may not consciously have plotted his actions, but kids sense more things than we might think. Two-year-olds normally begin testing the limits at their age, so why can't we assume he's expanded those limits to include you?"

Whether Cole was right or not, his theory sounded plausible. Could it be as simple as Cole described?

"Brody's actions aren't the real problem, are they?" he asked. "You normally don't freak out because we stopped at a burger place on our way home. What gives?"

Sara sat, chagrined that she'd overreacted. "I'm in a bad mood, I guess."

"Over what?"

"A lot of things." She paused. "No, mainly one. I phoned Dorothy's children. Stepchildren," she corrected.

"Your call didn't go well, I presume."

Sara shook her head. "One never answered the phone. The son was rude and told me not to bother him again. The third, a daughter, was more polite, but she basically told me that Dorothy wasn't a part of her family. Even when I shared..." Her voice cracked and she cleared her throat. "Dorothy asked me to tell them that she was sorry, but neither of the two I spoke to responded positively. The son laughed and suggested that she was only trying to appease her conscience before she went to meet her Maker."

"Any idea on what she was sorry for?"

She shook her head. "None. Oh, Cole. I feel so badly for that woman. To be her age, sick and nearly dying, and know that you're alone has to be depressing."

"You don't know the circumstances," he pointed out. "Blended families are hard to create. For all you know, she might have been the worst stepmother in the world."

"She might also have tried her best."

"That's true, but the point is you can't measure their experience against your frame of reference. Families like yours are more rare than you can imagine."

"I know. I keep telling myself that."

"As sweet as Dorothy seems now, she may have been a real shrew and those kids couldn't wait to leave. Abuse comes in many forms," he added soberly. "So don't judge them too harshly until you hear their side of the story."

"I've been telling myself that all afternoon, but you aren't going to be the one who tells Dorothy that her family doesn't care if she lives or dies."

"Don't take it personally," he told her. "You did what your patient asked and if her family doesn't respond, it isn't your fault. Your responsibility ended when you made contact. As they say, the ball is in their court."

"I know." She sighed as she met Cole's gaze. "It's just so *hard* not to try and fix what's broken."

"Yeah, but the trick is knowing what can be repaired and what can't."

She thought of his own family relationships. "What would you do if you got a call about your aunt? That she was sick and or dying and wanted to see you?"

"I'd like to think I'd be a bigger man and would meet her one last time," he mused, "but, honestly, I don't know what I'd do until I was faced with that situation. With all the bad feelings between us, I'd probably be just as disinterested as Dorothy's stepchildren are."

She'd suspected as much. Given the few stories he'd shared with her, she couldn't fault him for that decision. "I have to admit, the whole stepmother-stepchildren relationship is frightening."

"How so?"

"Of the three families I know with that sort of family dynamics—yours, Dorothy's and now ours with Brody—do you realize two of those situations turned out badly? Given those odds, what sort of chance do we have for success? Brody already thinks of me as the enemy. Will he eventually hate me, too? I don't want him to grow up so scarred that his future relationships suffer because of it."

There, she'd said it. She'd finally voiced the worry that

had plagued her all afternoon. The idea of someday being alone to face a serious illness without family support sent a cold shudder down her spine.

"Sara," he chided gently, "you have nothing to fear. I can't speak for Dorothy, but you are not like my aunt by any stretch of the imagination."

"Yes, but maybe she'd tried to reach out to you, too, and you didn't realize—"

"I was old enough to see what my aunt was doing and I was also old enough to understand the vitriol she spewed at me for years as well as on the day I left. You, on the other hand, are as loving as any mother could possibly be."

"Brody might not agree with you," she said darkly.

"Of course he does. If he truly was afraid of you and hated you, he wouldn't try to push your buttons. He certainly wouldn't be happy sleeping beside you at night, but he is, so don't be so hard on yourself."

"It's hard not to," she admitted.

"Try," he ordered kindly. "My psychiatry skills are a little weak, but in my opinion he's only trying to decide if he can trust you to stick around. When he decides that you will, when he realizes that he can't push you away, he won't ever question your role in his life."

She wanted to believe him.

Cole threaded his arm around her waist. "You'll see I'm right. Just be patient."

Patience seemed to be the answer for everything. It was a word she was beginning to hate.

Two days later, Sara stopped by CCU during her lunch break to check on Dorothy. "Has any of her family come by or phoned to check on her?" she asked one of the nurses.

The other woman shook her head. "Not that I'm aware."

"Okay, thanks. How's she doing?"

"So-so. She's somewhat depressed, which isn't unusual in heart patients. The good news is that her tests don't show any residual damage. You may have her back on your floor in a day or two."

Pleased that Dorothy was doing well, physically at least, Sara wondered if her depression was partly due to her family's lack of interest. As Sara couldn't drag Dorothy's stepchildren to visit and she was certainly a poor substitute, she could at least pop in and let her know that someone cared.

"Thanks for stopping by, dearie," Dorothy said, looking far more frail than she had two days earlier. "I appreciate your concern."

"It's my pleasure," she said cheerfully. "I hear you're doing so well you might be back on our unit before long."

"So I hear," Dorothy said.

Sara talked of non-consequential things for a few more minutes, then, conscious of Dorothy's flagging energy, she left.

Back on her ward, she ran into Cole. "Where've you been?" he asked, sounding curious.

"I went to see Dorothy. Oh, Cole, it's so sad. I know she'd feel better if her children came to visit."

"You don't know that for certain," he countered.

"No, but it couldn't hurt," she insisted. "I wish there was something I could do…"

"Don't meddle in affairs you don't know anything about," he advised. "What if they came and were hateful toward her? Do you really think she needs that right now? Can you risk it?"

She hadn't considered they might be more of a hindrance than a help but, given their attitudes on the phone, it was entirely possible. As Cole had suggested, she couldn't risk upsetting Dorothy. "No, I can't."

Even so, there had to be something she could do…

* * *

The next afternoon, Sara was at home with a fussy Brody, trying to find ways to amuse him, when the phone rang.

"We had a cancellation for a three o'clock appointment," Eller's nurse told her. "Would you be interested in taking that spot instead of coming in on Friday?"

"You have the lab results already?" Sara asked, thrilled by the news.

"Yes, and Doctor would like to discuss them with you today, if you're free."

"We'll be there," she promised. Then, after disconnecting the call, she swung Brody around in her delight. "Did you hear that, buddy? They have my results. Oh, dear. We have to find a sitter, don't we? And I have to call your dad."

She dialed Cole's number, but he didn't answer, so she left a message. Then, knowing Millie was off duty today, she phoned her, and thankfully her friend agreed to watch Brody. With child care organized, she tried Cole's phone again. When he didn't answer this time, she called Georgia because he spent quite a bit of his time on her floor.

"He's really swamped today," the ward clerk told her, "but the next time I see him, I'll tell him you called."

Sara hated to go to her appointment without Cole, but what choice did she have? Waiting for an extra two days seemed like unnecessary punishment. Today patience wasn't a part of her vocabulary.

Cole read the text message on his phone and his heart sank. If only he'd read it earlier, but he'd been so busy that he hadn't heard the distinctive ring tone telling him he had a text.

Cancellation at Eller's office. Meet me there at three if you can.

It was four o'clock now, which meant that he'd missed the appointment. He hated knowing that Sara had gone without him because, whether she heard good news or bad, she'd have to deal with it alone when that was news best handled together.

He half expected her to come by the hospital, but she didn't.

When he tried to phone her, his call went straight to her voice mail.

He tried not to jump to conclusions, aware that not being able to reach her could mean anything, but he was quick to leave when his shift ended.

As he pulled into the driveway, the lights in the house were on and the Christmas lights hanging from the guttering twinkled as usual. He walked in, and found her sitting at the kitchen table, watching Brody chase his sliced hot dogs and macaroni across his plate.

"Sara," he said, "I'm so sorry I didn't get your message until it was too late. How did your appointment go?"

The minute she raised her head, he saw the red-rimmed eyes and he knew... "Tell me," he said.

"The test was abnormal," she said dully. "Not just a little abnormal, but a lot. My FSH was high."

"How high?"

"High enough that I won't ever have children of my own." She swiped at a single tear trailing down her cheek. "Gosh, I hate this. I've cried buckets all afternoon. You'd think I was cried out by now." She blew her nose for emphasis.

"Is he certain? Absolutely certain?"

"There isn't any doubt. I won't get pregnant on my own and I'm not even a candidate for IVF. According to Eller, my results are such that an IVF facility won't even consider me for the procedure. And if one would, chances are I'd have a low pregnancy success rate—about five percent.

He also said that my poor egg quality may have been a factor in my miscarriage."

"Oh, Sara." He scooted a chair close enough so he could hug her. "I'm sorry. I know how much having a baby meant to you, but surely Josh suggested other options."

He had, but she'd been too numb to listen carefully. "He mentioned something about IVF with a donor egg."

"That's good news, isn't it?"

She stared at her husband. "But the baby wouldn't be *mine*."

"Then you won't consider the possibility? Is knowing Brody is my biological son and not yours that big a problem to you?"

"It's not a problem as such," she countered. "I wanted to give you something that no one else could, something that would be yours *and* mine. I wanted our kids to be *ours*."

"Then what are you saying?" he demanded. "If you can't have your own baby, you don't want to be *anyone's* mother?"

Was that what she wanted? "No," she said slowly. "It's just that I pinned my hopes on giving you a *part* of me, but I can't. Knowing that makes me feel so…" she searched for the right words "…inadequate. A failure."

"You are not inadequate *or* a failure." He spoke vehemently. "Absolutely do not say you are."

She met his gaze, her eyes wounded. "What would *you* call not being able to give you a son or a daughter? How would *you* describe it when I can't convince Brody to accept me as his mother? I couldn't even talk an old woman's stepchildren into visiting her after she suffered a heart attack. If those aren't failures, then I don't know what is.

"And to add insult to injury," she added, without giving him an opportunity to interrupt, "of all the health problems I could have had, mine is so elemental that it's part of being a female. And if I'm flawed in that area, then—"

"You are not flawed," he said fiercely. "So your body has a few issues. So Brody is slow at coming around and you couldn't break through three people's stubbornness. You're still a kind, thoughtful woman who has a heart bigger than she is.

"As for giving me something that no one else could, you already have," he said simply. "You've given me your love, your forgiveness and your understanding. Everything else is window dressing."

Touched by his comment, moisture trickled down her cheeks. "Thanks, but—"

"There's no buts about it," he said, moving in close to rest her forehead against his chin. "Those things mean more to me than you'll ever know or understand."

Cole sensed that he hadn't convinced her, probably because she was too mired in her own misery. She was grieving for her lost dreams and wouldn't hear what he had to say until she'd worked through the worst of her sorrow.

No matter. He'd repeat himself until she finally accepted his comments as truth.

The whole problem was that Sara needed to be needed. Even as a child, that had been evident, and recent events had raised those old doubts about her role in her family. It was up to him to convince her that the instances she'd named were simply rocky spots and not utter failures.

"Now," he said with mock consternation, "I want you to focus on all the things I told you—the positives and not the negatives—but the main thing I want you to dwell on is that I need you, Sara. You bring out the best in me. No one else can fill my empty places like you can."

"But, Brody—"

He cut her off. "A strand of thread is just that, a strand,

and it's easily broken. However, two strands woven together make a cord that is stronger and more able to handle pressure. Together, we make that cord, Sara, the cord that's held together by mutual love and respect. Together, we'll be the best parents we can be to Brody, which means he needs us. Not us as individuals, but us as a team."

"You make it sound so simple."

"It is," he said. "Burdens shared are burdens halved."

For the next few hours, Sara moped. She tried to count her blessings, to look at her situation through rose-colored glasses, but it was a constant battle.

As Brody became more recalcitrant and fussy, she wondered if she was only deluding herself that she had any mothering genes in her at all. However, slowly, but surely, Cole's comments popped into her head periodically.

You are not inadequate or a failure.

You've already given me something that no one else has. You've given me your love, your forgiveness and your understanding. Everything else is window dressing.

I need you, Sara... Together, we're whole.

Slowly, but surely, she accepted what she couldn't change. What she had to do was focus on what she *did* have, and right now she had a very crabby little boy on her hands.

By the next morning, Brody's cold hadn't improved. He'd been running a mild fever and his nose was perpetually congested in spite of her best efforts throughout the night to give him relief. His dry cough had worsened, too, and the combination had made him out of sorts, when he normally woke up bright-eyed and ready to greet the world. To make matters worse, he refused to eat or drink.

The thought of whooping cough occurred to her, but she didn't want to be one of those overreactive mothers who thought her child had caught every disease making the rounds at the time. After all, his records indicated that he only lacked the final booster which was given around age four, so the odds of that particular scenario were slim. Even so, she watched him carefully throughout the morning, monitoring each symptom and weighing it against the previous one.

Unfortunately, by midafternoon she still hadn't been able to coax him to drink his favorite grape juice and he'd grown more listless than she'd ever seen him. After she checked his diaper and found it dry when it normally would have been soaked, she phoned his pediatrician.

"Bring him in," she was told. "We won't know if it's whooping cough without swabbing his nose and throat for culture."

So, with growing concern because he didn't fight the coat and hat routine as he normally did, Sara drove him to the doctor's office.

An hour later, after blood tests that revealed an elevated white blood count as well as dehydration, and an X-ray that—thank goodness—didn't show fluid in his lungs, she was on her way to the hospital, experiencing the in-patient process from the side of the consumer rather than the caregiver.

With a heavy heart, filled with remorse and self-recriminations, she carried Brody to the pediatric wing, accompanied by Amy, a forty-year-old pediatric nurse.

"Room 440 will be yours," Amy mentioned as she led her to the room in question. "There's a sofa that opens into a bed, as well as a rather comfortable recliner for you to use. If you'll have a seat, I'll get my supplies and we'll get the two of you organized."

As she left, Cole strode in, his face lined with worry. "I got your message. What's wrong?"

Relieved to see her husband, she sank onto the recliner with Brody in her arms. "Dr. Keller suspects whooping cough."

Cole stared at her. "You're kidding."

Sara shook her head. "I wish I was. She won't know for certain until the culture report comes back, but she's going to treat him as if that's the problem. The good news is that he doesn't have pneumonia. She would have sent us home with an antibiotic, but he's severely dehydrated and she wants him on IV fluids. Oh, Cole…" Her eyes watered. "This is all my fault."

"How so?"

"I've been so focused on me and my disappointments that I didn't notice how sick Brody had gotten. I should have—"

"Stop berating yourself," he told her. "I saw him last night, too. If you're looking to blame someone, blame me. I'm the physician in the house and I dismissed his symptoms, too."

Cole obviously considered himself as much at fault as she did. "Maybe we're both being too hard on ourselves," she admitted. "I really didn't notice a change until this morning and then he seemed to go downhill as the day progressed."

"Thank goodness you were alert," he said fervently. "If he does have whooping cough, he'll get antibiotics before he has a chance to develop a secondary infection."

Brody opened his eyes at the sound of Cole's voice, but didn't raise his head off Sara's shoulder. Cole stroked his son's baby-fine hair with a shaky hand. "Hey, big fella," he crooned. "Aren't you feeling good today?"

Brody's smile was halfhearted and he closed his eyes as if too exhausted to pay attention.

Cole's phone beeped. With movements suggesting frustration, he checked the message and mumbled a curse. "I can't stay," he said flatly. "There's a patient—"

Although she wanted Cole with her, his other obligations came first. She offered a tremulous smile. "It's okay. There's no point in both of us watching Brody sleep."

He frowned, then nodded, his expression resigned. "I'll come back when I can."

"We'll be here."

"Call if anything changes," he ordered.

"I will." With Cole gone, Sara felt the need to do *something,* so she helped Amy, the peds nurse, settle Brody into bed. As he was already wearing his footed pajamas, they only had to remove his coat. The worst part came when it was time to start his IV.

"Some of the medical staff want to do the honors themselves when it comes to their own children, but I wouldn't recommend it," Amy said somewhat apologetically. "Right now, he needs to associate you with comfort, not pain."

Sara hadn't considered taking on that task at all and if she had, she would have dismissed the idea immediately. "That's okay. My hands aren't steady enough right now to hit anything smaller than the Alaskan pipeline."

It was a testament to both the nurse's skill and the severity of Brody's illness that he merely flinched when Amy inserted the needle. Afterward, he refused to lie in the strange crib with the tent over it.

"I'll hold him for a while," Sara offered.

"That might be best. Meanwhile, I'll start the vaporizer, which should help soothe his lungs and loosen the respiratory secretions. Although he's getting plenty of fluids now, try to convince him to drink on his own."

"I will."

For the rest of the afternoon Sara held Brody in her lap, mentally willing his health to improve. As she stroked the hair off his hot forehead and heard a couple of carolers in the background, she wondered when Brody had wiggled his way into her heart. As much as she'd resented his origins, now they no longer mattered. He was theirs to nurture and protect, much like another baby had needed nurturing and protecting some two thousand years ago—the same baby who'd eventually become responsible for the Christmas season.

She dozed herself, not realizing the late hour until Cole strode in after his shift had ended, minus his lab coat and tie.

"I'll take him," he said, reaching for Brody. "You need a break."

Although she knew he was right, she handed over the little boy reluctantly. She helped herself to the Popsicles in the ward's kitchenette and watched as Cole painstakingly urged him to eat. After Brody had nibbled away half of it, he closed his eyes and fell asleep again.

"Why don't you go home and rest?" Cole suggested. "I'll stay with him."

She started to protest, realizing she sounded like Mrs. Berton and so many other mothers whose children were in the hospital.

No, that wasn't right. She didn't just *sound* like a mother. She *felt* like one. And if she felt like one, she needed to *act* like one. Mothers did not leave their children.

"Just for a while," Cole coaxed, as if he understood the reason for her hesitation. "An hour or two is all."

An hour. She could do that, even though she really didn't want to go. "Okay."

"Good. Oh, and when you come back, bring something I can lounge in, will you?"

"You're staying, too?"

He nodded. "What would I do in an empty house by myself?"

What indeed? "Do you want dress clothes for tomorrow?" she asked.

He nodded. "I can shower and change in the doctors' lounge before I go on duty."

"I'll be back soon," she promised.

At home, she showered, changed clothes and threw Cole's things into a duffel bag. As she headed out of their bedroom, Ruth's letter caught her eye.

I'm sorry Brody got so ill, she silently murmured. *I should have been paying closer attention.*

But if you had, a little voice asked, *what would you have done?*

The question brought her up short. As a medical professional, she knew doctors didn't intervene just because a child developed a cough or a cold. Even if she'd taken Brody to the doctor yesterday, chances were they would have been sent home to try the home remedies she'd done on her own. Instead of blaming herself, she should do as Cole had suggested. She should be grateful she'd noticed a change when she had.

She would, she vowed. Then, as she took another step forward, her little voice spoke again.

Read the letter.

This isn't the right time, she told herself. She was on her way back to the hospital. Besides, with the disappointments and trials of the past few days, not to mention her struggle with feelings of inadequacy, did she really want to read a message from a dead woman now?

And yet would there *ever* be a good time to hear Ruth's last words?

CHAPTER TEN

UNDECIDED about the wisdom of her actions or her timing, Sara hefted the envelope in her hand. But as she debated, she realized she was tired of having the letter's contents hanging over her head like an ax about to fall. It was now or never.

She dropped the duffel bag onto the floor, sat on the edge of the bed and after a deep breath carefully slid one finger under the sealed flap.

Dear Sara,

If you're reading this, it means that I'm asking a favor of you that I never wanted or planned to ask. I know you must be devastated at the news that Cole is my son's father, but forgive me when I say our choices that night eventually led to the best thing that ever happened to me. I have nothing but the utmost respect for your husband and the few pleasant memories I have of my youth always included Cole.

For what it's worth, Cole could only talk about you during the time we were together. It won't be easy for you to forgive him or me, but for Cole's sake and the sake of his son, I hope you will. You see, the people we really needed weren't there that weekend and consequently we turned to each other, not realizing we would hurt the very ones we loved.

If you're reading this letter, it means I'm not a part of my son's life, which saddens me a great deal. However, I won't regret that Cole could be Brody's father, should you allow him to fill that role. There are many people who would gladly take on this responsibility, but you and Cole are the only ones I'd choose. Cole is a special man—I knew he would be even when we were teenagers—and if he chose you to be his wife, then I know you are just as special. Because of that, and because I believe Brody will need both of you to help him become the kind, caring man I want him to be, I'm asking you to open your heart and let him inside. As wonderful and as strong as your husband is, he can't accomplish this job alone. You, Sara, are the one who has softened Cole's rough edges during the time you've been together and I trust you'll produce the same results with his son. From what Cole has said, I have utmost faith in you.

Time is so short and our lives so fleeting that I hope you'll not only tell Brody every day that I loved him, but that he'll experience a mother's love from you on my behalf. He's the best of both Cole and me, but he's more than that. He's a clean slate, waiting for <u>you</u>—Sara noted the word was underlined—*to write beautiful things on it.*

Someday, perhaps before too much time has passed, you'll have forgiven both of us for the pain we've caused and you'll think on me with fondness.

Sincerely,
Ruth

Sara brushed away the tears on her cheeks. At this moment, she certainly didn't feel like the right woman for the job Ruth had given her, but for all of her faults, flaws and failures, she was the one who was available.

Lost in her thoughts, she returned to the hospital, where she found Brody nestled against Cole as the two men in her life dozed. As she gazed at father and son, love welled up inside her until she thought she might burst. Brody might not share her genetic makeup, but love and acceptance had made him her son, too. Although she'd never implied otherwise, it was an earth-shattering revelation to her and she couldn't wait to share with her husband.

Cole didn't know what startled him awake, but he opened his eyes and saw Sara sitting on the sofa, paging through a magazine. Who would have thought that holding Brody would have made him stiff and sore?

"Have I been sleeping long?" he asked.

She chuckled. "Define long. I've been here for the past hour."

"That's long. What have you been doing?"

"Reading. Making phone calls."

"Phone calls? To your parents?" he guessed.

"And to Dorothy's stepchildren. This time I didn't hold back."

"Oh, my. They won't issue a complaint against you, will they?"

"No, because I didn't call as Dorothy's nurse. I called as her friend. I told them that this was Christmas and surely they could give Dorothy a chance to make amends."

"Will they?"

She shrugged. "Who knows? If my stirring speech doesn't soften their hearts, then she's better off without them."

"My wife, the crusader." He stirred, shifting Brody in his lap. "He's really a bag of bones, isn't he?"

"Want me to take him?" She dropped her magazine on the seat cushion and rose.

"Let's see how he does in his bed."

Carefully, they maneuvered him into the toddler-size crib. When he didn't stir, merely let out a sigh, they breathed their own sighs of relief.

"Have you had dinner?"

"No." She shook her head. "I brought you a sandwich, though. Ham on rye with extra mustard, just the way you like it."

"Thanks."

As he dug into his food, he watched Sara gaze at Brody. He couldn't define it, but something about her had changed. She seemed more at peace than ever before.

"I am," she admitted when he remarked on it. "Sitting with Brody here in the hospital, worrying about him, made me feel like his mother for the first time."

He grinned. "It took you long enough to figure it out."

"Afraid so. Anyway, I finally realized the biology doesn't matter. Anyone can become a parent, but it's the *parenting* that's most important."

"Wasn't that what I said all along?"

"Yeah, well, I had to figure that out for myself. Afterward, I read Ruth's letter."

"And?"

"She must have been a remarkable woman," she said simply. "I want to help him become the son she'd be proud of."

For all of Sara's efforts, he'd sensed she'd been holding back a part of herself, but now it was as if she'd finally made a firm commitment to the task of raising Brody. He wanted to shout his happiness, but the noise would create

MILLS & BOON Book Club

2 Free Books!

Get your free books now at
www.millsandboon.co.uk/freebookoffer

Or fill in the form below and post it back to us

THE MILLS & BOON® BOOK CLUB™—HERE'S HOW IT WORKS: Accepting your free books places you under no obligation to buy anything. You may keep the books and return the despatch note marked 'Cancel'. If we do not hear from you, about a month later we'll send you 5 brand-new stories from the Medical™ series, including two 2-in-1 books priced at £5.30 each and a single book priced at £3.30*. There is no extra charge for post and packaging. You may cancel at any time, otherwise we will send you 5 stories a month which you may purchase or return to us—the choice is yours. *Terms and prices subject to change without notice. Offer valid in UK only. Applicants must be 18 or over. Offer expires 28th February 2012. **For full terms and conditions, please go to www.millsandboon.co.uk/termsandconditions**

Mrs/Miss/Ms/Mr (please circle) _____

First Name _____

Surname _____

Address _____

_____

_____ Postcode _____

E-mail _____

Send this completed page to: Mills & Boon Book Club, Free Book Offer, FREEPOST NAT 10298, Richmond, Surrey, TW9 1BR

Find out more at
www.millsandboon.co.uk/freebookoffer

Visit us Online

0611/M1ZEE

Find, try & love
more books like this!

Visit millsandboon.co.uk

MILLS BOON®

You can find all Mills & Boon titles at our web
millsandboon.co.uk

For a limited time only, we are offering you an
EXCLUSIVE 15% OFF when you order online.
Simply enter the code **15NOV11** at the checkout
But hurry, this offer ends on 30th November 2011

PLUS, by ordering online you will receive all these extra benefits:

- 🌹 Purchase new titles **1 MONTH AHEAD OF THE SHOPS.** Available in paperback and as eBooks

- 🌹 Order books from our huge backlist at a discounted price

- 🌹 **Try before you buy** with Browse the Book

- 🌹 Be the first to hear about exclusive offers in our eNewsletter

- 🌹 Join the M&B community and discuss your favourite books with other readers

Terms and Conditions:
- Offer expires on 30th November 2011
- This offer cannot be used in conjunction with any other offer.
- Code can only be redeemed online at www.millsandboon.co.uk
- Exclusions apply
- Discount excludes delivery charge.

NOV

a furor on the ward and bring down everyone from code-blue teams to security personnel.

Instead, he abandoned his food and rose to take her into his arms. "You are, without a doubt, the most fantastic woman in the world. I love you."

She grinned. "You are the most fantastic man. And I love you, too, Cole Wittman."

As if on cue, Brody began to fuss. Cole went to the crib and while Sara unlatched and lowered the rail, he reached in to pick him up. To his surprise, Brody shook his head. He said one word as he held out his arms toward Sara.

"Mama."

His wife's eyes immediately filled with tears as she took their son into her embrace. He couldn't imagine a better gift he could have given her on this Christmas Eve.

Christmas Eve, four years later

"Mama," Brody bellowed at the top of his lungs as he entered the kitchen, where tins of Christmas cookies covered the counter and the air smelled of apples, cranberries and cinnamon. "We're home."

Sara smiled as she greeted him with a smile and a hug that wasn't easy with her growing belly in the way. "I see that," she said softly. "But can you please use your inside voice? Alison is sleeping."

Alison was their two-year-old daughter, thanks to the efforts of IVF and a donor egg. She had her daddy's brown eyes and a cute little nose that obviously came from her genetic mother, but she was what Cole affectionately called "her mama's girl."

If all went well, their new son would arrive in February, also courtesy of the same medical technology that had brought them Alison.

"Sorry," her son said, lowering his voice. "What time will Grandma and Grandpa get here?"

"Anytime now," Sara answered.

"I'm gonna watch for them." He raced off just as Cole walked in, his cheeks as rosy as his son's from the cold.

"Where's he going so fast?"

"To the living room and his lookout post. My folks should arrive any minute," she reminded him, "and you know Brody. He has to be the first one to spot them."

He snagged a celery stick from the vegetable tray on the counter. "Alison?"

"She's sleeping."

Cole grinned as he threaded his arms around what once had been her waist. "Then we're alone?"

"For the moment, yes."

"And Junior's behaving himself?"

She rubbed the bump in front of her. "He's quiet right now."

"Good, because I want to kiss my wife in private."

In the background, Sara heard Brody squeal with excitement. "You'd better hurry because we're about to get company," she warned.

"Now, Sara. Some things are simply not meant to be rushed."

Sara smiled at her husband. "I couldn't agree more."

* * * * *

FIREFIGHTER WITH A FROZEN HEART

BY
DIANNE DRAKE

First published in Great Britain 2011
by Mills & Boon, an imprint of Harlequin (UK) Limited.
Harlequin (UK) Limited, Eton House, 18-24 Paradise Road,
Richmond, Surrey TW9 1SR

© Dianne Despain 2011

ISBN: 978 0 263 88612 2

Harlequin (UK) policy is to use papers that are natural, renewable and recyclable products and made from wood grown in sustainable forests. The logging and manufacturing process conform to the legal environmental regulations of the country of origin.

Printed and bound in Spain
by Blackprint CPI, Barcelona

Damn, he shouldn't have kissed her.

Should have left well enough alone—especially since they'd come to an understanding. But the urge... Well, he'd hoped it would be quelled. It wasn't, though. Didn't even come close to it. In fact, one kiss had whetted his appetite. He wanted more. But he knew the result of that, didn't he?

Now that her children have left home, **Dianne Drake** is finally finding the time to do some of the things she adores—gardening, cooking, reading, shopping for antiques. Her absolute passion in life, however, is adopting abandoned and abused animals. Right now Dianne and her husband Joel have a little menagerie of three dogs and two cats, but that's always subject to change. A former symphony orchestra member, Dianne now attends the symphony as a spectator several times a month and, when time permits, takes in an occasional football, basketball or hockey game.

Did you know these are also available as eBooks?
Visit www.millsandboon.co.uk

CHAPTER ONE

"It's not your call, Corbett. You took in a lungful of smoke, so you go to the hospital to get checked out. Not my idea, not my rule either, but you do it, or you take a suspension." Captain Steve Halstrom folded his arms across his chest, looking properly stern in his edict. "You don't have a choice in the matter."

Jess didn't need to go, though. He didn't have a damn thing wrong with him. Wasn't coughing. Okay, so he'd broken enough rules for the day. He got it, this was the punishment. Meaning he'd have to leave his buddies behind at the scene, feel guilty as hell walking away from them while they were still fighting the worst of the blaze, just so he could pay the so-called piper. If his years as an army surgeon had taught him one thing, it was the value of working as a team. Today, against his better judgment, that team ethic would prevail, and he'd be sidelined. Do the deed, do the time. He'd done the deed, couldn't argue the point...*much.* "Even though I'm a doctor, and I know—"

"What you know is that it's policy. You take in smoke, you take a ride to the hospital."

Jess looked up at the building—a three-story apartment, fully engaged. Everybody had got out, and that was the good news. The bad news was the wind, and the old

building sitting so close to the one on fire that its demise was likely.

"Damn, this is lousy timing," Jess muttered, shrugging out of his turnouts—personal protective gear that was turned inside out when not in use so that the firefighter could quickly step into them and pull them on. A hundred pounds of heavy was what they called it, and it was a far sight different from the surgical scrubs and occasional lab coat he had worn when he'd been a surgeon. But that was just part of the career trade-off. He was okay with it most days.

Today, when he'd pulled that child out of the burning apartment and carried him down the stairs, letting him breathe *his* air, he'd been very okay with it. The child had been hiding in the back of an old closet. Couldn't be seen from a normal vantage point. Parents nowhere to be found. But one elderly lady had mentioned there might be a child up there, and that's all it had taken to raise the hair on the back of his neck. Granted, he hadn't known if the kid was still in there, but that hadn't stopped him. Not when there had been a possibility. "If I check out okay, I'm coming back," he told Steve.

"If you check out okay, you get three days off. This was a close one, Jess, and you brought it on yourself. So, you're on leave, *not suspension,* and if you argue with me, it'll be a week. Got it?"

"After what the lady told me, I should have just left the kid in there?" Jess snapped at his supervisor, instantly regretting it.

"You know what? Doesn't matter how you check out medically, take the whole week so you'll have plenty of time to think. Oh, and in case you've forgotten protocol, let me remind you that you are *required* to let someone know where you go. It's not an option. We don't do this

job alone." He shrugged. "I don't want to have to hang you up like this, Corbett, but it's all I can do. This time you're off the hook easy. Next time I'll do something official."

Steve was right about this. Jess knew it. Didn't have to like it, but he did know it. So now he had a whole empty week ahead of him. That, if nothing else, was his demon to deal with. "Then I'll see you in a week."

"Next week," Steve said, waving Jess off to the ambulance where *he* waved off the paramedic who tried to help him in.

"I'm fine," he grunted at her. Sitting out on the job, the way he was being forced to do, didn't square with him. But, different from the days when he had been head of trauma in the army, he wasn't head of anything now. Just another one of the many. Actually, one of the nearly fifteen thousand New York City firefighters and paramedics. One who was close to the bottom of the ladder. It was a good way to get lost, which was all he wanted. Get lost, stay lost. Do his job. Forget the rest of it.

"Which is why you're in my ambulance?" she asked, following him in the door. "Because you're fine?"

"Look, just do what you have to do, skip the comments and leave me the hell alone. Okay?" Plopping down on the stretcher inside the ambulance, Jess closed his eyes, even though the light was dimmed to almost total darkness. All he wanted to do was shut out the extraneous noises, but he couldn't. In Afghanistan, there'd always been noise... screaming, crying, artillery going off. Here, the sounds weren't the same, but they all amounted to suffering. Here, though, he got there first, made a *different* difference. Then he moved on, no commitments left behind.

"Too bad. The comments are the best part," she quipped.

Nice voice. A little throaty, which wasn't bad in the feminine variety...if he'd been looking for the feminine

variety in anything. Which he wasn't. So he laid his right forearm over his forehead, not so much because it was a comfortable position but more to shut out what he'd see when his eyes adjusted to the dark. The equipment, the storage bins, the paramedic...not his life anymore. "Then comment away, *after* you check me out and release me," he said, not wanting to be a grouch about it. She was, after all, just doing her job, and being tough on her because of it wasn't his style.

"Well, it says here you took in some significant smoke, which means you get a free ride to the hospital like it or not. So, for starters, I need to put the oxygen mask on you..."

Now he was annoyed. He didn't need oxygen. Didn't want the damn mask clamped down on his face.

"No, thanks," he said, finally opening his eyes and shifting his arm up just enough to have a look when his eyes adjusted enough to make out a blur. First sight, red hair. Spunky red, even in the dimness. Short, boyish, in a pixie sort of a way. "Skip the oxygen. My lungs are fine, no matter what my captain thinks."

She moved toward him, carrying both an oxygen mask and a blood-pressure cuff.

"Blood pressure's okay, too. Unless you put that oxygen mask on me."

She laughed. "Scared of a mask, fireman? A little bit claustrophobic?"

"Not scared or claustrophobic. Just don't need it," he said, now wishing he could get a better look at her. He was pretty sure she was shapely. Nice curves in silhouette. Oddly familiar to him, even in the dim light.

"Says you?"

"Says me. I'm a...used to be a trauma surgeon."

"I'm impressed, fireman. But not swayed. You get the mask, I get your blood pressure. And I don't negotiate."

"But do you compromise?"

"Whoa, the fireman has an offer to make?"

He couldn't help but chuckle at that. His paramedic was downright stubborn, and he liked it. "Not an offer. A compromise. I'll cooperate unconditionally when you take my blood pressure if you let me wear a cannula instead of a mask." Prongs up the nose were better than a mask any day. The thing was, when he geared up to go on a run, he was all about masks and other equipment. But a simple, lightweight, green oxygen mask…that was his last memory of Donna. Garbled words she'd tried saying to him through her oxygen mask. Words he'd wanted to understand but couldn't. Words he should have heard if not for that mask.

"So, fireman, are you always this uncooperative?"

"Only when I have to be."

"Let me guess. In your opinion, that's most of the time."

He chuckled. "You've got some bedside manner, paramedic."

"I try." She pulled the cannula from the drawer and handed it to him. "Since you seem to know my job, you do the honors while I crank this baby up to full squeeze." She was referring to the blood-pressure cuff she was dangling over him.

Damn, he really wanted a better look at her. She was tweaking his memory and all he could see right now were big protective eye goggles and a surgical mask. Smart move, considering all the soot and debris flying around out there, but very frustrating. "Is that a threat?"

"A promise." She took his blood pressure then tossed the cuff back in the drawer.

"One twenty over eighty. Pretty good, for a man in your

disgruntled and extremely dirty condition. Here, let me clean some of that soot off your face." Grabbing a bottle of sterile water, she twisted off the lid then soaked a gauze pad and started to dab at his face. But he caught her wrist and stopped her.

"One twenty over eighty? Did you mean to tell me it was a *perfect* blood-pressure reading rather than just a pretty good one? Oh, and the dirty face is fine, it comes with the job."

She wrestled out of his grip. "And the fireman gets a demerit for the worst manners I've met all day."

"What the fireman wants is to get the hell out of here and get back to work."

"Like I said before, you get a trip to the E.R. After that, you're out of my hands." She gave a pound on the glass between her and the driver, indicating they were good to go, then handed him the wet rag. "Wash your face. I don't want you getting soot in your eyes. And no arguments, okay? I just want to get this over with. You're my last patient on my last run as a paramedic, and I don't want any hassles. Think you can manage that for me, fireman?"

"And I suppose you expect me to smile, too?" he asked, half cracking that smile.

"What I expect is that I'm going to do the paperwork now, and you're going to answer my questions. Smiling is optional." Sitting down on a fixed bench across from him, she picked up the clipboard, clicked her pen and wrote the date on her transport form. "Do you have a name?" she asked.

"It's Jess. Jess Corbett." He thought he heard a little gasp from her.

"Okay, *Jess*." She twisted until her back was almost to him, as the ambulance lurched forward, then lowered her

mask and pulled off her goggles. "So, tell me, how did you end up here?"

"Kid trapped in a closet. I gave him my oxygen. My captain wasn't happy that I didn't go in with backup. You know, same old story." Now, this was frustrating. He thought she looked like…no, couldn't be. Voice was different. Hair much shorter. Curves more filled out. Julie had been a couple pounds shy of skinny, with long straight hair. Thin voice. Pretty, not gorgeous. But his paramedic, what he could see of her, was gorgeous.

"I mean *here,* in New York City, fighting fires. How did that happen?"

"That's on the paperwork?"

"No, but getting to know my patients gives me a better sense of what's going on with them. As in, are you always so grumpy or is this a reaction to your smoke inhalation?"

"Trust me, it's a reaction to my smoke inhalation, but not the kind of reaction you think it is." But she could be Julie. Except, Aunt Grace had told him Julie was working in the south. "In answer to your question, though, let's just say that I got tired of my old job, quit it and decided to try something new."

"Well, I suppose quitting is good…*for some people,* isn't it? You know. As in running away."

Julie! He sat up, swung his legs over the side of the stretcher and yanked off his oxygen cannula. "I thought you were working down south someplace."

She turned to face him, full on. "This is south, compared to Lilly Lake." She reached up, switched on the bright overhead so he could see everything. "Julie Clark, R.N., paramedic." Said in all bitterness.

Well, this was certainly awkward. His first love. His first…everything. It was so awkward he didn't know what to do. Bail out of a moving ambulance, lie back down, shut

his eyes then pretend she wasn't there? Let her have it out with him before they got to the hospital? Which was long overdue, actually.

With the way her eyes were sparking now—the same beautiful blue eyes that kept nothing hidden—jumping from the ambulance seemed like the best way out of this mess...for him. But he'd been the one who'd laid out that mess back then, and running away a second time sure didn't feel like the honorable thing to do. Hadn't then, didn't now. So, Jess gritted his teeth for the confrontation, and since this was Julie, he knew there would be one. Being feisty had always been part of her charm, and he didn't expect any of that had changed.

"It's locked," she said, as if sensing his thoughts. "You're not going anywhere."

Was that a barbed smile crossing her lips? "So, what's the protocol here, Julie? Do I ask how you've been? Should we sit here in silence and stare at each other? Or would it be easier if you beat the hell out of me and just got it over with?"

"If I weren't on the job, I might just take you up on that one. But since I am, here's an idea. How about you be a nice, cooperative patient and lie back down, and I'll be the paramedic who watches your vital signs and makes sure you don't go into respiratory arrest as some aftereffect of the smoke inhalation? Does that work for you, Jess?"

"Are you going to put a pillow over my face and smother me?"

"Is that what you want me to do? Because I can."

"Look, Julie..."

She shook her head, and thrust out her hand to stop him. "Lie down. Now! And don't argue with me."

"Sure," he said, doing just that. "And I suppose if you really want me to wear a mask..."

Julie laughed, but it had a cutting twinge to it. "Jess Corbett, trying to comply. It doesn't become you, Jess. Not at all. Besides, I'd rather watch you lie there and be uncomfortable around me. Good show, watching you squirm."

He did stay down for about a minute, hating every blasted inch of silent space around him. Then he popped back up. "You said I'm your last patient. Does that mean you're quitting?"

"Moving on. Went to nursing school part time for years, all the way through to my doctorate, and now I'm going to work as a full-time nurse."

"Congratulations," he said, still pretty much at a loss for words. It wasn't every day that you ran into a childhood sweetheart, one he'd actually had feelings for. Of course, he'd made fast work of that. But, still, Julie... She *was* a memory-maker. Gone from his life, but never forgotten. "Well, I hope you have a good career. Aunt Grace would have been proud of you." What a lame thing to say, but he really couldn't think of anything else except, maybe, to apologize. After all this time, though, that seemed so trite, and under these circumstances so contrived.

"Oh, I intend to. So now, unless you have a medical concern or question, be quiet. Okay? I don't want to talk to you anymore. Don't want to listen to you either."

Too bad, because he liked the sassiness in her. He'd liked it seventeen years ago, and it hadn't changed much. But once they dropped him off at the hospital, that was going to be the end of the line for Julie and him...*again*. It was for the best, he thought as he sank back down on the stretcher, shut his eyes and tried to blank her out. Definitely for the best.

"Signing out for the last time," Julie said, handing in her badge. This was it. After so many grueling years in the

back of an ambulance, she was finally moving on to the place she'd always wanted to be. And it was a good move, being a nurse. Grace Corbett had helped her, had made everything possible. Had dreamed the dream with her. She sighed, thinking about Grace, missing Grace. "And glad to be moving on."

"Well, you take care of yourself. It's not going to be the same without you around here, Julie," her supervisor, a tall, big-boned woman named Gert, said, giving her a hug.

Good times, good memories, being a paramedic. Better ones ahead of her, though. *She hoped.* And two hours later, when she was tossing the last of her few incidentals into a cardboard box, she was still looking forward, not backward, because looking backward would be filled with thoughts and memories of Jess Corbett...the last person she'd ever expected to find in the back of her ambulance tonight.

Jess...darn! Now she'd opened the floodgates, and he'd poured through in a huge way. The funny thing was, she didn't try holding him back. In fact, she shut her eyes for a moment and indulged herself. Jess... He was bigger than he was last time she'd seen him. More muscled. Lean. Fit. Broader shoulders. Face more chiseled, edgier lines to it. His eyes, though...still the same sapphire blue, but harder. Much harder than she remembered. No laugh lines around them either, which made her wonder if he ever smiled. His hair was the same, though. Sandy, maybe a little darker than it had been seventeen years ago. Clipped a whole lot shorter than she'd ever seen it on him. She liked the stubble on him, too. Made him look...masculine. Not that Jess, as a teenager, hadn't been masculine. But Jess *then* compared to Jess *now*...actually, there was no

comparison. Jess the man and Jess the boy, the man won hands down.

"But I'm not going to think about him," she said, heading down three flights of stairs, grappling with the last of the things she was taking to her new life. She had an emergency room to expand. New responsibilities to think about. And thinking about Jess distracted her. So she wouldn't. That's all there was to it. She would not think about Jess Corbett.

An hour later, as she turned onto the interstate taking her north, she was still trying not to think about him. Of course, this new life she'd chosen for herself wasn't going to make that easy, was it? Not when her destination was Lilly Lake, and Lilly Lake was the place they'd almost started a life together.

For early spring, the evening was pleasantly warm. Tonight, the sun was setting in gold hues over the lake, and in the distance the wail of a loon saddened the expanse. Heard for miles, across land, and from lake to lake, it was the haunting call of mates looking for each other, mates lost to each other and calling out to find them. Jess knew what that was about, what it felt like to search. "So that's the long, sad story of my exile from New York City."

"Smoke inhalation?" Rafe Corbett snorted a laugh. "They grounded you a week for smoke inhalation?"

"*Two* weeks," Jess grumbled, then chuckled. "Let's just say that I overstepped my bounds. After my clean bill of health I shot off my mouth when I should have kept it closed, and my captain decided to put me on ice for a little longer to think about it."

"In other words, you don't play by the rules."

"And you do?"

"Okay, so the Corbett men do things their own way. But

for me, that's fine. I'm an orthopedist, I don't really have to get into much of the team spirit the way you do."

An orthopedist who, not so long ago, hadn't been all that different from Jess. Except now Rafe was a married man with a daughter, and another one on the way. The picture of perfect contentment, and happy to be in that place. "Well, team is where it's at. And between us, big brother, I do have some problems with that. I'm more used to…"

"Doing it on your own?"

Jess winced. It was true. He was a loner in most aspects of his life. In fact, he could probably count on one hand the number of times he and Rafe had actually sat down and talked as brothers these past dozen or so years. "Yep, doing it on my own. But I get the team concept, realize how important it is, even if I get ahead of myself sometimes."

"Get ahead of yourself? You ran into a burning building without telling anybody you were going in. That's a hell of a lot more than getting ahead of yourself, Jess."

"You're going to give me a lecture, too?" he asked, clearly annoyed, not with Rafe so much as with himself. He'd been wrong. He'd admitted it. But there was something inside him…something he just couldn't control at times. Sometimes he had to act, consequences be damned. "Because I've already heard it, and now I have two weeks to reflect on the *error* of my ways."

Rafe held up his hands in mock surrender. "Then it's over, okay? Not another word. So, do you want to come stay up at Gracie House? We've got better accommodations. Molly would love having her favorite uncle there to play with." Six-year-old Molly was Rafe's new daughter and part of his newfound contentment.

"No. The cabin's fine. But tell Molly she'll be seeing enough of me over the next couple of weeks that she'll

probably get sick of me." In truth, he liked the cabin. Liked its rustic charm. A mile from nowhere, with just enough amenities to call it modern, it kept him isolated. What more could he want? "Tell Edie, though, I appreciate the offer, and that I wouldn't mind stopping in a couple of times for a good home-cooked meal if she's up to it. I don't want to put her out, though, considering…"

"She's pregnant, working until her due date if she can and she loves to cook. How about tomorrow night? That'll give her the chance to plan it, and give you the chance to settle in."

"You can do that, just make plans for your wife like that?"

Rafe chuckled. "Hell, no. But Edie didn't figure you'd stay at the house with us, so she told me to invite you over tomorrow night for dinner."

"And you're just trying to score points with me, making me think it was your idea."

"I need some points, because I've got a favor to ask you."

"Sounds ominous."

"Not ominous. More like a matter of practicality. And to be honest, I'm glad you're home because I was going to come to the city next week to talk to you about it."

Jess twisted in his seat. Was on the verge of getting up and going inside. Shutting the door on what Rafe was here to discuss. "Another time?" he asked, trying to put off the talk for no good reason other than he didn't want to deal with it at present. In fact, his preference would be signing his share of Lilly Hospital over to Rafe, then be done with the whole thing. But that's not what Rafe wanted. So Jess was hanging on, but in title only.

"Look, Jess. I understand it's hard for you, and if there

was any other way to do this, I would. But we are co-owners..."

"One of which who wants nothing to do with the hospital. So, here's what you can do, Rafe. Anything. *Anything* you want. I trust your judgment, and I'll give you my blessing but, please, leave me the hell out of the decisions. Okay?"

"What I want, Jess, is to take Rick Navarro on as a partner. He's earned it. He deserves it. And he has good ideas for expansion..."

Jess waved him off. "What, in the definition of *anything* don't you understand?"

"For once, just listen to me, okay? Before you start spouting off your opinion or telling me all the reasons you don't give a damn, just shut up and listen!"

Jess huffed out an impatient sigh. "Do I have a choice?"

"You've always got a choice, but I was hoping you'd give me some support in this."

"You've got my support, Rafe. Just not my attention." He pushed himself up out of his seat and headed toward the front door, but stopped before going inside. Change of heart? Not at all. But a sure change of mind. Rafe was the only person he had in this world, and it wouldn't hurt him to listen to his big brother. After all, Rafe had taken the beatings for him, quite literally. All those years, all the tirades, Rafe was the one who'd stood up to their old man and taken the punishment. So at the least he owed him another minute to listen. "Okay, tell me, but don't expect anything from me other than listening. Because I'm not going to get involved in this."

Rafe stood, and went to lean on the banister across from the front door. "Fine. I'll make it fast. We're expanding pediatric services, which you already know. We're looking into some growth in obstetrics, too. But the first thing

we're taking on is an expansion to our emergency services, because what we have isn't good enough."

At the mention of emergency services, Jess winced. Being a former trauma surgeon, this was probably where Rafe wanted to wheedle some kind of commitment out of him. *Come back and work temporarily until we can find someone else to take over. Or be a consultant.* That's what he expected, but he was going to hold his ground. No involvement, no way!

"Rather than sending major trauma cases to the hospital all the way over in Jasper, or someplace even farther away, we're going to expand enough to handle what we need and help with overflow from other areas. So we've hired a nurse-coordinator to oversee the first phase of growth. She has an amazing trauma background, a doctorate in nursing…"

"A doctorate?" he asked, feeling his gut churn.

"A doctorate. And for where we are right now, she's the perfect person to put in charge of coordinating the plans. Um, Jess…we hired…"

"Let me guess. You hired Julie Clark?" He hadn't seen her in seventeen years, now here she was, front and center, twice in two days. How could that be happening?

Rafe frowned. "Either that was an amazing wild guess, or you've been in touch with Julie."

"In touch. *Not* by choice."

"Anything you want to talk about?" Rafe asked.

Jess shook his head. Didn't reply, so Rafe continued, "Well, she was the right one. Has the credentials we need, as well as the experience…" He paused, studied Jess's frown, sucked in a deep breath. "Look, Jess, since you're not here most of the time, and when you are you never leave the cabin, I didn't think it would matter."

"Why *would* it matter?" Jess snapped, then stormed inside his cabin and slammed the screen door behind him.

"Jess?" Rafe called after him.

"Nothing matters," Jess yelled back. "Not one damned thing." Except for those couple of weeks of Julie's pregnancy scare hell. Those had mattered a lot.

CHAPTER TWO

"It's strange being back after all this time," Julie said, dropping down into the chair across from Edie Corbett's desk. "I have good memories of Lilly Lake, and I appreciate all the help you've been, helping me get settled here again."

"I was new in town just about a year ago, so I know what it's like trying to get yourself established, even if you did live here before."

"It wasn't for long…just a few years, but let's just call them my formative years. And I really do want to thank you for letting me take a tour of Gracie House the other day. I didn't mean to just stop on your doorstep and beg to be let in, but…" Julie smiled fondly. "But I couldn't help myself. I needed a few minutes to come home."

"And you're welcome to *come home* any time you like. Our doors are always open."

"I'll bet I'm not the first."

Edie laughed. "As a matter of fact, no, you're not. Several of Grace's children have stopped in, and Gracie House seems to be a focal point in their lives. For me, it's interesting to meet the people who've passed through her life… and her doors." She glanced fondly at a picture of Molly, her new daughter, and Grace's former ward. "Interesting and life-changing."

"Well, I spent the most important years of my life there. I was kind of a wild child, all my various adoptive parents threw me out, I had nowhere to go other than the juvenile home, and Grace stepped in and offered to take me. She made the difference, and it wasn't always easy for her, dealing with me. But she had so much..."

"Patience?" Edie asked.

"That. But I think it was faith. She never saw the bad side or the difficulty in people. Whatever the situation, she always managed to turn it into something positive. Like the time I stole a couple hundred dollars from her and took a bus ride to New York City. I don't think I really intended on running away so much as exploring the world, but the minute I stepped off that bus, aged sixteen, it was like all my small-town ways just wanted to pull me back. I was scared to death. Didn't have enough money left for a decent meal. Nowhere to go. No one to help me. I mean, I was overwhelmed, and not as smart as I thought I was. So I called Grace, and she said she'd come get me. And she wasn't angry, Edie. In fact, she told me it would take a few hours for her to get there, so I might as well wander around, see the sights while I could. She even suggested a couple places I should go. *Julie, take advantage of your adventure*...that's what she told me. And when she finally picked me up, she asked me if I'd had a nice day. A nice day? I was expecting the wrath of God to fall down on me, and instead she took me to a very swanky restaurant, we spent the night in a glamorous hotel and the next morning she actually took me shopping. Then, when we got home, she asked me if I'd learned my lesson. To be honest, it took me a while to figure out what it was because to a crazy sixteen-year-old, it seemed like I'd been rewarded for my so-called crime."

"So, what was the lesson?"

"To trust and rely on the people who love you when you have a problem. That they won't let you down if you give them the chance to help. She told me if I'd have let her know how I was feeling, told her how much I wanted to go to the city, she could have taken me. But I didn't give her that chance because I figured she would say no. I didn't trust her enough to be honest with her." Julie laughed. "A mistake I never made again. Oh, and she did require a little extra work from me in the stables to pay her back for the money I took…work in the form of a shovel and pitchfork. Which, actually, is why I'm here. I was wondering if the foundation could use an extra volunteer. I loved working with the horses when I was a teenager. I think that's probably what grounded me more than anything else…being the person trusted with the care of another life. It certainly made me find things in myself I didn't know were there. So now that I'm back—"

"Always!" Edie interrupted. "It seems like the more horses we take in, the further our reputation spreads. Rafe's in the process of coordinating the building of another stable, one for the more critical horses. Sort of like an intensive care, I think. And we're renovating both the old stables, enlarging them and modernizing the facilities. So we can use all the help we can get, and then some."

"Well, I can still shovel…"

"There's plenty of that to be done. And lots of other things, if you decide that shoveling isn't quite the exciting time you remember."

"Never exciting, definitely not the thing I wanted to be doing, but it was quite a character builder. Of course, Grace knew that when she put me on the task. And I'm not too proud to do that again, or anything else you need. I have a lot to pay back, and with the way Grace loved her horses…" A stray tear slid down Julie's cheek. "Working

with Grace's horses again is one of the biggest reasons I applied for the job here in Lilly Lake. I'd just hoped to be doing it with Grace."

"I miss her, too. And I didn't know her for very long. But she made such an impact on my life in such a short time...brought me together with my husband, gave me my daughter. I owe her everything."

"Me, too," Julie whispered reverently. "Everything."

On the verge of tears herself, Edie cleared her throat. "Well, then, why don't you stop over this afternoon, after you get off work, and have a look at the horses we have right now? I'll let Johnny Redmond know you're coming, and I'm sure he'll have some details and schedules for you to go over by then. Oh, and I'd love to have you stay for dinner, if you don't have other plans. It's spaghetti night at Gracie House. Nothing fancy. But it's Molly's favorite meal, so please, join us if you can."

"I'd love to, if it won't be an imposition."

"No imposition. But bring an appetite. Molly helps cook, and let's just say she cooks *big*."

"Then I'll see you later on, with a big appetite," Julie said, standing to leave. "So, if I may ask, when are you due?"

Edie instinctively laid her hand on her belly. "Another month. A little girl. Do you have any children?" she asked.

"No. Never been married, never been a mom. I'm more of the career type, I think."

"I was the career type, too, and look at me now." She glanced again at Molly's picture, then the one of the three of them—her, Rafe and Molly. "I'm into family in a huge way, and loving every minute of it. It's everything I *never* knew I wanted," Edie said, laughing. "And I wouldn't have my life any other way."

There was a time she'd thought that, too. But then she'd

been a kid with enormous, romantic delusions. Luckily, she'd grown up. A little of it the hard way, maybe. She'd learned her lessons well, though, in large part thanks to Grace Corbett. "Well, I'd better get back to work. So I'll see you later, Edie," she said from the hall. Turning, she hurried back to the emergency department, where she was responsible for more things than she'd ever thought she'd be responsible for. Thanks, in part, to Grace Corbett, too. Actually, thanks in full, since it was Grace's benevolence that had made paramedic training first, then nursing school afterward, possible.

"Looks like we're feeding an army tonight," Jess commented on his way into the dining room. The spaghetti bowl in the center of the kitchen table was heaped to overflowing, and the bread plate had enough garlic bread piled on to feed half the population of Lilly Lake. It reminded him of coming home to Aunt Grace for a meal.

"Uncle Jess!" Molly squealed, launching herself into his arms with such a force it nearly toppled him over backward. "I've been waiting for you to come visit us. I have a new pony…actually, I have two ponies now. Lucky, my old pony, and she's not really that old. Johnny says she's about two, so that really makes her my new pony, since Snowflake, my new pony, is really about six, which makes her my old pony."

"Whoa, slow down," Jess said, laughing. "You're talking too fast, and I can't keep up. So, your old pony has a new pony, and Lucky Snowflake is who?" he teased.

"Lucky is my pony, and so is Snowflake, silly," Molly replied.

"Oh, now I get it. You have two ponies. Lucky is one, Snowflake Silly is the other."

"Not Snowflake Silly," she said. "His name is Snowflake."

"Didn't you tell me his name was Snowflake Silly? I'm positive that's what I heard." He looked at Rafe for support. "Isn't that what she said? Snowflake Silly?"

Rafe smiled, threw his hands into the air in surrender and backed away. "I'm leaving this one up to you two while I go help my lovely wife toss the salad." With that, he backed all the way into the kitchen, stopping short of Edie, who was wielding a large butcher's knife, going at the lettuce with a vengeance. "It really is a lot of food," he commented offhandedly.

"I invited someone else this evening," she said, eyeing a big, juicy red tomato for her next chopping chore. "Someone from the hospital."

"Anybody I know?"

"Maybe. She's fairly new on staff. Very nice. Originally from Lilly Lake, so you might know her. Her name's Julie Clark."

Rafe, who had picked up a carrot to munch, nearly choked. "Well, this ought to be interesting."

"How so?"

"Julie and Jess have history."

"What kind of history?"

"Big history." He patted his wife's belly.

"You're kidding. They were...?"

He shook his head. "False alarm. But it had us all going for a while."

"So, what should we do? I don't want either of them being uncomfortable. Especially not Jess, with everything he's been through—a war, the death of his fiancée, a career change."

Rafe gave his wife an affectionate kiss on the cheek.

"Well, I'm sure eating spaghetti with a former girlfriend will shrink in comparison to all that."

"You may be a great doctor, but you're not so smart about relationships, are you?"

"I get ours right, don't I?"

"You get ours perfect. But we don't have history...torrid history."

"I didn't say it was torrid."

"No, but..." She patted her own belly. "That sure implies it, don't you think? Anyway, he's here and Julie's down at the stable, talking to Johnny, so she'll be up in a few minutes. And you, my dear husband, are in charge of dealing with the situation."

Rafe shrugged, then gave over to a smile. "Like I said, could be interesting. Jess needs something to shake him up, and Julie might be it."

"What might be it?" Jess asked from the doorway.

"This might be it," Edie hedged, holding up her butcher knife. "The best one I own. This one might be...*it*."

Jess gave them both a half smile. "Domesticity has really dulled you two down, hasn't it?" he asked. "So much ado about a knife?"

"Hey, little brother. Believe me when I tell you there's nothing dull in this house. In fact, I think you're about to find out just how un-dull Gracie House is going to be."

"What's that supposed to mean?"

"Me, Jess. I think Rafe's referring to the two of us having dinner together." Julie looked at Edie. "Molly let me in, by the way. Hope that was okay? Oh, and I brought non-alcoholic sparkling grape juice. Knew you couldn't do wine, but I thought this might go well with the spaghetti." She held the two bottles out to Edie, but Jess was the one who took them and marched straight to the refrigerator on the other side of the room—as far away from Julie as

anyone in the kitchen could get without opening the back door and continuing on into the yard.

"Thank you. So, I take it you and Jess remember each other?" Edie asked, with a sly wink at Rafe.

"Actually, we had the chance to catch up with each other just a few days ago...in New York," Julie said. She was clearly not as uncomfortable as Jess was at this meeting. If anything, she was almost too noncommittal. Trying too hard to stay unaffected. "In the back of my ambulance. He was my very last patient as a paramedic."

"So, that's how it was. Jess was your patient." He arched an amused eyebrow at his brother. "Bet he wasn't a very good one, was he?"

"No, he wasn't."

"Did you have to strap him down?"

"Do you two realize I'm standing right here?" Jess cut in.

"Sure we do, little brother. But since you're not contributing to the conversation—"

"Look," Julie interrupted. "It's clear I'm the outsider here. How about I take a rain check for another night? That way Jess will be able to enjoy the lovely meal Edie has prepared without getting tied up in knots having me sitting on the opposite side of the table from him."

"If anyone should leave, it's me," Jess said. "You're the guest, I'm just the—"

"You're both overreacting," Edie broke in. "This is a meal. A simple meal. That's all. Food, conversation...don't read anything else into it. Molly's excited, having both of you come to dinner, and we're not going to disappoint her. So, Jess, have a seat at the table. Julie, sit anywhere you'd like. Rafe, go tell Molly dinner's ready." She sucked in a deep breath, then dropped down into one of the kitchen chairs. "Oh, and in case you didn't notice, we're eating

in here tonight. I didn't want to make it formal by setting the dining room. So relax, be casual." She smiled sweetly. "Sit with your backs to each other, if you must. But let me warn you. I have a ton of food, and neither of you is going anywhere until that spaghetti platter is clean."

Julie laughed. "I think I can manage my fair share, in spite of Jess being here."

"Ditto," Jess grumbled.

"Do you two want some time to air some dirty laundry before we eat?" Edie asked. "Because you're welcome to use the den."

"No laundry, dirty or otherwise," Jess said, taking his place at the table.

Julie took her spot diagonally across from Jess. "None at all. Not one single, solitary piece of it."

"Why don't I believe you?"

"So I suppose now's the time to ask," Jess said. He'd followed Julie halfway to her car, trying to decide what to do. Truth was, he didn't know what was proper here. They'd made it through dinner, kept the conversation light enough. But those sideways glances he'd caught her giving him...no mistaking her feelings. Now here they were, ex-lovers, ex-friends—Jess wasn't even sure what they were—standing six feet apart in the driveway on a starless night where the moon didn't even have the decency to exit its cloud cover, both of them so stiff they wouldn't have even swayed in a wind squall.

"Ask what?"

"Several things, I think. First, how are you?"

"After all these years, that's the best you can do?"

"Okay, let me try something else. How have you been getting along?"

"You mean, how have I been getting along *without you?* Is that what you want to know?"

"Okay, stupid question. Let me try again."

"There's nothing to try, Jess. If there were, you would have tried it, or said it, the other day in the ambulance. But you didn't."

"Because you told me to shut up."

Julie shook her head. "Look, let me make this easy on you. I live in Lilly Lake now, work at the hospital *you* own, and that may put us into close proximity from time to time. Which means we need to learn how to deal with... us. What we were, what we weren't."

"What we were, Julie, were kids, doing the things kids do."

"Not all kids do what we did. I mean, I'm assuming you're not forgetting..."

"No, I'm not forgetting. Believe me, I've thought about us, about what happened, over and over all these years. Thought about how it could have turned out differently, where we might be now, if it had. The thing is, I'm not that same person, Julie. I've lived a lifetime since then, had regrets you can't even begin to imagine, and all I can say to you right now is that I'm sorry. I was a stupid, thoughtless kid. I should have trusted you more. But I didn't. I said some bad things and I am sorry."

"So am I," she said, her voice flat. "Sorry you thought I was trying to trap you, but I'm also sorry I didn't tell you the truth sooner than I did. And that I didn't get to apologize. But you left me, Jess. You walked away from me and never gave me the chance."

Jess shut his eyes, heaved out a heavy sigh. "You were sixteen, Julie. I was seventeen. We really didn't have a lot of choices. And you didn't have anything to apologize for." He opened his eyes to look at her, but she had turned away

from him, staring at her car. "There really wasn't a right or a wrong way to get through it, and I suppose all either one of us can say about it now is that we did the best we could."

"Or maybe there was a better way, and we just didn't take enough time to figure it out. Anyway, you said you're not the same person you were back then, and I'm certainly not the same person I was, so let's just not dwell on the things we messed up. Okay? I have a good life going. A great life, thanks to your aunt. She was everything to me, Jess, and because of that, I don't want to fight with you. So can we agree to be cordial with each other?" She truly wanted to add *not looking back* to that request, but she had looked back, more than once over the years, and she always would. Because there'd been a few days when she'd dreamed of being a wife and mother. Those dreams had made her happy, probably the happiest she'd ever been because she'd been in love with Jess. Totally, completely in love. With the qualifier that it had been the love of a rather immature sixteen-year-old. With a baby on the way... Or so she'd thought until the test had come back negative.

The dream had come and gone so quickly. It had taken her some time to come to terms with it, come to terms with the end of her future fantasy life, but the day she'd gone to tell Jess the truth... She still had nightmares. What she'd done to him, the pain she'd caused him...

Her pain, too. But she'd thrown herself into making a better life. And succeeded. Which was why she was surprised by her feelings now. Surprised by the pain that was slipping its way back in. Seeing Jess again was good, but it hurt.

"Cordial is good," Jess agreed. "I'm not expecting anything. Don't deserve anything. And, God knows, you've got every right to hate me. What I did was inexcusable."

"No, it wasn't. Like you said, we were kids." Kids who never got a chance to be kids. Maybe that's why their emotions had been so intense. At such young ages, they'd both known so much pain. "Anyway, it doesn't matter now. But I'm curious. Did Grace ever know I thought I was pregnant? Did you ever tell her?"

Jess shook his head. "I never told her, but she probably knew anyway. That's how she was."

Yes, that's how she had been. "Well, that was around the same time she started talking to me about making *real* plans for my life, trying to show me some options for finding a better way. Anyway... I need to get going. I'm heading back in to work the night shift in a little while, and I'd like to run home and grab a quick shower first. So... I'm glad you're feeling better after that incident in New York. And I'm really glad you have such a good family here to take care of you while you're recovering. You're a lucky man."

"Well, I'll be here next week for spaghetti night, and I'm sure my family would love to have you come back, if you can. So maybe I'll see you around..."

"Maybe," she said, heading for her car. Although she wasn't sure she wanted to. Or wasn't sure if she could. Because right now her head was spinning and her chest hurt. All she wanted to do was get into her car, drive away and go someplace where she could cry for the things that had never been, and the things that never could be. All of them about Jess.

Puttering his way along the back road, Jess wasn't in any particular hurry to return to his cabin. It wasn't that he minded being alone. That's the way he spent most of his life now. In many ways, it was preferable. Getting involved, having someone be the center of his life...what was the

point? As much as he'd loved Donna, he hadn't been able to make the real commitment to her, the one every future bride should expect from the man she'd consented to marry. He'd tried. Gotten involved in the plans, smiled when she'd talked about the dream. *Their dream.* But she'd known he'd been struggling with all that…permanence. Had asked him about it, even though he'd denied it. Yet it had been something he hadn't been able to hide, and the closer they'd got to that permanence, the more it had shown on him. Then he'd hurt her and for that he'd never forgive himself. She'd loved him and in return he'd broken her heart.

Was that what she'd been thinking about when she was killed—her broken heart, his inability to be everything she deserved?

Even now, two years after Donna's death, there wasn't a day that went by when he didn't replay those last few moments with her. Could he have done something different? Been different for her? Maybe faked the feelings? Faked the whole *happy with the domestic lifestyle* thing until he had settled in and it had become a habit?

Donna Ingram. Beautiful. Smart. Full of life. She'd always led with her heart and, in so many ways, he envied that. All she'd wanted had been a normal life with a man who'd never had normal in his life. Impossible odds, as it had turned out. And overwhelming regrets.

Tonight Donna was on his mind, as she often was. Tonight, though, Julie Clark was also on his mind, but for other reasons. Julie had been his first love and, once upon a time, they'd made plans, too. Sure, their plans had been childish. They'd talked about running away together. Or maybe getting jobs and saving their money so they could backpack or bike across America, or Canada, or the whole of Europe. Impractical plans that had seemed so real and

so exciting for a short time. But then Julie had thought she was pregnant, and, stupid kid that he was, he'd been thrown for a big curve. So he'd taken the easy way out by listening to his dad. *It's a trap, Jess. That's all it is. She's setting a trap for you. So, don't be stupid, son. Kick her to the curb before it's too late, before she ruins your life.* Yeah, great advice from a drunk child abuser and overall mean slimeball of a man who'd masqueraded as the town doctor. The hell of it was, he'd listened. He'd accused, he kicked, then he'd run. What a jerk!

But that was only the first time. He'd pretty much done the same thing with Donna, hadn't he? Maybe not kicking her to the curb so much as edging her there. Being gentle, trying not to hurt her in the process. But it was all the same and, in the end, he'd hurt her anyway.

Now, tonight, an entire lifetime of miserable failures was poking him from every side, and he just wasn't in the mood to be poked alone. So, turning off the main road, Jess headed back to Lilly Lake. Brassard's Pub was as good place as any to be in a bad mood. He didn't drink, didn't smoke, didn't care to play darts. But he craved the noise. Wanted it all around him. Wanted it to permeate every pore in his body, reminding him that he was still alive since he wasn't even so sure about that. So, yes, Brassard's was the place. Loud jukebox, louder bartender, and on a good night, a crowd that could be heard halfway over to the next county. Yes, it was exactly where he wanted to be.

"Jess!" the bartender yelled across the noisy room. The owner-bartender, Will Brassard, was also head of the Lilly Lake Volunteer Fire Department. "I heard you inhaled."

Jess thought about waving him off in favor of an isolated corner, but Will was a nice guy, married to a nice woman, father of some nice kids. Living the life Jess had

thought he'd have by now. "Twice," he shouted back. "I inhaled *twice*."

"So what did they give you for it?" Will shouted. "A commendation?"

If only... "Two weeks *vacation*." Rather than shouting the story, which he knew he was about to tell, he shoved his way through the crowd, half of them dancing to the music, and made his way to the bar stool on the end, the one where he didn't have to sit and face himself in the mirror behind the bar. "Two long, restful weeks up at the cabin, looking at the walls, pacing the floor and taking up knitting because...let's just say that I didn't follow orders as well I should have. Funny how that works out, isn't it?"

Laughing, Will held out his hand in greeting. "Well, my wife knits, and it's not all it's cracked up to be, because if you don't follow the knitting rules, you end up getting... well, to me it looks like a big ball of knots. So, if you're looking for some activity..." He pointed to the far end of the room, where several of the locals were engaged in what seemed to be a rather bland card game...one eye on the cards, one eye on the old, large-screen, rear-projector TV where reruns of a college basketball game were wobbling across the screen in hues of green and orange.

"Not my thing, but thanks for the offer. Likewise, don't do darts."

Will started to point to the beer tap, but stopped. "That's right. You don't drink either, do you?"

"Because I'm boring as hell. I work and I sleep. And when I get back to Lilly Lake, I don't even do that much."

"So, why are you here tonight? You've been coming back home off and on for a year now, and I don't think you've ever been in here. In fact, other than passing you on the road a time or two, this is the first time I've seen you, period."

He genuinely liked Will. They'd known each other in school. Not too well, but well enough to know that the boy Will Brassard had turned into a good man. "It seemed like a good place to stop, and since I was in a stopping mood…"

"Coffee?" Will offered. "Or a soft drink?"

"Coffee's good."

"And let me guess. You'd rather have it over there at the table in the corner, so you don't have to put up with me talking to you, or asking questions."

"Actually, that was my intent when I came in here. But I think I'll stay at the bar, if you don't mind a non-drinker taking up a perfectly good drinking spot."

Will laughed. "Any firefighter is welcome at my bar, for any reason, any time. No matter what they're *not* drinking. Stay as long as you like."

It was a friendly invitation, and Jess appreciated it. But by the time he'd polished off his third cup of coffee, he was restless again. Even the noise and activity weren't enough tonight. Problem was, he wasn't sure what was. No point in staying here, though. Not when the night was young and someone paying for more than a cup of coffee might want his seat. So Jess dropped a generous tip in the tip jar, saluted his farewell to Will, and headed for the door. But before he got there, a shout above the crowd stopped him.

"We've got a run, Jess. Grease fire in the kitchen, out at the lodge. Care to join us?"

Jess's heart lurched. Did he care to join them? Hell, yes, he cared. In fact, the adrenalin was already pumping.

"May have a couple of minor casualties we have to run into the emergency room," Will responded. "How about you being our medic on this run?"

Hadn't Julie said she was working Emergency tonight? Suddenly, he wanted to see her again. He wasn't sure why, and didn't have time to think about it as Will tossed his

bartender apron to one of the waitresses and leaped over the bar. So maybe this wasn't going to be a bad *vacation,* after all. At least, not this part of it.

CHAPTER THREE

"IS EVERYBODY out?" Will Brassard shouted across the ruckus of firefighters struggling to get through the line of bystanders watching the flames shooting out the kitchen roof. Set against the backdrop of the black night, the orange glow was an astounding work of art, mesmerizing its watchers, stalling them in place, causing congestion in the area. Also, the hundred or so patrons evacuated from the restaurant, combined with the two hundred guests at the lodge hotel and various guest cabins who were leaving by a sundry of exits, were causing quite a commotion, some in shock, some confused, some simply looking for a safe place to go. Consequently, by the time the Lilly Lake volunteer firefighters had arrived and readied their equipment to face down the fire, about a third of the population of Lilly Lake was either there, or on their way to watch the show.

"Not yet!" one of the volunteers practically screamed at the top of her lungs. "I think we've got three more people still in the kitchen, doing God only knows what. Manager of the lodge says they're trying to account for everybody registered right now, and they'll let us know in a minute if we've got to worry about that."

"Like we have a minute," Jess snorted. He was suited up and heading in through the cluster of people. Not thrilled,

though, to be called to paramedic duty. Of course, Will probably thought he was a natural, maybe even assumed that's what he did in the city. But it wasn't. He shunned medicine now. Yet here he was, carting medical equipment through a crush of gawkers, getting ready to do something he didn't want to do. Except there was no way he could turn his back on these people. No way to tell Will he wouldn't do it. It wasn't in him. Wasn't like him to turn his back. Probably one of the few good character traits in him, thanks to Aunt Grace. "So, where are the injuries? And do we know what we have so far?"

"We've got them in a couple of places. The less serious injuries are out back in the caretaker's cottage," Will shouted. "We have a couple of more serious ones going to the third guest cabin down from the pool. Decided to put them there because transport out will be easier, and we're clearing the parking lot and road in right now for the ambulances. Got five coming in, by the way. The one from here has an ETA of less than five minutes, and the other four coming in from Jasper and Hutchings are still twenty to thirty minutes out. And, Jess...one of my men just radioed, and we've got what looks to be a bad injury on the way down. Burns, maybe something else cardiac. They couldn't tell, but he's going in and out of consciousness."

"Okay." Jess took a harder grip on the medical kit Will had thrust at him once he'd climbed out of Will's SUV. Serious injuries, one ambulance in town and the possibility of a long response time. "What about a helicopter, if we need it?"

"We can get one, but time out on that's going to be forty-five minutes, if we're lucky." Will was running hard to keep pace with Jess. "Give me the word, and I'll get it ordered."

"So that's all we've got in the way of transportation?" It wasn't good enough and, frankly, he was surprised he hadn't known the status. But what did he know about anything concerning the medical or emergency needs in Lilly Lake?

"Well, we can get them into the hospital here pretty fast, but until the expansion on the emergency department begins, they're limited in what they can do."

Which frustrated the hell out of Jess. He wanted, no, he'd always *demanded* immediate response and the best facilities, yet he owned a hospital that wasn't yet ready to offer what he would demand...if he still practiced as a doctor. He needed to talk to Rafe about it, see what they could do to fix it, in a hurry. Back away from his plans to *not* get involved and get involved in this one thing. "But the hospital's ready to receive, what? The less serious injuries?"

"It's ready to receive whatever we send them. They're a good bunch there, and they'll do whatever they can to get those we can't keep out to facilities that can handle them. So, don't worry about that end of it. It'll work." The voice answering wasn't that of Will, though. It was Julie, and she was following on Jess's heels, running just as hard toward the guest cabin as he was.

"What are you doing here?" he shouted at her.

"Came to help. Like I said, I've got everything well covered at the hospital, got staff that came back in the minute they heard about the fire, so Rick...*Dr. Navarro*...asked me to come out to the field and coordinate efforts here. They do that in Lilly Lake, send hospital personnel out when there's a need."

A klatsch of women too busy watching to notice the rescue operation in progress swarmed over the path leading to the guest cottages, essentially swallowing up the

passageway. Jess swerved to avoid them, but Julie pushed her way right through. "Look, ladies, you're going to have to move back," she said, stopping for a moment. "All the way to the other side of the building."

"Anything we can do?" one of the women asked.

"As a matter of fact…" Julie motioned them closer to her. "We've got a lot of personnel coming through here now, with more on the way. Maybe you ladies could keep the area clear for me, make sure people stay back, sort of take control of the pedestrian traffic flow."

Jess smiled, hearing the words. She was, essentially, turning part of the problem into the solution. Smart gal. Natural leader. He admired that.

"I didn't know you were so resourceful," he said, once she caught back up to him.

"I was living on the street when Grace took me in. You get to be very resourceful when you don't have a roof over your head or a meal in your belly."

Apparently, there were a lot of things about Julie he didn't know. "I guess I never knew that either." What, exactly, had he known about her back then, other than she'd attracted him like crazy? He thought about it for a moment, and came up with nothing.

"Nobody knew. I didn't want anybody's pity, and Grace was respectful that way, not telling anyone."

That, she had been. And he missed her more and more each day. "She was," he agreed, still fixed on the image of Julie being homeless. He'd been young, but how could he have not known?

Arriving at the guest cabin where the more serious of injuries were being brought, Jess was first in the door. Greeted by several volunteers, townspeople who all stepped away when he strode in, he looked first at the log rail bed in the corner of the room where a middle-aged

man was being attended by a woman still clad in her black-and-white checkered chef pants and a white jacket. She was putting cold compresses on his head, and a second appraisal showed he was the only patient in there, so far. Meaning the bad one was still en route.

"Okay, I'm Jess Corbett," he said above the murmur of the bystanders. "Doctor…er, firefighter. So, what do we have here?"

"Chest pains," the woman said. "Shortness of breath. And he's looking a little…pale. His name is Frank Thomas, he's our head chef."

Jess was immediately at the bedside, taking the man's pulse. Rapid, thready. He was diaphoretic…sweating. Shortness of breath becoming pronounced.

"What do you need?" Julie asked, peering over Jess's shoulder.

"Get his blood pressure, get him on oxygen, then get an IV, normal saline, ready." He looked at Frank. "Frank," he said, assessing the man's responsiveness. "Are you allergic to anything?"

"Cats," Frank managed to whisper.

Jess laughed. "Well, then, I won't be treating you with any cats today. Any medicine allergies, or reactions you can recall?"

Frank shook his head.

"Good. I want you to take an aspirin for me." He looked around, saw Julie strapping the blood-pressure cuff to Frank's arm. "Anybody here got an aspirin?"

With that, three different people produced a variety of types, and Jess chose the low dose, then popped it into the man's mouth. "Chew it up, Frank, and swallow it."

The man did, with great difficulty. "Am I going to be okay, Doc?" he forced out.

Doc. It had been a long time since anybody had called

him that. Strange how it sounded. Kind of nice, though. "We're doing our best, Frank. Right now, we're going to get you stabilized, then send you to the hospital, where they'll be able to run tests to see exactly what's going on."

"My wife," Frank gasped.

"I called her," Julie said, stepping up with an oxygen mask. "She's going to meet you in the emergency room." With that, Julie placed the mask on his face, then whispered to Jess, "It's low, ninety over sixty." After which she immediately set about the task of finding a vein in Frank's arm and inserting an IV catheter. "You're going to feel a little stick," she said, as the needle slid in as smooth as melted butter. She glanced over at Frank, saw that he didn't respond, not even a tiny flinch to being stuck, and she nudged Jess, who was busy hooking EKG leads to Frank's chest. "I think Frank, here, is on the verge of taking a little *nap*."

"Frank!" Jess shouted, giving him a little shake. "Wake up, can you hear me?"

Franks's eyes fluttered open.

"Do you have any history of heart disease?"

"No," he sputtered. "Healthy…"

"Ever had chest pains that you can remember?"

This time Frank didn't respond. Rather, he stared up at the ceiling.

"Come on, Frank," Julie said, slapping him on the wrist, trying to stimulate him back into paying attention. "Stay with us, okay? We need you to try hard and answer the questions Dr. Corbett is asking you. It's important."

Frank nodded, but didn't look away from the ceiling, and it appeared he was having difficulty even doing that. Jess gave a nod to Julie who, without asking, knew to get the defibrillator ready, just in case. She was impressive, taking his nonverbal cues, setting out drugs that might

have to be administered, getting the endotracheal tube and laryngoscope ready. It's what she did in the normal course of her day, and what Jess used to do, too. But somehow, seeing Julie work the way she did knotted his gut. She was so…good. So confident. She'd gone so far beyond anything she'd ever thought she could be back in the days when she'd wanted him. Good for her, he thought. *She did better than anything I could have ever been for her.*

"Frank, you're having a cardiac episode…heart attack," Jess explained. "Are you on any kind of medication, for *any* condition?"

The man shook his head, a wobbly, feeble attempt at it, but the effort was more than he was able to endure, and his eyes dropped shut. "Damn," Jess snapped, immediately scrambling into assessment mode, trying to locate a pulse. Which he did, thankfully. "Weak," he said. "Respirations getting more shallow, quite a bit more labored, too." Meaning Frank was winding down. "Julie, could you check his blood pressure again? I have an idea it's dropped."

She did, then tried a second time. "Not hearing it," she said, pumping up the blood-pressure cuff a third time, on this attempt feeling the pressure with her fingertips. "Palp at fifty," she finally said.

"So when can we get him transported?" The three or four minutes they'd been working on the man seemed like an eternity, and the thing was, in the field there was little or nothing they could do for him unless, God forbid, he crashed. Which was getting perilously close to being the case. But in even the most scantily equipped hospital, which he hoped *his* hospital was not, there was a world of options and miracles that would save Frank's life, once they got him through the door.

"Someone, check on transport," Julie shouted to the

three or four people in the cabin who seemed to have no function other than wait. "Go find Will Brassard, the fire chief, and tell him we've got a patient we've got to get out of here right now!"

"Big voice," Jess commented, plowing through the kit containing the cardiac meds. He wanted something to kick-start the heart in case it decided to stop, and he found it in the form of a tiny vial of epinephrine. "Don't remember that on you before."

"That's because it's an acquired talent. I had to work on it. Bad patients in the back of my ambulance need a big voice sometimes. Patients like you were."

He chuckled. "So you took shouting lessons?"

"Something like that. Part of some assertiveness training Grace had me take."

"Money well spent," he said. "You're about as assertive as anybody I've ever known."

"In a good way?" she asked, taking the vial from Jess and drawing the liquid into a syringe, getting ready to act.

"In a good way." A very good way.

"They're ready to take him," one of the volunteers called from the door. "And they said to tell you they're bringing in a critical from the kitchen right now."

It was almost an amazing switch. As one Frank Thomas was carried out the door to the nearest ambulance, one Randolph O'Neal was rushed in and deposited in the very same bed Frank had just vacated. Only, right off the bat, both Jess and Julie saw the grim prognosis for the restaurant's sous chef. He was burned extensively on his legs, shoulders and chest, a combination of second- and third-degree burns. His breathing was raspy, gurgly. He wasn't conscious. He also had a gaping, bleeding head wound. "I need saline," Jess shouted, then looked at Julie. For a

moment they exchanged knowing glances…glances that spoke volumes in the span of a fractured second.

"I'll get a helicopter in," Julie said.

Jess, already in assessment mode looking for pupillary reaction in the man, simply nodded, already seeing the bleak reality. Unfortunately, the bleakness was only confirmed when Jess pried open O'Neal's eyelids, flashed his penlight, saw fixed, dilated pupils. No reaction to light. "Nothing," he said, cursing under his breath and at the same time, strapping a blood-pressure cuff on Randolph's arm.

Julie didn't even bother asking what it was because, judging from the grim expression on Jess's face, it wasn't good.

"Oxygen, IV, saline for the burns…" he said, on a frustrated sigh. "You know the drill."

Julie immediately turned to the group of bystanders, all but one of whom had gone out the door when Randolph O'Neal had come in. "You got any kind of medic training?" she asked the boy, who appeared to be a busser at the restaurant.

"No, ma'am. Except I can do that squeeze thing if somebody's choking."

"Can you pour liquid over this man's burns?"

"Yes, ma'am. I can do that."

And just like that, Julie had recruited a volunteer who stepped forward to assume an important part of their patient's treatment.

"Got a broken leg," someone shouted from the door.

That someone turned out to be Rafe, who was leading the way for two firefighters carrying yet another patient on a stretcher.

"It's about time you showed up," Jess quipped.

"Well, I'll be damned. You're the medic in charge?" Rafe asked.

"I'm the medic in charge, which means you take the broken leg because..." He looked back at his patient. Didn't finish his sentence as Randolph O'Neal's breathing had just gone agonal...into near-death mode. Rafe must have seen the same thing, as he tried stepping between his brother and O'Neal.

"Look, you don't need this right now, okay? You take the guy we just brought in and I'll deal with this."

"Because I can't?" Jess snapped.

"Because you shouldn't." Rafe stepped up, took Jess by the arm, tried to move him. "Jess, his pupils are blown," Rafe whispered. "He's not going to make it. Not to a hospital, not anywhere."

"I don't give up on my patients, Rafe," Jess growled, bending down over the man.

"Jess," Julie said, laying a hand on his shoulder. "Rafe is right. We can't... There's nothing..."

A hush fell over the cabin as the inevitability became apparent to everybody there, and within seconds the cabin cleared of everybody but Jess, Julie, Rafe, the two patients and James Orser, the young man who was still, dutifully, dousing Randolph O'Neal's chest with saline, even as O'Neal exhaled his final breath.

Julie laid a hand on James's arm, whispered for him to stop. "Go sit with the patient who was just brought in," she said. "I'll be over there in a second." She looked at Rafe, whose agony for his brother showed in his face. Then she looked at Jess, who seemed...numb. "There wasn't anything we could do," Julie said to Jess, as Rafe went to treat Max Fletcher, the man with a compound leg fracture that had happened outside the lodge, well away from the fire... a bystander who'd come to watch and gotten in the way

of a pick-up truck. "He was so badly injured, he wouldn't have made it to a trauma center, and even then..."

"I know," he said. He was a trauma surgeon, after all. Well, trauma surgeon, past tense. But he still had all the knowledge, still had the same feelings, present tense. And this was why he'd left medicine. It was too late. O'Neal had come to him too late. He had needed to be there sooner. And Jess had needed to be the first one to look, not the last one. All his years of medical training yet by virtue of being the surgeon he was always the last one in line. That's what he'd figured out on the battlefield. What he still knew. What he still hated.

Suddenly, nausea welled up in Jess like a water balloon stretched to its limits and ready to explode. Without saying a word to Julie, he ran outside, straight to the bushes and retched until there was nothing left inside him, then gave way to dry heaves after that.

"Leave him alone," Rafe said, stepping up to Julie, who was halfway to the tree line, running after Jess to help him. He grabbed her by the arm and forcibly stopped her.

"Why? Can't you see he needs help?"

"What he needs is to be alone, to work it out."

"He lost a patient, Rafe. He's taking it hard."

Rafe let go of her arm. "He lost a fiancée in Afghanistan. Almost two years ago now. And, yes, he's still taking it hard."

"Oh, my God," Julie whispered. "I didn't know."

"He doesn't really talk about it.

"I'm so sorry, Rafe." She turned to look at Jess, who'd finally straightened up. "That's why he left medicine? Did he lose heart?"

"I don't think he lost heart, or else he wouldn't be out trying to save lives in a different way. To be honest, he's

never told me what's going on with him. I've asked, but he shuts me up, tells me it's nobody's business."

"But you can't let him go through this alone right now, even if he thinks he wants to be alone. You know that's true. So which one of us going to go over there to see if he's okay?" she asked.

"That would be you, because I'm going into the hospital to operate on Max Fletcher's leg. Headed there right now. And, Julie, just so you'll know, Jess is as apt to push you away as he is let you in. Don't take it personally. Jess loved Donna and she died in his arms. I'm not sure how you get over something like that. Or if you can. But Jess is stubborn. He won't let anybody get too close, and you do know some of the reason for that."

She did. "Thanks for telling me about Donna."

She gave Rafe a squeeze on the arm, then went to Jess, but before she could say anything, Jess held his hands up in surrender. "I don't need help," he said. "I'm fine."

"You don't look fine," she said, handing over a bottle of water. "In fact, you look like hell."

He took the water, uncapped it, swished some around in his mouth, then spat it out. "He told you, didn't he?" he said, wiping his mouth on his sleeve.

"Some. Not much. And I'm sorry, Jess. I didn't know."

"Well, it's not exactly captivating conversation." Taking one more swig, he rinsed and spat again, then capped the bottle. "So you see why I'm a firefighter now...the story of my shame. I don't do trauma so well."

"Not shame, Jess. A lot of other emotions, but not shame. And as for not doing trauma well, that's only your opinion. I saw you work in there, saw the way you took care of Frank Thomas and tried with—"

"Oh, so now you're being nice to me?" he interrupted. "Pity the man who's off vomiting in the woods and offer

him some good-hearted words that you wouldn't have offered him an hour ago?"

"And you would have me do, what? Ignore someone who needs my help?"

"Who the hell told you I needed help?"

"It doesn't take a genius to see what you're going through, Jess. I just thought—"

"Don't. There's nothing here worth wasting your thinking on. What I was, what I am now…they don't connect, okay? Don't think you're going to play the part of some little do-gooder who's going to step in and make things right for me, because it's not going to happen." He stepped around Julie, appraised the scene. "Looks like the fire is squared away. Why don't you go see if there are any more injuries that need treating."

"Is that how it's going to be, Jess?"

"How what's going to be?"

She shook her head. As badly as she felt for him, there really wasn't anything she could do to help. Rafe had been right about that. Jess had shut his brother out as masterfully as he was shutting her out. And if life had taught her one thing, it was never to force herself into a place where she wasn't wanted. Clearly, she wasn't wanted here. Even so, her heart did break for Jess. She'd loved him once. Had wanted to have his baby once. And, apparently, she still had a few leftover feelings for him. Feelings from the past, though. *Only* from the past.

"You still here?" Julie asked Jess, looking up from the desk she was slumped over, finishing up the last of the paperwork from the injuries at the restaurant fire. In total, six treated in the emergency room and released, two admitted, one of them gone to the operating room and now in

Recovery, one under cardiac observation but doing well. And one fatality.

"Just checking on Frank Thomas."

"He's resting easily. Dr. Navarro doesn't think he needs to go to a hospital with a cardiac care unit because, so far, the tests are showing that his heart attack was fairly minor."

"You look like you should be resting," Jess commented.

"I'm fine. I've worked longer and harder than this. And as soon as I put my signature on this last piece of paper, I'm out the door."

"Would you like to stop somewhere for a cup of coffee on your way home?"

Actually, all she wanted to do was go to bed, sleep hard, sleep long. Because she was scheduled to be back on duty much sooner than she wanted to be. But something in Jess's eyes, something in his voice, compelled her to accept his invitation. "Look, how about I meet you at the coffee shop down on Main Street in about twenty minutes? I can't stay long, but a nice caramel mocha latte sounds good."

He chuckled. "I didn't figure you for the fancy stuff."

"A girl's got to have her indulgences, Jess. Caramel mocha latte happens to be one of mine."

"Then I'll have one waiting for you," he said, then turned away. But before he was away from her desk, he spun back to face her. "Look, Julie, about last night, and some of the things I said…"

She waved him off. "Just go get us a table and order the coffee, okay? The rest of it doesn't matter." Even though it really did. But she wasn't going to be the one to fix it for Jess. He didn't want it, and she couldn't afford the involvement. As long as she kept that in mind, she'd be fine.

"I ordered you a large," he said, a little while later, as

she sat down across from him at the table located in the front window.

It was like they were on display, the ideal couple drinking coffee together that anyone strolling by would see. The perfect place, if you wanted a place that lacked intimacy. Which this table did. In a way, she was grateful for the public display, because that kept things honest. And with Jess, this time around, that's all she wanted. Honesty. "Thank you."

"And a blueberry muffin. You used to love blueberries, didn't you?"

"You remembered that?"

"Actually, I hadn't thought about it for years, but when I told the server that I was ordering the caramel mocha for you, she told me you usually get a blueberry muffin with that, so I ordered one. And that's when I remembered you loved blueberries."

For a moment, she was disappointed. Then she chided herself for having some stupid, romantic notion that, after all these years, he would have remembered something so trivial. Of course he wouldn't. Just like she wouldn't remember something trivial about him, like...like... "Do you still have an aversion to pepperoni on your pizza?"

He chuckled. "Still hate it with a passion. How'd you remember that?"

Truthfully, since that night when she'd treated him for smoke inhalation, she'd remembered a lot about Jess Corbett. Too many things, probably. "Don't know. I suppose it just came to me."

"Well, for what it's worth, my pizza taste has gone to all veggies. Don't eat any meat on them nowadays." He took a sip of his chai tea. "Still don't like coffee either."

"That's a new one on me. But we were kids. I don't suppose we ever had the occasions to do coffee, did we?"

"Donna was the one…she used to tease me about my peculiar appetite. She drank probably ten cups of coffee a day, black, no sugar, no cream. Definitely no caramel."

"And you two served together?"

He nodded. Looked out the window, fixed his gaze on something in the street. "She was a medic. Damned good in the field." He cleared his throat. Blinked hard. "Look, I appreciate you trying to help me last night, and I apologize for being such an idiot about it. But that's my history, isn't it? Being an idiot at the most inopportune times."

"Well, we were young at that particular inopportune time. Different problems, different…ideals, I suppose. And history's just that…history. In the past. We learn from it and move on. Or hopefully learn and move on. No need to apologize for last night either. Rafe had warned me that you probably wanted to be alone, and I should have listened to him. But sometimes I'm headstrong, sometimes I go getting myself into situations where I don't belong, and what you were going through…I clearly didn't belong there. So it's me who should be apologizing to you for bothering you. But I truly am sorry for your loss, Jess. I blundered right in where I shouldn't have."

"It wasn't you, Julie. And whatever Rafe told you about how I push people away, he was right. I do. It's easier that way. You know how we were raised, Rafe and me…my old man. Even though I wasn't the one who got the beatings…I was there. Saw what he did to my brother. Wasn't able to do a thing to help Rafe. Wasn't able to do a thing to help…" He took a sip of his tea. "Anyway, enough of that. Let's talk about something more pleasant, like what a good nurse you are. I'm impressed. Not surprised, though, because you were always strong."

She smiled. "Well, I don't know about being strong so much. But I'll admit, sometimes it impresses me, too. Not

that I'm a *good* nurse so much as that I am a nurse. It was my little-girl dream, the only one I ever had, really."

"You never wanted to be a fairy princess?"

She shook her head. "Always a nurse."

"But you were a paramedic? How did that happen?"

"It didn't take as long to get through the training as it did to study to be a nurse, and being a paramedic got me into the medical field while I was studying. A practical choice on my way to nursing, I think. And I'm nothing if not practical. Oh, and Grace figured into it, too."

Jess chuckled. "Why am I not surprised? She seemed to have a plan for everybody she loved, didn't she?"

"Grace…she expected something of me. No one ever had, but Grace always did, and when I messed up, which I did a lot, she didn't criticize. She just stood by me, showed me better ways. I think her offering me paramedic training was her way of testing my dedication to medicine, since I didn't really display much dedication for anything else, except the horses. She knew that side of me…the side where I acted first and thought about the consequences later. I was barely eighteen, and all I wanted to do was go to nursing school. I didn't think about all the years of education on a university level I'd need. My grades were so poor in high school I barely got out. And there I was, begging to embark on this long journey of even more education.

"Grace knew I wasn't ready for it. So I knocked around in odd jobs for a while. Then she offered me a shot at paramedic training. Less in the academic pursuit, more in practical experience. She was testing me, Jess, to see if I could do it. To see if I could dedicate myself enough to pass the first hurdle. Which I did, because I loved working with people who needed help…needed *my* help."

"But you still wanted to be a nurse?"

Julie nodded. "That never changed."

"So Aunt Grace eventually paid your way to nursing school?"

"No. Somewhere along the way, I figured out that getting through nursing school was something I had to do for myself. It would have been easier letting Grace support me all the way, which she would have done. But I didn't want easier. I wanted to earn my way in the world, which I did as a paramedic. Grace gave me my start, and helped me here and there when I needed it, but it was by her example more than her bank account that I found my way." Julie smiled fondly. "And it was hard, working my job full time and going to school. There were times I wanted to quit... or drop out for a semester or two. But Grace believed in me...the only one who ever did.

"I'm sorry I missed her funeral, but I had university exams and Grace wouldn't have wanted me to postpone. My thoughts were with your family that day, though."

He reached over and squeezed Julie's hand. "You're right. She would have definitely had an opinion about you missing your exams. A strong opinion!"

Julie brushed back a tear. "Look, I really need to get going. I have to be back on duty later, and some sleep between now and then would be a good thing." She pushed away from the table. "It was nice talking to you, Jess. When we were kids...well, that was different. *We* were different and we made a mess of things. But like I said, that's history. Maybe now we could be friends? I think Grace would have liked that." Funny, how easily that had come. All these years, all the harsh feelings...they didn't matter now. Because what she said was right. They *had* been kids. That's all. Just kids who hadn't been smart enough to know how to deal with their problems.

"I think she would have liked that," Jess said, standing. Grace would have liked that. But Jess hadn't said he would. And that was disappointing. Bitterly disappointing.

CHAPTER FOUR

"SEEING anything interesting?" Julie walked over to Jess, who was leaning against the wall in E.R. Exam 3, and leaned next to him. It was near the end of her shift now and, good Lord, was she ready to go home! Between her normal duties, meeting with an architect to go over expansion plans *ad nauseam,* ordering E.R. supplies, conducting a brief E.R. staff meeting, interviewing one candidate for a full-time nursing position and fretting over the fact that Jess Corbett was simply hanging around, watching, she was wiped out. He'd been there over three hours now, hadn't really said much to anybody about anything, including her. More like he was an impressive, immovable presence standing off by himself in one spot or another, making her uneasy for reasons she didn't want to get into.

"Lots of things," he said, his voice so sharp it could have cracked glass.

"Anything I should know about?"

In answer, he shook his head. That's all. One shake of the head. Well, that wasn't what she'd expected from him. Somehow she'd hoped for friendly, or cordial, or even semi-sociable. "So, are you interested in a guided tour of the area…or something? There's probably not much that you haven't already seen, but maybe I could answer some questions or show you some of the ideas I'm working up

for the expansion." She was pretty sure he wasn't interested or else he would have already said something. But he owned the place, and she felt obligated to try. More than that, she was worried about him.

"Appreciate the offer, but I know my way around. And, yes, I'd like to see your ideas."

Well, that was a step in the right direction. Twenty minutes later, when they were sitting together in the cafeteria, drinking coffee, and she was running through a list of things she absolutely needed to make the expansion successful, she was wondering if they were still going in the right direction because, as usual, Jess was rigid, all observation, no talk. "Space-wise, we could use more room," she pressed on, wishing he'd say something, make a noise, at least grunt. Which he hadn't done so far. "But the architect believes that in order to stay inside the basic footprint he's laid out, we're going to have to sacrifice a little of what I'd hoped for in order to keep the whole layout more efficient. Apparently, I'd planned too much wide open space he considered wasted."

Finally, something provoked him enough to speak. "Wide open space is wasted?" Jess broke his rigid posture by crossing one long leg over the other then leaning back in his chair. "Why's that?"

Julie shrugged. "I thought it would be nice to spread things out so people won't feel so cramped or claustrophobic when they're in here. But he said wasted space is wasted money. In other words, why build something that's not going to generate revenue?"

"Sometimes it's not about the money."

"Well, you and I might agree on that, but Mr. Masters has a good reputation for his medical facility designs and he's probably right."

"So you're just going to back down?"

"If I get what I want, Jess, something else has got to give. If that happens, then I blow the budget I was given to make this work."

Jess drew in a deep breath, then let it out slowly. "Have you factored in a bigger ambulance bay?"

"What we have is fine."

"For one ambulance. But one isn't enough, which means that whole area is going to have to be expanded. And I want the doors from it leading straight into Emergency, rather than the way it is now, where the patient is offloaded and has to take a long trip down through what is, essentially, the administrative offices."

Julie raised her eyebrows, quite surprised to hear that Jess had actually thought this through. "Well, I'd actually come up with an idea to relocate the ambulance bay at the back and have admittance through a small triage area. You know, first assessments."

"But?"

"But budget."

"Yeah, well, it's not about the money. So I say to hell with the budget. Design your ideal, then we'll see what we can do. And in the meantime, I may toss in some ideas of my own." He pushed back his chair, then stood. And for the first time in hours finally cracked a smile. "You're not what I expected, Julie."

"What's that supposed to mean?"

"Back when we were kids, I think the thing about you that attracted me the most was your wild side. We were a lot alike in that respect. But what you've made of yourself... I know you give Aunt Grace all the credit, but the credit belongs to you, too. I guess I didn't think you could change so much because, in lot of ways, I haven't changed so much. Sometimes I'm still that teenaged boy who's trying to figure it out."

"And sometimes I'm still that wild child who's just fighting to get through any way she can."

"Oh, you're getting through, Julie. I'm just glad that the hospital is reaping the benefits." With a nod of the head, he turned and exited the cafeteria, leaving Julie to wonder what that had been all about. Jess, getting involved in the expansion plans. Jess, being so complimentary.

It was nice of him. Strange, but nice. She liked it. Hoped she'd see it again because whether he recognized it or not, the Jess Corbett who'd just walked out of here had gotten through, too. Only thing was, he still hid from it.

"Julie...*Julie?*"

Somewhere in the distance someone was snapping fingers at her. Then Rick Navarro's voice shook her out of her thoughts. Much to her surprise, he was seated in the very same spot Jess had been, and she hadn't even seen him come up. "I'm sorry," she said, trying to click back to reality mode. "What was it you were saying?"

"I was just telling you to go home. You look tired. After last night, and with the day we've been having in Emergency, you need to get some rest. Doctor's orders."

She really liked Rick Navarro. As a hospital administrator, he was strong and fair. As a doctor, compassionate. As a person, he was just about as nice as anyone she'd ever met. She remembered him from when they were kids, although she'd never really had much to do with him. He was the son of Lawrence Corbett's maid. Had taken a lot of hard knocks from the kids at school because of it. It couldn't have been easy being the maid's kid when you were growing up in an affluent little town like Lilly Lake, and that was something she understood all too well. It hadn't been easy being the wild child either...the one all the parents had forbade their children from being friends with. Outcasts, both of them. A common bond. Maybe

that's why she liked Rick so much. They shared similar history, and had come through rather well at the other end. It's probably the reason she'd jumped at his job offer, too. "I'm okay. Just a little distracted. Jess and I were just going over the expansion plans, and—"

"Jess?" He looked genuinely surprised.

"He has some ideas. Doesn't care if we go over budget either."

"Did you feel his forehead?" he asked.

"Why?"

"To see if he was burning up with fever. He's gotta be sick, delusional. The Jess Corbett we all know doesn't want to be involved here."

"Well, the Jess Corbett who was sitting in your seat only minutes ago got involved."

"Any idea why?"

Julie shook her head. "I think it might have something to do with last night. After Will Brassard called him out to work as a medic, I think he might have seen a different side of things."

"That can only be good. If Jess stays on this and we actually reap the benefits, I'll be happy."

"Then prepare to be happy. For what it's worth, I don't think Jess is going to back off." Said in all due tentativeness, though. She was pretty sure Jess meant what he said, the way he'd meant every word he'd said to her back when they'd been kids. The only question was, for how long? After all, he did have that history of running away. Yet he'd seemed genuinely interested in the expansion. Given that he didn't want to be here in Lilly Lake in the first place, though, she did wonder. "Anyway, I need to get back to work. I've got some papers to shuffle before I call it quits for the day."

"Paperwork can wait. You need to go home. You've al-

ready put in more hours than we allow, so I might have to get tough with you if you don't follow doctor's orders."

Julie laughed. "That's the best you can do for a threat? Where I come from, Navarro...actually, where you come from, too, you've got to back up those words with action."

"Like picking you up and physically removing you from the building?" He cracked a broad smile, arched playful eyebrows. "I can do it, if I have to."

"You, and what man's army?" She stood, though, glad to get the reprieve since she really did want to get out of there. Needed some space to breathe, to think...about Jess.

"Look, tough girl. Don't make me call Security on you."

"You know, it's good to be home. I really missed Lilly Lake, missed all my friends." Impulsively, she threw her arms around Rick and gave him a big hug. "Missed you, too, Navarro. So tell me, have you and Jess made up yet? Something outside the meet and greet and be cordial stage?"

Rick's expression sobered. "Rafe and I did when he came back. Jess is the tough one, though. He's keeping his distance."

"Well, Rafe told me about Jess's fiancée. I honestly didn't know anything about it." And she was a little hurt Jess hadn't been the one to tell her. "It's terrible, and I can't even begin to imagine what he's gone through, or is still going through. So I think he's having a hard time adjusting. I know I would. Also, I know, for a fact, he's not happy about having to take time off from work. But he brought some of that on himself."

"Brought it on being Jess?"

Being Jess. People who knew him knew exactly what that meant. "There is that side of him, isn't there?" she said, half smiling. In truth, that unpredictable side was part of what she'd found so exciting all those years ago. "And the

problem is, *being Jess,* as we call it, has got him as many write-ups for taking what the fire department calls unnecessary risks as it has commendations for bravery."

"Grace worried about that. She was also pretty upset when he just up and quit medicine. Every time she tried talking to him about it, suggest that maybe he should keep some options open, he'd just shut her out." He shrugged. "God knows, I've had my share of trying to figure out where I want to be in life. Not sure I've got it all worked out yet, to be honest. So I know what Jess is going through."

"Well, right now he's pretty focused on the E.R. expansion, so I say we just take advantage of that and hope it works out as well for Jess as it will for the hospital." She meant that, too. She really did want it—whatever *it* was— to work out for Jess.

"And I think maybe I'll take the first *big* step with Jess, and see what happens. I mean, I really don't have anything against him anymore. Making up with Rafe made me realize a lot of things about myself. The biggest, probably most important thing being that, as a father, I have to be an example to my son. Telling Christopher to do one thing and doing just the opposite isn't being that example."

Julie reached out and squeezed Rick's hand. "I'll bet you're just the greatest dad in the world. And I can't wait to meet Christopher. Anyway, as far as Jess is concerned, just give it a try and see what happens. He's a nice guy who really needs someone to reach out to him."

"Have *you* tried?" he asked.

Not enough. Sometimes the memories were too painful. Besides, what would happen if she did get through to him? They couldn't go back to being what they had been all those years ago and, for them, there was no going forward. So why bother? Actually, why even think about it? "Our history..." She shook her head. "He's not going to

respond to me. I mean, professionally we can work together. That'll be fine. But I'm not the one who needs to be reaching out to him in any other way." Because it would hurt too much. As it was, she could hide behind her professional feelings when it came to Jess. That was easy to do. But she was discovering that her personal feelings were still raw. It was a surprise, after so many years, but there was nothing she could do about it except protect herself as best she could. Because this time, like last time, Jess would leave. Only this time she was forewarned. *Caveat emptor.* Let the buyer beware. Except she wasn't buying.

All the way home to change her clothes to go to the stables, and for the next hour after that, Julie wondered why she felt this overwhelming need to do something when she'd thought her recharged position on staying uninvolved was pretty clear. On the one hand, Jess was in a bad place right now, a place she'd been before. Half her life had been spent in a bad place, and if not for Grace Corbett…well, there was no telling how it would have turned out. Probably not as well as it had so far. Besides all that, Grace had done so much for her, and she wanted to give something back. Helping Jess… Grace would have liked that. Would have wanted it.

But could she stay away from him on an emotional level? That's what scared her. Not the history, not even the bad way they ended so much as the little twinges she felt, even now, when she thought about him. She remembered those twinges, remembered where they'd got her before. All those years ago, when the teenaged Julie Cark had encountered Jess Corbett for the first time, it had only been for a good time. That's all. That's who she'd been. But those twinges has sunk her. Done her in. Bowled her over when it had come to Jess. Which was what was making

the so-called mature woman Julie Clark very nervous. In a life where she was pretty confident of herself at long last, this was one realm where she wasn't confident at all. So, in this whole debacle over what she wanted to do, could do, should do, literally any and everything after the next couple hours tending the horses was up for grabs. In other words, she had a great job and outside that, she was clueless, thanks largely to all this confusion surrounding her feelings for Jess.

One thing was certain, though. She did have to help him get through whatever was messing up his life. For Grace. Even for Jess. For herself, too, if she ever hoped to straighten out her own personal tumult.

"He's beautiful!" Julie exclaimed, standing on the opposite side of the stable, looking across at the gray Arabian Johnny Redmond, the stable manager, was showing off. "Except for the fact that he needs a few pounds on him, he's stunning." With its distinguishing head shape and lofty tail carriage, the Arabian was clearly one of the most aristocratic, most beautiful horse breeds in the world. At least, in Julie's opinion. It was a breed with speed, endurance and strong bones. Also, in her opinion, an Arabian stood out because of its good nature, its ability to learn quickly and, most of all, its willingness to please. Grace had often compared her to an Arabian, but she'd always known better. Those weren't her qualities. Far from it, in fact. But standing in the presence of those noble attributes, the way she was now, only solidified her conviction to help Jess. In her estimation, *he* was the one with the qualities of a good Arabian, even if those qualities were shrouded. "And he's got great spirit. It hasn't been broken. You can see it in his eyes." But there was distrust in those eyes, too. Or maybe just wariness from the abuses he'd suffered.

Again, she thought of Jess.

"You always did have a way with the horses," Johnny said. A retired jockey, Johnny was one of Grace Corbett's longtime employees, a vital part of the Gracie Foundation, where abandoned and abused horses were rescued, treated, brought back to health and adopted out, or given a home for life if adoption wasn't an option. Right now, Johnny looked after nearly a hundred horses, an odd assortment of mules, some donkeys and a small herd of wild, starving burros rescued from out West and relocated to Gracie Foundation's acreage. "Grace always hoped you would help run the foundation someday. Maybe now you'll get your chance."

Maybe she would. Although, it had been years since she'd had any good horse time. Coming back to it, though, and being entrusted with this stunning creature was just one more reason she was glad to be back. "Well, how about I start off slowly then work my way back into it, beginning with this handsome fellow?"

"That's what I had in mind for you, but you're going to have to be careful. He's shy," Johnny warned. "And he spooks easily. I'm also a little worried that he's off his feed and, so far, we haven't been able to get any substantial amount of nourishment in him. Vet's been out to check him a couple of times, doesn't see much wrong physically except he's underweight and generally weak. So if we can't get him to eat in the next couple of days, we're going to have to force-feed him, which I'd rather not do."

This poor creature had suffered too much pain and anguish and, in a sense, turned himself into a ghost. Like Jess, in some ways. But he still had his spirit, the way she knew Jess still had his. It was just a matter of getting to know that spirit and nourishing it. "Does he have a name?"

"Normally, we let little Molly choose the names. That's become her official role in the Gracie Foundation, which

is why our horses have names such as Ice Cream, Licorice and Pretty Girl. But we haven't let her in here with this one because when we got him in, we weren't sure he was going to make it and we didn't want Molly exposed to something like that. She gets really involved and there's no reason for her to see the ugly side of how some people abuse these animals. So, no name."

"Then he's Ghazi, which is Arabic for conqueror, because he *will* conquer his abuses and be strong again. I see that in him." In Jess, too.

Johnny smiled in appreciation. "Then Ghazi it is. I'll go record it in the registry and, in the meantime, maybe you could take Ghazi out for a walk…if he'll walk with you. So far, he hasn't responded to anybody, but if you can get him out, the bonding experience would be good. For both of you. Also, he hasn't shown any mean tendencies, just skittishness, but I don't think he's ready to be mounted yet. So for now I think we should just lead him around the paddock then let him tell us when he's ready."

This horse deserved better than what he'd had before now, Julie thought. And soon he would get better. *She was sure of it.* "So, Ghazi," she said, approaching him directly, so not so spook him, "we're going to be friends, you and me. Best friends, if you'll let me."

The horse eyed her suspiciously, stepping back each time Julie stepped forward. But the stall was small, and he only took a few steps backward until he was trapped against the wall. She was instantly alerted, as this was when some horses would buck and rear. But not Ghazi, it seemed. He simply stood. Actually, he almost cowered, which made her wonder what could have happened to him to cause so much sadness. "I know I'm supposed to give you healthy foods like carrots, and Johnny would kill me if he knew what I was about to do, but do you like sugar

cubes?" she asked, pulling a couple from her pocket and placing them in the palm of her hand. She got close enough that Ghazi could see the sugar, then let him make the next move, which was to move back toward her outstretched hand to take it. Risky business, if he decided to nip, but she didn't see meanness in his eyes. All she saw was sadness and fear...and so much spirit desperate to break through. "It's okay, sweetheart," she said in her gentlest of voices. "Whatever happened to you in your other life, it's never going to happen again. I promise you, you are safe here, and we love you. From now on, you're going to have the best life any horse could possibly have."

Because Ghazi was her horse now. She *would* adopt him. Beyond the shadow of any doubt, she knew he was meant to be hers. Which meant Lilly Lake had truly just become her home because she had a horse here—a horse that needed her care. No matter what else happened in life, she *was* home to stay. Heaving a sigh of relief, Julie swiped at the tears streaming down her cheeks. Home...it had such a nice feel to it. So much safety. It was good to be back. "Look, sweetheart, you need to make the first move. I know that trusting me might not be easy yet, but this is about you. So, please, just take the sugar." She stretched out her hand to him just a little farther, and this time Ghazi stretched his neck toward her.

"That's good. Now, try to take one more step."

Which the horse did. Then so did Julie, happy that she and Ghazi were making some kind of instant connection. It renewed her faith in her ability to judge horses. Hopefully, the same would hold true for people. Namely, Jess. "Okay, baby. Just a little closer." She extended the hand holding the sugar cubes just a little farther toward Ghazi, then waited for his next move. Which was another inching toward her. "Good, sweetheart. Just keep coming."

Finally, when she was close enough to Ghazi to feel the moist exhalation from his nostrils on the palm of her hand, she took one final stretch and held herself steady there until the horse, at last, took the sugar cubes from her. She was pleased to find he was as gentle as a kitten, pulling back his lips and barely touching her flesh with his teeth. Ghazi was a mild-mannered soul, and she was totally, head over heels, in love with him.

"That was amazing, what you just did with him," Jess whispered.

Startled, Julie spun around. "How long have you been standing there, watching?"

"Almost from the beginning. Something about giving him sugar instead of carrots, and not telling Johnny, who by the way, in case you never knew, keeps a stash of sugar cubes hidden in his office, in his file cabinet, third drawer from the top."

"And you know that, how?"

Jess grinned. "Youthful inquisitiveness. Also knowing that Johnny is a creature of habit, and that some things never change. So, tell me about the horse."

"I called him Ghazi. And he has a kind soul," she said, not sure what else to say.

"So do you, Julie. You are going to keep him, aren't you? You were always partial to the Arabians, weren't you?"

"You remember that or did someone have to tell you, like they did the blueberry muffins?

"Actually, yes. I remembered."

"I'm flattered." Pleased as well. "And you liked the quarter horse, if I'm not mistaken." She smiled over a memory of Jess sitting astride his glorious palomino quarter horse, and her thinking he was the most handsome boy she'd ever seen in her life. Then the memory clouded, and

her chest tightened. "Look, I've got to get back to work. I promised Johnny…" She stepped back. Tried turning away from him, but he grabbed her arm.

"I brought over some hospital plans for you to look at. Additions to what you've already done. I know we can't do this on a personal level, Julie. You make that clear every time you're around me, and I understand why even though you say you want to be friends with me, you can't. But we still have to deal with the hospital. And I don't want to make that tough on you." He should have just left the plans on the table by the door and gone. But he'd got himself caught up in the moment, watching her gentle up to the horse the way she had. It was a beautiful thing. Julie was a beautiful thing. She'd truly come home, and for a second he'd wished he could come home again. *Almost.* Then the reality had risen back up to bite him. He didn't have a home anymore. Not in any real sense. Didn't want one. Didn't need one. Julie's reaction to him only emphasized that.

"For the hospital," Julie said, then turned her back on him, pulled another two lumps of sugar from her pocket when Ghazi braved up enough to nudge her in the arm for it. "And it's not about not being friends, Jess," she said. "It's about so many things. Things I haven't figured out yet. Just give me some time, okay?"

"All the time you need." Because it didn't matter. He wasn't staying. She was. And she knew the score. Knew him. Watching Julie, all he could think about were the opportunities he'd missed along the way. His fault, every last one of them, so he couldn't complain. But, damn, he felt the sting anyway. And being here with Julie, it was more acute than he'd expected. More acute than he wanted because he knew…*dear God,* he knew…what he couldn't have even when he slipped up and let himself wish or hope

or daydream a little. He was Jess Corbett, though, and he didn't get wishes or hopes or daydreams. Not now, not ever. Because whenever he touched anything, or even got close to touching it, it always turned out the same. *Bad.*

That was a thought that depleted him as he dropped his notes on a worktable, then marched out of the stable without so much as a goodbye. And it was a thought that still depleted him as he spun tires on the dirt road toward the lake, driving much too fast on what amounted to little more than a wide path that barely ever saw automobile traffic. It was also the thought that was still depleting him when he missed a turn in the road, spun off to the side trying to overcorrect in order to get back to where he needed to be, then plunged straight down into the ravine and finally, after a long, bumpy descent, came to a slow, jerky stop only when he hit a tree.

Missed opportunities…that was the only thing on his mind as Jess Corbett lost consciousness in one of the most out-of-the-way areas on the entire Corbett estate. Around him, the early evening shadows threatened to carry him along into the night, where the darkness would have no choice but to swallow him into oblivion or cradle him until morning.

CHAPTER FIVE

THE jingle of her cell phone awoke Julie with a start, and she immediately rolled over on her side to look at the clock on her bedside stand. It was a little after three. At this time of the night, the only phone call that could conceivably come in would be about a hospital emergency, so Julie was already sliding out of bed, preparing herself, mentally, for whatever was about to happen. "Hello," she said groggily, stifling a yawn after she'd clicked on.

"It's Rafe Corbett. Sorry to wake you up, Julie," he said. "Wasn't sure who else to call, so…"

He paused, and Julie responded without waiting for him to finish. "Not a problem. And I'm on my way, Rafe. Give me ten minutes to grab a shower and get dressed, then I'll be out the door. See you there in twenty, tops." Her feet dropped to the floor and she propelled herself up. "So, what's the emergency? Can you give me some idea of what should I be expecting when I get there?"

"It's not a hospital emergency," Rafe said. "It's personal. Jess…"

He hesitated, and she heard his audible sigh. Suddenly, the hair on her arms stood up.

"I haven't been able to get ahold of him. I've been trying for hours, and I wondered… Actually, Johnny told me the two of you spent some time together earlier today…

that would be yesterday now, wouldn't it? Anyway, I was wondering if you knew where my brother was going after he left there? Did he say anything to you, or give you any kind of indication what he was going to do?"

She slid back down to the bed, sat on the edge of it, blinked hard a couple of times to clear her head, which wouldn't clear because an image of Jess planted itself in the forefront. "I'm sorry Rafe, but I don't know. He left in…well, we'd had a little disagreement, I suppose that's what you could call it, and he left."

"Was he angry?"

"Not really. More like he was quiet." And now she was blaming herself. Jess had been good, but she'd been… unresponsive. "I heard him drive off, but it was probably ten hours ago by now. Maybe even closer to eleven." Her stomach was beginning to churn. "I mean, I'm sure he's okay, Rafe. He probably just wants to be alone, or maybe he had an appointment to meet someone, or a hot date. So have you called the police department? Maybe Rick knows where he is."

"I've made the calls. No luck anywhere. And as far as I can figure out, you were the last person to see him. You're probably right, though, that he's okay. Hopefully on that hot date you mentioned, losing track of time. I mean, that would be good…my brother dating again."

An image she definitely didn't want in her mind.

"Or maybe he's off doing the solitary-man thing. We Corbett men have always liked our alone time. That's probably what this is about. Just Jess doing what he does."

Rafe's words sounded good on the surface, but nothing inside them sounded convincing to Julie. In fact, they sounded just the opposite, which caused the lump in her stomach to double instantly. "He's always been a little headstrong." Putting it mildly. "So, you know what, Rafe?

I could go out, have a look around." She wasn't sure where, but the rest of the night was shot for her. Too much worry and guilt equaled no more sleep for her until Jess was found. "Cruise up and down a few streets and see if I can spot his car. Check the all night diner out on the highway, and Will Brassard's bar. I could also stop by the hospital and see if he's there, maybe in one of the on-call rooms. He was hanging around there earlier, just watching, so maybe he's gone back. Would it help if I went out?" Truthfully, it would be like looking for that proverbial needle in the haystack, but searching out that needle would be better than simply sitting around, waiting for it to appear.

"I don't really see much point to it, Julie. I actually think he might have gone back to the city. Jess is, well... unpredictable. Anyway, I appreciate the offer, and as soon as my brother checks in, I'll let you know. Thanks, and sorry to have bothered you."

The click of Rafe's phone was like the rumble of ominous thunder in her ear. Then, suddenly, she was alone in the dark, worrying about Jess. "He's a loner, but he's not irresponsible," she reasoned with the emptiness around her. "He's abrupt, but not inconsiderate." In other words, she didn't believe he'd simply left Lilly Lake without a word to anybody. Especially *not* without saying something to his brother.

That was the belief that got her showered and dressed in record speed, and moved her out the door to her car. It was also the belief that put her behind the steering-wheel for the next hour and a half, driving up and down deathly quiet streets where the only signs of life were the moths that flickered around the incandescent glow given off by the streetlights, and all-night dives with their flickering neon welcomes.

"Maybe he's back at his cabin by now," Will Brassard

suggested. Will was still hard at work in his own pub, cleaning up after the last customer had gone home. Julie liked Will. They'd been friends back in the day. Never close friends, but more than acquaintances.

Propped on a bar stool, drinking coffee left over from the sober-up pot Will always made for his last-of-the-night stragglers, Julie was glad for the warmth of the beverage. Even though the April early morn wasn't so chilly now, something about being out all alone in the earliest hours was disquieting, maybe even a little sad. "I've called him every fifteen minutes for the last hour or so, and if he was anywhere near here, he'd have answered. I have an idea Rafe's been calling just as often as I have."

"Jess would answer...*if he could.*"

If he could... But what if he couldn't? *That* was the thought she didn't want to think. The one she could see reflected on Will's face. "Or maybe he's too far away now. Not in a good reception area. Could be, too, he simply forgot to turn on his phone."

"Or we might have to face the possibility that he's hurt," Will said, then tossed down his bar rag. "Look, there's no point standing around here wondering about it. Jess is a firefighter...one of *us*..." Meaning the unmistakable bond between all firefighters. "I'm going to call out a few volunteers and go have a look. As best as I can remember, there are probably four different ways to get back to his cabin, so by first light we should be able to get them all covered pretty quickly."

"Well, normally I'm not so reactionary, but that may be a good idea. Jess is..." She really didn't have the right words to describe what she was trying to say. Sad. Impulsive. Lost. All accurate, but she didn't think they truly conveyed what Jess was going through right now. And to describe him in any more detail would give Will,

or anybody listening in, cause to think she had feelings that went beyond simple friendship.

"He's Jess," Will supplied, then chuckled. "Isn't that what people always said about him? He's Jess."

Rafe was dependable. And Jess was Jess. "But Jess, being Jess, isn't irresponsible. Impulsive, yes. Stubborn, definitely. But not irresponsible. So, where do you want me to search?"

Will shook his head. "Can't let you do it, Julie. This could get dangerous, considering some of the territory we're going to have to cover."

"I know the area," she argued.

"But you haven't lived here for years. So you might have forgotten…"

"Can't stop me, Will." She sat down her coffee mug. "I'm a paramedic, remember? Worked in New York City. Seen tough, done tough, *am* tough. Considering the part of the city I worked in, a walk in the woods is a piece of cake. I'd rather do this with you and your men, but if you're not going to let me, then I'll be out there on my own."

"You haven't changed," he said, motioning her to the front door with him. "Stubborn when you were a kid, stubborn now." He chuckled. "In a lot of ways, just like Jess."

"Well, the *just like Jess* part I might have to debate with you. Actually, the part about not changing, too. Because I *have* changed. Back when I used to be stubborn, I didn't have anything to back it up but a bad attitude and some pretty ill-conceived ideas. Now I have skills you'll need out there if Jess is injured." She prayed, though, they wouldn't be needed.

Jess expelled an irritated sigh. He wasn't hurt so much as trapped. And at some point, when someone noticed him missing and came to find him, that whole embarrassment

thing was going to kick in. But on the bright side, he wasn't hanging upside down. That was the only point of consolation he'd had over these past, interminably long, boring hours. He'd worked a couple of rescues where the victim trapped inside the car had been hanging upside down, or in some other uncomfortable position. So sitting here in his seat, with his damned foot trapped under the gas pedal so tight he couldn't move it without causing at least two or three significant metatarsal fractures, with a couple of broken phalanges thrown in there for good measure, while it wasn't comfortable, it certainly wasn't as uncomfortable as it could have been. The thing that probably hurt the most was the abrasion on his cheek that had happened as a result of the air bag inflating. That, and a splitting headache.

"Okay, now would be a good time to come and get me," he said to his cell phone, which wasn't picking up any kind of a signal. Not that he thought anybody would come for him. At least, not now. Not in the middle of the night. Actually, according to his watch, going on to morning. Of course, the big thing was, with the way he kept himself isolated, how long would it be before anybody actually started to miss him? Well, the answer to that was ten hours now, and counting.

"Ten hours," he muttered, shutting his eyes. Ten empty hours where he'd done everything in his power not to think about anything. Problem was, the one thing…the one *person*…he couldn't keep out was Julie. In fact, even now, in the dark, sitting at the bottom of a ravine, he could still see her as clearly as if she were here.

"No way he'd take his car up that road!" Will exclaimed. He was pacing back and forth at the entrance to a very rough service road leading to the far side of the lake. "I

mean, I was down that way a couple months ago, on a routine inspection, and it's bad."

"But it's a shortcut to the lake," Julie argued. And the place she and Jess had made love for the first time.

"If you're crazy enough to take it."

"And Jess is Jess," she reminded him, narrowing her eyes and looking down the road as far as she could see in the emerging light. "Nobody's seen him anywhere else, so this is the last place to try, if we think he stayed on the estate." Intuition told her he had. Or maybe that was her heart indulging in some wishful thinking.

"Then we're going in on foot, because I can't risk getting our department vehicles banged up if we don't know for sure he's down there."

"How about horseback?" Rafe called down from his mount, Donder. He was riding with Johnny and Rick. With them, they had brought another horse, a fine-looking bay filly Molly had named Lollipop. Lollipop was saddled, but without a rider. "The four of us will go in, take the road all the way down to the turn, then let you know what we find."

"Works for me," Will said. "And in the meantime, I'm going to send a couple of people back around to the other side to make sure we didn't miss anything. Also, I've got someone out on the road to Jasper, which is the way he'd have to go if he was returning to the city. Oh, and Rafe, I did call his department, talked to his chief, let him know we were looking for Jess, in case he turns up back in the city. And, um...well, now's not the time to talk about this, but they're concerned about him."

Julie shut her eyes, rubbed her forehead. Maybe she should have said something to Rafe about Jess's proclivity for taking risks, but invading Jess's privacy...it just didn't sit well with her. Jess might be a little out there, as far as some of his coworkers were concerned, but that didn't

mean he was crazy, or a danger to himself or anybody else, for that matter. He was simply a man who was trying to work out his issues his own way, and she respected that. Sure, it worried her. But, deep down, she trusted Jess to do the right thing because that, too, was part of being Jess. "He just took in a little smoke," she said, trying to head off the conversation. "I was the paramedic who treated him that night, and it wasn't anything serious." Okay, so she wasn't being exactly forthcoming with everything but, somehow, she felt the need to protect Jess. Especially now, when he wasn't there to defend himself. "And right now we really do need to keep looking for him."

Will opened his mouth to speak, had second thoughts, then simply nodded. "She's right. Let's get back to work."

"So, is the bay for me?" Julie asked.

Rafe nodded. "You ride as well as the rest of us. And once we get to the bend, we're going to split up in pairs. So…" He pointed to the horse, and Julie mounted without hesitation.

"Do you know what Will's talking about?" Rafe whispered to her, as they headed out.

"What I know is that your brother has received more commendations in the short time he's been in the department than most people receive in the course of a career. The rest of it he'll have to tell you about. He's a good firefighter, Rafe. He cares."

"You're a loyal friend, Julie. Too bad he didn't hang on to you years ago. Things might have turned out differently for him."

Things might have turned out differently for her, too. But there really was no point in going over all the *what ifs,* because they didn't matter, and sometimes all they did was cause heartache.

* * *

"I see his car!"

Jess's eyes shot open and he looked at his watch. Eight o'clock. He'd been here, what? Fourteen, fifteen hours now? The effects of mild dehydration were beginning to set in, and his muscles were cramping something fierce. Plus, he was downright hungry and his throat was sore, partly from the dehydration, partly from giving in to frustration several times and simply yelling for help.

"Down at the bottom of the ravine. Up against a tree!"

Jess tapped the horn to let them know he was fine, but it didn't sound, the way it hadn't sounded every other time he'd tapped it in the past dozen or so hours. So he shouted, to no avail, unless the chipmunks scampering around the base of the pine tree just outside the car cared to listen.

"Any sign of life?"

"Not yet. I'm going down."

Was that Rick Navarro's voice? Rick and...Johnny Redmond, he thought.

"No, I'm going down," another voice shouted, and it didn't take any guessing to know who that was. It was Julie. She was taking charge.

Jess heaved a heavy sigh of relief, and relaxed.

"You don't do rescues, Rick," she continued.

"Go, Julie," Jess whispered. "Show them what you're made of." Good stuff. No, great stuff. In spite of himself, he enjoyed watching her rise to the occasion. The thing was, there was always this niggling thought just on the edge of his mind reminding him that she could have been his. She'd loved him back then, told him all the right things, wanted all the things that would have made for a great life. Sure, they had been young. And that had been part of his excuse for running out on her. The other part... Damn, why did his mind do this to him? Why did he have to keep replaying the way he'd messed up, first with Julie, then

with Donna? With his whole damned life? "Shut up," he whispered to himself. "Shut the hell up!" Like that would stop the barrage of thoughts.

"But I do have that experience," Julie went on. "I'm trained. So I'll go down there first. And, Rafe, tell Will to get emergency equipment in here right now! Don't know what I'm going to find, but I want to be prepared. Also, I want an ambulance ready and waiting, and alert the E.R. that we'll be bringing Jess in shortly."

"Won't need an ambulance," Jess whispered. But then he began to worry. Julie, Rafe... It was his fault they were here. His fault they were putting themselves at risk to rescue him. Part of him wished everybody would go away and just let him work out his demons right then and there... Get it right in his head first, even if it took another day or two. Then come and rescue him. With Julie in charge, though, that wasn't going to happen. Truth was, he liked the barrier of avoidance he'd raised around himself. Once he learned how to keep it up all the time he'd be fine. *Just fine*...he thought, staring out the windshield, listening to the voices up above him.

"Rafe, Rick...once I'm down," Julie called, "one of you be prepared to follow me after you know what I need, and one of you stay up top."

"Damn it," Jess muttered. "How many more ways can I mess up my life?"

Lucky for him, he didn't have time to count the ways, as Julie's voice rang out from somewhere in front of the car just in time to save him from an even deeper descent into his own private hell of regrets. "Jess, can you hear me?"

"Yes," he shouted at the top of his lungs, which wasn't very loud.

"Jess, answer me!"

She was getting closer.

"Jess?"

"I'd answer if I could," he said, his voice traveling only into the windshield then stopping. Then he dropped his head back against the headrest and waited. What else could he do?

No answer. She could see the car ahead. It had cleared several large rocks, any number of trees and thankfully was sitting on all four tires, looking like it had taken a cruise down the hill and decided to come to a rest against the pine tree. Car was a mess, and she was praying Jess wasn't. But he wasn't answering, which worried her. So she doubled her pace, until she was practically running.

"Jess, answer me! Jess!" She was almost there. Couldn't see anything in the rear window from her vantage point. Nothing moving. Nothing obviously bloodied and mangled, though, thank God.

"Anything yet?" Rafe called from up top.

"Car's totaled. Can't see anybody inside." And most of her didn't want to take a look. But she was closing in, moving even faster… "Jess, can you hear me?"

No answer, but…was that something moving in there? A hand…waving? "Got a visual on something," she yelled, sprinting around the side of the car and coming to a stop on the driver's side. Sucking in a deep breath, she braced herself to look in, and saw…Jess, and he was grinning at her. Sitting there, grinning the grin of one mighty embarrassed man. Immediately, the tension drained from her, and she said a silent prayer of thanks. Then yanked open the car door so hard it hurt her shoulder. "What the hell are you doing?" she yelled at him, immediately dropping to her knees, pulling out a penlight and flashing it in his eyes.

"Waiting for you to come find me," he whispered. "Nice bedside manner, by the way."

"Probably better than you deserve. You had us scared to death, Jess. Half of Lilly Lake is out looking for you, your family…well, they can tell you how they've felt for the last several hours. And here you are, grinning." Eyes reactive. Bright, actually. "Got him," she yelled. "Alive, apparently well enough."

"Definitely well enough," he said. "No internal injuries, nothing serious, unless you consider humiliation an injury."

She gave him a fleeting glance, then mustered up a grin of her own. A very mocking grin. "Well, you know what they say about your worst humiliation being someone else's momentary entertainment."

"What? No sympathy for the wounded man?" he teased.

Letting down, now that the emotional edge was off the moment, Julie gave herself over to a laugh—more of relief than anything else. "You're incorrigible, Jess. Do you know that? Has anybody ever told you how incorrigible you are?"

"Not quite so nicely as you put it. But in other words… yes. I've heard that a time or two in my life. Oh, and thanks. I'm glad it's you who came down to witness one of my less glorious moments."

"Less glorious moment…I'm glad that's all it was, Jess."

"You were scared, too?"

She nodded. "Back when I was a paramedic, the discovery was the part I didn't like. That moment when you don't know if your patient is alive or dead, that instant when you open the car door to find out… I loved that part where I got to take care of them, but I hated the discovery."

"I'm sorry you had to go through that with me," he said gently, reaching out to brush a thumb across her cheek.

One touch, and her heart raced. That's all it took from Jess. Then, now…that's all it had ever taken. To fumble her way around the realization that she still had strong feelings, Julie diverted her attention by taking Jess's blood pressure. Put everything she had into the simple task, gave it her undivided attention. Or, at least, tried. But even strapping the blood-pressure cuff to his upper arm caused… Oh, no! Those familiar twinges! She focused even harder on her task, squeezed her eyes shut as hard as she could to listen…to block him out totally.

Then, when she was done, and there was no way to avoid looking at him again, Julie pulled the stethoscope from her ears, braced herself to be professional and looked point blank at Jess. "Seriously, what happened to you? How did you end up here? If it's my fault, I'm sorry. I didn't mean to be so…"

"What I did was missed the turn. Haven't been down this road for years and I underestimated it. Meaning I took a detour straight down the embankment and hit the tree. And it's not your fault, Julie. We're not making it click right between us yet, and that's all it was. It didn't result in…this." He pointed down to the way his foot was wedged underneath the gas pedal. "Would have climbed out, but I'm on the verge of snapping a few vital parts of my foot. Maybe have a wrenched knee and shoulder, too. Decided to sit this one out and wait for someone to come find me."

"*You* sitting around, waiting it out? What's this world coming to?" She bent down, took a look. Not only was his foot wedged under the pedal, it was actually locked into something underneath the dashboard. "It's pretty stuck, Jess."

"That's your professional opinion?" He relaxed back into the seat, but didn't take his eyes off Julie. "So, what's the verdict?"

"Describe your sensation to me."

"Other than being mighty glad to see you?"

"Am I going to have to call your big brother down here in order to get a straight answer out of you?"

"Okay, you win. I'll be more serious. I don't think my foot is broken. I can wiggle my toes, twist my ankle a fraction of an inch. No excruciating pain. Circulation's still pretty good, I think."

All of it good. Had he not been taking in every tiny move she made, she'd have sighed a sigh of relief over that one, but she didn't want to give herself away. Not even in the little things. Definitely didn't want Jess to think she cared in any way more than superficially. "Need help extricating him," she yelled back up. "And, Rafe, I may have some orthopedic injuries, so you should come down here and have a look. Oh, and a definite yes on the ambulance, because we're going to have to take him out on a stretcher." She glared over at Jess. "No arguments."

"Don't need a stretcher," Jess argued anyway.

Julie smiled at him. "This is the second time you've been my patient, and the second time you *have* to do what I tell you. So you might as well loosen up and go with it, because you don't have another choice." Then she reached over and squeezed his hand. "I'm glad you're injured and not gone."

"Injured and not gone?

"Well, slightly injured. And, yes. Injured and not gone."

"What you're telling me is that people thought I'd up and left Lilly Lake without telling anybody?" he asked, sounding regretful. "I guess I deserve that, don't I, with the way I act sometimes?" He shrugged. "I think I have some apologies to make, especially to my family."

Julie uncapped a bottle of water she pulled from her emergency pack and handed it to him. "Look, I understand.

What you went through losing your fiancée was…well, I can't even begin to imagine. And I'm sure it catches up with you. You're right, though, that there was some thinking along the line of you just leaving without saying anything to anybody. People do expect that from you, Jess. That's how you've always been. But I know you wouldn't do it right now, not when Rafe needs you to help him with the hospital plans, especially with Edie getting ready to deliver. I mean, you've got a whole, long list of faults, and I'll be glad to go over them with you, in detail, once we get you out of here…" She smiled at him. "But you're not inconsiderate."

"Look, I know we've had our differences in the past… I said things, did things that were really stupid. So I do appreciate your sympathy toward me now, even though I don't deserve it." He drank greedily from the bottle, then heaved a sigh of relief. "Now, let me guess. You were the one who initiated the search."

"Something like that. Rafe called and—"

"I'm pretty sure *he* was one of those who came down on the side of me going back to the city without telling anybody. I think, over the years, Rafe has borne the brunt of my lifestyle more than anyone else. Borne it, compensated for it, tried explaining it away to other people. So he'd be the first one who'd expect me to bolt." He shrugged. "And I can't blame him."

"He was worried, Jess. Really worried, so don't fault him for anything because there's not much anybody can do in the middle of the night. He and Johnny saddled up at first light, though, along with Rick, and they rode. I went to see Will, who got some volunteers together, and…well, this is where we are. Oh, and just so you'll be prepared, Will did call your department in New York City and talked to your chief."

"And Steve said…"

"Don't know for sure *what* he said, but I think it was probably what you'd expect him to say. You do go against the grain, you know."

"Which means Rafe knows everything. Meaning he expects even less of me now than he did before."

"So you should probably be the one to tell your brother what's going on with you so he won't think any less of you. I checked on you, Jess. After your smoke inhalation, I was worried because of some of the rumors I'd heard. So I checked, and I found out…"

"That they don't like the way I work. That I take risks… big risks."

"It's not so much the *way* you work. You've done amazing things in a short amount of time. But the risks you take…" She nodded. "That's the thing, I think. Those risks…"

"Save lives," he snapped. "Which is what my job is about. See, Julie, you don't like that first discovery, and I understand that. But that's where I shine. It's what I do best. It's why I'm a firefighter and not a doctor."

"It's also why you've had so many commendations. *And reprimands.* And, no, I haven't mentioned this to Rafe or anybody else because, as dumb as this may sound, considering that I worked so closely with the fire department and respected the rules, I think what you've done is admirable. I also think that you know exactly what you're doing each and every time you rush in. But to always put yourself in the way of harm, to put yourself out there in front of everybody else…"

"It's not always black and white out in the field, Julie. You, better than most, should understand that."

"I do. I've been out in that very same field. But the rules aren't made to be broken."

"Sometimes, though, they can't be followed."

Julie heaved a frustrated sigh. What he said was true. She couldn't argue the point. Especially not when Jess had been personally responsible for saving dozens of lives that might have otherwise been lost. He *did* know what he was doing. He *did* shine at the discovery. It was a salvation for many, and the cause of fearful dread for some. "Look, I'm not going to talk about this right now because the men are on their way down the hill and we need to figure out how to get you out of this mess. But later, Jess. We're going to talk about it later and, in the meantime, you might want to say something to Rafe because he's going to find out. Be fair to him, okay? Let him hear it from you."

"Thank you," he said, lifting the water bottle to his lips again.

"What for? I haven't done anything yet."

"You've done more than you know," he said. "Much more than you know."

CHAPTER SIX

BASICALLY, there was nothing wrong. According to the chart, Jess was bruised, with an air-bag abrasion to his right cheek, he did have a marginally sore shoulder of no consequence, slight concussion with no aftereffects, his knee was a little puffy but none the worse for wear and his foot was, according to Rafe, *just a little bit sprained.* Julie was glad to read the results of a couple of hours of tests. Now he could go home. "I'm on my way to give him the good news now," she said to Rick Navarro in passing.

"Well, say something to him about his driving, too, while you're at it," Rick quipped.

Suddenly, she prickled with defensiveness. "It wasn't like he intentionally drove off the road. Accidents happen. We see the results here in the E.R. all the time."

Rick arched skeptical eyebrows, then shrugged. "Whatever," he said indifferently. Which made Julie prickle all the more.

"Do you think he did it on purpose? Is that what this is about?"

"What I think, Julie, is that Jess lives large and maybe not too cautiously. That's all I'm saying. Anything you want to infer from that, well…infer away. Your guess is as good as mine when it comes to Jess Corbett."

Trouble was, with her, it wasn't a guess. She knew. "It was an accident," she said emphatically. "He missed the turn."

"He missed the turn in an area *no one* travels. Think about it, Julie. Before you go getting yourself involved with Jess, just think about it. Okay?"

"I'm not getting involved with him," she said, trying hard to keep all inflection from her voice. "We dated years ago. And now…we're friends in the loosest sense of the word."

"Friends in the loosest sense of the word don't take offense the way you just did. And they don't go all red in the face either." He sucked in a sharp breath, let it out slowly. "Look, Julie. I'm not exactly the best one to be giving relationship advice here. I mean, look at me, look at the mess my personal life's been in for a while. I made mistakes, bad mistakes. So I know how it feels to have mixed emotions the way you do with Jess. But just be careful where Jess is concerned. I know he's not the guy we grew up with, but sometimes he seems angry like he did back then, and I'm not talking about the surface kind of anger where you go blow off steam somewhere and it's over. Jess's emotion is pervasive. It's eaten its way into a deep place, and at some point, if you do get more involved with him, it's going to pull you in, too. So as a friend just watch out for yourself. Okay?"

Julie stepped across the hall and gave Rick a quick hug. "I appreciate your concern, Navarro. But it's not the way you think it is between Jess and me."

"Are you sure? Because I remember how you were with him the first time, remember that look you used to get on your face every time you saw him or someone talked about him. Saw it then, see it now. Go look in the mirror, Julie, if you don't believe me." With that, he headed down

the corridor leading to Admittance while Julie turned and went down the corridor toward the cubicle where Jess was waiting, impatiently, to be dismissed.

"What I'm saying, Jess, is that you can't keep doing it." Rafe's voice lowered so not to be heard. "I appreciate you telling me, but it's not like I haven't been seeing this in you for a while."

"There's nothing to see. I do my job. People perceive me to be reckless, but I'm not. It's all a matter of interpretation."

"Is it? Because you're sitting out there at the cabin for two weeks, and I don't believe that it's because you needed a vacation or you inhaled a little smoke. You don't have to say the words, Jess. I know."

"Know what?" Jess snapped.

Out in the corridor, Julie stepped back, caught up in the dilemma about whether to let the brothers argue it out without her standing there, listening or breaking it up by barging in. Honestly, she thought the air needed to be cleared between Jess and Rafe…for Jess's sake as well as Rafe's. So she stepped back again, but not entirely away because what she heard next glued her to the spot.

Rafe looked his brother straight in the eye, determined to get through to him. "What the old man did to you. While he was beating the hell out of me, he was turning the psychological battle on you. Don't you think I heard the things he used to call you?"

"Just words," Jess said.

"Words," Rafe snorted. "Believe me, Jess, there were times when I was grateful he was only beating me. A bruise heals, but being told you're worthless doesn't."

Julie drew in a sharp breath. She'd known. Yet she hadn't known…not the extent of the abuse. And suddenly she could see Jess and Rafe as boys…Rafe with the bruises,

Jess with the attitude and the strange, haunted look in his eyes. Too many people had known, too many people had found it easier to look away.

"I don't want to talk about it," Jess snapped. "He's dead. I've moved on."

"But to where, Jess?" Rafe asked. "You went to medical school, you joined the military, now you're a firefighter. Is that how you're going to live your life, always moving on?"

"You know, you got lucky, Rafe. Edie, Molly, another one on the way…you're one lucky guy and I envy you what you've got. I almost had some of it, but then I blew it. Stepped right in front of myself and put an end to something that could have been good because I know that I'm not the settling-down kind. But at least I recognize that… recognized that before it was too late. Donna and I…we didn't make it to the end. I pushed her away for her own good. At least, in my opinion it was for her own good. Told her I couldn't go through with it, then an hour later she was…" His words broke off. He shut his eyes.

"My God, Jess! I didn't know."

His eyes snapped back open. Angry eyes. Eyes filled with rage. "Well, you should have. Because that's how I've always been. It's who I am."

"Or who you choose to be."

"What the hell do you know about me, Rafe? Other than that we share blood, what the hell do you really know?"

"That you're running from the same thing I am… turning out like the old man. We hated him, and we see his traits in us. We're doctors, Jess. We followed in his footsteps there, and even though that's where I know I'm supposed to be, don't you think it bothers the hell out of me some days when I let myself think about it?"

"Except I'm not a doctor."

"Sure you are. You can deny it all you want, but it's still there inside you. Maybe buried a little deeper than it used to be. But still there. So it's got to scare you sometimes when you think about it, like it does me. I understand the fear of being like the old man. And I understand pushing people away so you don't have to face yourself, because that's what I did when I first met Edie."

"Well, you didn't push hard enough, and it worked out for you. I'm glad. But I'm not getting that close to anybody again because it's not what I'm supposed to have, not who I'm supposed to be. So, yes, maybe my life is always going to be about moving on, and that may include taking some of the bigger risks since I don't have to think about a wife and children first, in case I get killed, or critically injured. But I don't have a death wish, big brother. I don't do stupid things and nobody—*nobody*—is going to tell me the risks I take aren't necessary, because they are. And so you'll know, the only reason I even said something to you about what's been going on with me is because if I hadn't, Julie would have. She got on me about it even before you guys came down that hill and pulled me out of the car."

"Then good for Julie," Rafe said to his brother.

"Look, I'm sorry I didn't say something sooner. The thing is, none of it matters. I'm not going to change. I thought I could, but I can't. Julie couldn't change me all those years ago. When I thought she was pregnant, when I knew she wasn't... She wanted to be pregnant, Rafe. Wanted that baby. At the end of the day, when I was trying to look for a practical solution, all I really wanted was to get as far away from my mess as I could get. I knew she was hurt when she found out she wasn't pregnant, knew that somehow she'd built some fantasies around it, but I was glad it turned out like it did, Rafe. Glad I didn't have to deal with her pregnancy, glad I didn't have to deal with

her, glad to get away. Then when Donna and I were... Damn it, Rafe! I looked at home design catalogues with her, picked out color patterns, got involved in the decision about which duvet to buy. I wanted to do it, should have been able to. But when she started talking about that satiny, mauve duvet that would go so well with throw pillows, that's when I knew I couldn't go through with it and all I wanted to do was get away from it...from her.

"Donna deserved that domesticity, she deserved that husband who really cared about the details the way she did. And it wasn't me. The more plans she made, the more I was sweating it out. Literally getting sick to my stomach. But trying to be all she needed me to be. In the end..." He shrugged. "I should have been honest with her from the start. Told her who I really am. Then turned my back on her before we got to the place where she expected a duvet."

Outside the curtain, Julie bristled. He'd been glad to get away from her? *Glad?* She'd always thought it had been fear, never expected to hear it described as something that had made him glad. And that hurt. "Here!" she said, whooshing through the curtain and thrusting the discharge papers at him. "Sign them, then drop them off at the desk on your way out the door!" She brushed past Rafe and started to exit, but Rafe caught her by the arm and held her in place.

"I didn't have time to thank you for rescuing my brother."

"It's my job. What I do. That's all it was," she said, fighting for control even though right now it wasn't coming through for her the way she wanted. Because right now all she wanted to do was get away from Jess, not have to look at him, not have to have these awkward, mixed emotions she was feeling give her away to the man who most didn't want to see them.

"Julie..." Jess said, shoving to the edge of the bed. "You heard what I just said to Rafe, didn't you?"

"You're accusing me of eavesdropping?"

"There's no expectation of privacy here. I know that."

"I didn't want to interrupt."

"But you're part of this."

"No, I'm not. Because there's nothing to be part of, Jess."

Jess tried to stand, but came up wobbly on his foot. Which Julie used to her advantage, and backed away even more.

"You said you were glad to get away from me, Jess. I would have understood if you said it was fear. I would have understood if you'd said you were confused. But glad?"

"Not in the sense of being happy. More like..."

She shook her head. "No. We don't have to do this, don't have to do anything. I work here, I may run into you from time to time since, technically, I suppose you are my boss. There's nothing else, though. And that's something else you can be glad about." Maybe Rick was right about what he'd seen, but he wasn't going to see it again.

"Can we just talk about it? Let me try to explain what happened?"

"You know what, Jess? You can talk all you want. I'm not going to stop you. But I'm not going to be here to listen to you either. Summer Adair's coming on duty, and she'll make sure you're processed out. Or you can stay here. It's your hospital. Do what you want."

By the time she'd cleared the E.R. doors and was on her way to the cafeteria for a cup of hot tea, Julie's hands were shaking. Then, by the time that cup of hot tea was in hand and she was sitting alone in the farthest corner of the room, her back to everyone, her face to the window, her gut was knotted. Finally, by the time she'd raised the

cup to her lips, she was fighting back tears she refused to spill. Nobody made her cry. Nobody had for a long, long time and Jess wasn't going to be the one to do it. He didn't deserve that distinction. So she fought back her case of threatening weeps by focusing on her to-do list, and refused—*refused*—to let anything sidetrack her. She had bandages to order and a drug cabinet to restock. In Julie Clark's life right now, that's all there was.

"I know. It was stupid. I was stupid." Jess stood at the window overlooking Gracie stables. Julie was in there, and while he couldn't see her, he did take some comfort in knowing that he hadn't totally driven her away from everything she loved.

"She's just hurt," Edie Corbett said. "Give her time."

Jess turned to face his sister-in-law. Wonderful woman. Great mother. Rafe was a lucky man. "Time? That's not going to heal anything. I hurt her. Took a time in her life when she was so vulnerable... You know about the pregnancy scare, don't you?"

"Rafe told me."

"Anyway, I shot off my mouth, said I was glad to get away from all that mess I'd made. But back then she'd wanted that baby, and she'd been so hurt when she'd discovered she wasn't pregnant. Then the other day, what I said..."

Edie laid a comforting hand on his arm. "I don't know what's going on between you and Julie, but if it's something that's meant to be...friendship, more than friendship, you'll work through this."

"I can't do more than friendship," he said.

"Don't sell yourself short, Jess. Rafe did, yet look where he is now?"

"He's where he's supposed to be, with the right person."

"And you can't find that for yourself?"

"Oh, I probably can find it. It's what I do with it after I find it that's the problem."

"Well, maybe when it finds you, instead of the other way around, it, or *she,* will fight hard enough to help you overcome the obstacles. It can be done, Jess. Just look at me…" She patted her belly. "I fought hard for one of the Corbett boys, and won."

Edie was close to her due date now, and she really did glow. For a moment he caught himself wondering what Julie might have looked like at this point in her pregnancy, if she'd been pregnant. But as fast as that bit of melancholia hit him, he shook it away. "Rafe won."

"And you can't?" she asked. "Just look out that window, Jess. Maybe all you'll get out of this is a good friend, but isn't a good friend worth the effort?"

"But I don't want anything out of this."

"Then why do you keep staring out the window at her?"

Truth was, he didn't know. Even now, he was watching Julie simply stand there and stroke the gray Arabian's muzzle. What an astonishing thing, seeing how she could gentle an animal so easily. She could do that with people, too. With him… Already had with him. "Look, I think I need to hobble on out there and see if she'll talk to me. I do owe her an apology."

"Don't be too hard on yourself, Jess. No matter what you've done, or said, I know Julie won't be." Edie handed him the cane that was to be his companion for the next couple of weeks. "And if she doesn't want to listen this time, maybe she will next time, or the time after that."

Limping past Edie on his way out the door, Jess stopped and brushed a tender kiss to her cheek. "You know, if my brother hadn't found you first…"

Edie laughed. "Yeah, yeah. That's what they all say. Oh,

and Jess, invite Julie in for dinner later on. Don't know if she's actually ready to sit down at a table with you, but if she is, tell her it's chicken cordon bleu."

"Think she'd come if you put me in the next room and shut the door?" he asked, stepping out onto the porch.

"That's always an option."

Making his very slow path down the porch steps and off in the direction of the barn, Jess debated with himself if he really needed to be doing this. He'd already put Julie through hell, and he truly didn't want to make the situation any worse. But he had to talk to her, or try. Had to tell her he was a hothead who blew off steam without thinking first.

"Are you supposed to be walking around?" she asked him, purposely avoiding eye contact. In fact, her back was to him as she brushed Ghazi and she didn't so much as glance over her shoulder at Jess. "I thought Rafe told you to stay off your feet for a couple of days."

"Since when do I listen to anybody?" Jess asked. "Isn't that what I do best? Not listen?"

She didn't answer him. Didn't say a word.

"Look, Julie. What I said...what you heard. You're right. I did mean it. But not the way you think."

"There really aren't too many ways to interpret it."

"Okay, so I'll admit it. I wasn't ready for what might have happened if you'd been pregnant. I was glad you weren't, and that was purely selfish on my part. But what I had going on in my life back then..."

"I was your mess. I get it. And believe it or not, I even get why you ran away. I was a little girl dreaming grown-up dreams. But to hear that you were *glad* to get away from me... I don't suppose I expected that. Not from you."

"I was glad, though. But not for the reasons you think. See, I almost bought into your fantasy. It scared me. I'll

admit that. Settling down at seventeen into some kind of domestic arrangement, with a baby, no less. I don't think there are many seventeen-year-old boys out there who want that, or who even think that could be the outcome when they get sexually active. I sure didn't. And the way my old man was screaming at me… But the thing is, part of me actually believed I could make a go of it. I didn't want you near him, though. He'd have done to you what he did to Rafe and me, and I was too young to protect you from it." He cringed, thinking back to that time. The horrible things that had happened, the fear of what his old man would do. *What his old man had done.* "It is what it is, Julie. I can't go back and change it and even if I could, I probably wouldn't because I didn't want you dragged down to where I was. That's all I meant when I said I was glad to get away. I was. It gave me a new chance at life, and it gave you one as well. And look what you've done since then."

She finally whirled around to face him. "I appreciate your honesty, but so far all you've done is evade things that need to be dealt with, then get angry when you're backed into a corner. That's not who you are, Jess. Maybe you don't know that anymore, but that's not who you are." She expected anger, expected him to push her away like he did everybody else, but what she saw when she allowed herself to look into his eyes was sadness. "I'm sorry for your past, Jess. Sorry about Donna, too. Everybody is. The thing is, if you let people in, you'll make it easier on yourself. People want to be there for you but you make that impossible." She tossed her brush into a tack box and took Ghazi by the reins, ready to lead him back into the stable. "When I first came here, to Gracie House, even to Gracie Foundation, I pushed people away harder than anybody I've ever seen since. But Grace pushed back. She was the

first one. And she made me realize that all my pushing…
it was just fear. Here I was, thinking I was being all brave
and tough, and when I opened my eyes to it, what I found
was a scared little girl who simply didn't want to be hurt
anymore."

"And the little boy who didn't want to be hurt anymore
either."

Julie nodded. "So, aren't we the pair?"

"Can the pair be friends?" he asked, following her to
the stall, where she settled Ghazi in. "I know we keep trying, but is there a chance we can actually do it? Or have
we gone too far past that point?"

They'd been lovers but, given her feelings for him now,
could they be *only* friends, or would that hurt too much?
It was a brutal question, but an honest one for which she
had no answer. "That's an age-old question, isn't it?"

"You mean because we…?"

She nodded. "I mean, I don't ever remember us being
friends. We had the other thing going on…"

"Because we were kids. Kids aren't always that smart
when it comes to, well, that part of life. Act first, think
later."

"Like we did. Only I don't think we ever got to the part
where we were thinking about anything, did we?"

He leaned against the doorjamb, took the weight off his
foot. "Trust me, I was thinking. In fact, the only thing I
was thinking about all those weeks was you."

She laughed. "Yeah, typical boy thoughts. And we both
know what those are."

"Okay, so I'll admit I did have those thoughts. I mean,
come on. You were a looker. So how could a boy *not* have
those thoughts?"

"A looker?"

"I'm just being honest here. But I thought about you in

other ways, too. I liked your intelligence, liked the way you faced the challenges. Liked the way I felt when I was with you."

"I didn't know that."

"Because I was a typical guy and whenever we got together, all *those* things flew right out of my mind. So, do you think we can come to some kind of an understanding?"

"Why are you pushing me, Jess?"

"Because I still like your intelligence, still like the way you face challenges. Still like the way I feel when I'm with you. And—" he grinned "—you're still a looker. What can I say? I'm a man, I like to look."

In spite of herself, she laughed. How could she not? Even with his rough ways, Jess was a charmer. Had been when he was a boy, was more so now. And she was just as susceptible to that charm now as she had been when she'd been a girl. "So what am I supposed to do with that, Jess? Tell me, because I don't know."

"It's easy. Just accept me for who I am. And don't worry so much."

"Not worry? Are you kidding me? Because look what you do. You've been a firefighter for just a little under two years, and you're already a legend. It's a risky legacy, though. Who you are causes people to worry. So, I can accept you the way you are because that's not going to change and I don't think it has to, but the worry comes with it. It's conditional. And one more thing, while we're on the topic of worry. Tell me why you were out on *that* particular road. There are all kinds of speculations swirling around, nobody really understands why. But I want to understand, because it was dangerous, Jess. What you did was so dangerous."

He braced himself with a stiff breath. "Okay, in the in-

terests of friendship, the truth. And it's not very exciting. I used to go out there when I was a kid. Loved that area because I had the lake at my front and the foothill at my back, with trees everywhere else. I always felt...protected there. It was a long way from the house, and I knew my old man wouldn't come that far looking for me. Rafe had his haven up at Hideaway Bluff and that's where the two of us went together. But I had my place down at what I called Lake's Edge. It was perfect, nobody even knew I went there, except you, and I just wanted to go back to... think. That's all it was."

"I always loved that area, too," Julie admitted, her eyes softening as she thought of Lake's Edge. "After the first time you took me there, I used to go out there myself sometimes when I wanted to be alone."

"I was thinking about you and me there, on the picnic blanket under that big old oak tree... I think I just wanted to spend a little time in a place where my life never seemed complicated."

"It did seem simple then, didn't it, being young, and in love? Nothing else in the world mattered while we were there." Sighing, Julie shut her eyes. "I wanted us to build a house there. Never mind the impractical aspects of exactly how that could happen. I wanted a house, a proper Victorian with a wrap-around porch. White picket fence. Flower garden. Innocence of youth, even though I don't remember ever being innocent. But it's nice in a fantasy, isn't it?"

"Well, I never got around to imagining a house there. But I liked the solitude. The safety. And the memories. Which is why I was on that road. I wanted to go back there and pretend everything was the way I wanted it to be. I missed the turn because I wasn't concentrating on the road." A glint came to his eye. "Amazingly, the im-

ages of us there are still pretty vivid. But that's all it was, I swear."

A soft smile crossed her lips. "You're incorrigible, Jess, but I believe you."

He stood, winced, bore down harder on the cane. "So, friends...*finally?*"

"Friends don't let friends stand too long on an injured foot." Immediately, she stepped to his side, slid her arm around his waist and her shoulder under his arm. "You need to sit down."

"I know why my aunt loved you," he said, as they made their way over to a bench near the tack room.

Julie chuckled, helping him down. "I think love is a strong word for how Grace felt about me. Maybe she liked me..."

"*Loved you.* Because you were strong."

"I had to be strong, because I wasn't very smart about pretty much everything I was doing. So I needed something to compensate for my lack."

"You mean, not very smart about us?"

That's not what she'd meant because, no matter how badly it had turned out between them, she'd never had any real regrets about her brief love affair with Jess. And in her mind it had been a love affair. First lovers were never very smart, though, were they? "Let's just say that I wasn't smart about a lot of things. Eager, I'll admit. Because I wanted you probably in the same way most teenaged girls want their first love. Also, I always knew more than anybody else. Couldn't be taught, or told..."

"And your parents?"

"You mean my *third* set of parents? The ones who left me before Grace took me in? What's there to say? They were probably decent people, but I didn't give them much

time before I was looking for my way out, doing the things I knew would facilitate that."

"Three sets of parents? I don't suppose I ever knew that about you." He shifted on the bench and stuck his foot out, then bent down to adjust the hard plastic ortho boot Rafe had forced on him.

"When Grace took me in, I was on the verge of being declared a casualty. The state wanted to put me in a juvenile detention facility, wanted to lock me up until I was an adult, basically. Anyway, Grace found me. Took me in, and she respected me, Jess. She kept my wild-child ways private because she had faith in me. At least, that's what she always said. And you know what? I believed her. She was the only person I ever truly believed." She sat down next to Jess. "Now, I'm going to take that boot off you and see if your foot is swelling, because I'm betting it is."

"Then what?" he asked.

"After I adjust the straps, you either sleep here with the horses tonight or I help you back up to the house."

"It's swelling," he said, even before she'd bent down to have a look. "But it's worth it."

"How?" she asked as she slid the ortho boot off him.

"Because of this."

"What?"

"This." With that, Jess reached his hand over and turned Julie's face toward him. "You can stop me. Or not."

"This isn't the oak tree, Jess."

"And we're not kids."

And she hadn't been with a man since Jess. But he didn't need to know that. Didn't need to know anything. Neither did she, except…how, exactly, had this happened? How had they gone from nothing to friends to what was about to come into being in mere minutes?

"I don't do this with risk takers," she said, in her first

effort to put him off. Flimsy effort, though. "And you're hurt. Your foot is definitely swelling. You need to go prop it up."

"Which has nothing to do with anything."

He still had her face cupped in his hand...strong hand, nice. Not baby-soft like she remembered from him, but rough. Disturbingly, arousingly so. Every fiber in her body was urging her to close the distance, crush herself to him, wrap herself around him and kiss him until she was too weak to draw breath. But every fiber in her body was also screaming that this was Jess, and she knew how it had to turn out with him. "Jess, um...this isn't..."

"Isn't what, Julie?" His head dipped toward her. "Tell me," he whispered.

"We can't do this. It's not us, not who we are anymore," she finally managed to say. On so many levels, though, she wanted this...yet on so many levels it scared her. But she didn't have time to think, didn't have to do the usual Julie Clark thing and make a list of pros and cons. Grace had taught her to do that before embarking on any unsure venture and this was as unsure as it got. However, as the list was forming in her mind, specifically the one with all the reasons why she shouldn't be doing this, his lips brushed hers and, oh, they were soft, yet not tentative in the least. Not demanding at first, though, like she remembered from him before. In fact, his kiss started like a casual stroll, a walk in the park, exploring the pleasantries. Almost chaste, but not quite. Perhaps like he was exploring his own boundaries.

His touch was skilled as he slid his hand up her back, as he traced the outline of her lips with the tip of his tongue. Jess had, indeed, moved on in his lovemaking, while she had chosen to stay behind, stay in the past. It was obvi-

ous in his every move, as it was surely as obvious to him in her every move.

"Jess," she murmured against his lips, with every intention of pulling back. But she didn't, as once she did it would be over. It would have to be over. So she answered the quest of his tongue by nibbling and sucking his bottom lip, eliciting a groan from him. And at the sound of his deep, guttural arousal, fire darted through her veins, coursed through her pores, made her burn and tremble in places where only Jess had caused that to happen before. And, as hard as she was trying to hold on to her reserve, to not show any outward excitation, she must have responded where Jess could feel it, because instantly his tongue flicked to part her lips and delve inside.

There was nothing left in her to fight against what she wanted. Nothing left of her list, nothing left of common sense, and this did defy every ounce of common sense she possessed. Accordingly, she indulged herself in that blissfully sensual, erotic experience, giving herself over to her own explorations.

This isn't good, she thought to herself, or maybe she murmured it aloud…she didn't know, didn't care as she scooted to press herself even closer to him, not even thinking about how they were sitting on the tack-room bench where anybody could see them. None of that mattered just then, because Jess kissed her the way she wanted to be kissed by him, the way she'd allowed no one else to do to her. Skillful, passionate, emotional… Her heavy sigh was testament to that, a testament to feelings she'd kept buried, and that, tomorrow, she would wish had stayed buried. Because for Julie it had to be everything, or nothing. That's just the way she was, the way Grace had taught her to be. But Jess didn't want that. She'd heard him say it… *I'm not getting that close to anybody again because*

it's not what I'm supposed to have, not who I'm supposed to be. So, yes, maybe my life is always going to be about moving on...

The only thing he wanted was to move on emotionally. And emotionally all she wanted was to stay. That's all she'd ever wanted...that place where someone truly wanted her. Where that someone would never, ever leave her.

"Where are you, Julie?"

"What?"

"Where are you? Where did you go?"

It was only then that she realized she'd been the one to end the kiss, to pull back. To disengage herself completely from Jess. "What are we doing, Jess? We can't relive the past. Can't go back and make things right. So, what is this?" The uncertainty in her voice gave her away as she pushed herself away from him, bent down and fumbled to get the ortho boot back on him.

"I don't know, Julie. Wish I did, but I don't."

And he didn't want to figure it out. That was as plain on his face as embarrassment was on hers. "Okay, we've kissed. No big deal. Now I've got to get back to work."

"I never get it right with you, do I?" he said, taking hold of his cane and pushing himself off the bench. "Never have..."

Never will. He didn't say the words aloud, but she felt them in her heart. And they stung because what she didn't want to know had just become painfully obvious to her. She still had feelings for Jess Corbett. And he'd never stopped running away.

CHAPTER SEVEN

SHE was stunning, sitting astride Ghazi, bareback. He'd been watching her gentle the horse for two days now. Hadn't said a word to her, hadn't even gone close. His excuse was that he didn't want to spook the horse and everything seemed to spook that horse, except Julie. In truth, though, he didn't want to spook Julie.

Damn, he shouldn't have kissed her. Should have left well enough alone, especially since they'd come to an understanding. But the urge…well, he'd hoped it would be quelled. It wasn't, though. Didn't even come close to it. In fact, one kiss had whetted his appetite. He wanted more. But he knew the result of that, didn't he? Which made the acid churn bitterly in his stomach. One more screwup to add to his collection.

"She's making progress," Rafe said, sitting down next to Jess on the front porch. "Johnny wasn't sure that one was going to turn out good. Too abused. But Julie has her way with horses, doesn't she? Probably one of the best horse-women I've ever seen."

In answer, Jess shifted positions on the swing, then shifted his gaze to focus on a little chickadee hopping its way through the grass. Watching Julie, thinking about Julie…it was turning into a habit he had to break. Clearing his throat, he forced another thought into his head. "I

looked over her plans for the emergency department, added some ideas of my own. They're good, within the existing structure. But I've been wondering if it's time to go beyond that structure and do something worthwhile for the whole area, considering that we've got the space, as well as the resources."

"Didn't think you wanted to get that involved in the hospital again."

"I don't...didn't. But right now there's nothing else to do. Can't go back to work. Can't even walk around without injuring myself. And if I spend another day staring at the walls—" *or Julie* "—I'll go crazy. So I might as well do something useful." Something *with* Julie.

Rafe chuckled. "So, as a last resort, you're going to play at being a hospital owner? Which is fine with me, actually, because I could use some help."

"Well, don't go thinking I'll be returning to medical practice, because I won't. But I want to take a stab at seeing how we can manage more for Lilly Lake. There's a need. A big need. And before you tell me that's what you've been trying to get me to do for months, I know that. I should have listened to you. But I didn't, and I can't change it."

"Better late than never. And so you'll know, I'm not going to kick you in the butt over it, since I didn't exactly want to take up the cause either."

"But you got lucky and ended up with a good life here," Jess said, almost on a wistful sigh. "How is Edie doing this morning? She seemed a little tired at breakfast."

"I think she's anxious to get this pregnancy over with. I mean, I can't even begin to imagine what she's going through, but for me this is turning into the longest nine months of my life. Last summer when Edie and I met seems like an eternity ago in some ways, and a moment ago in others. And this pregnancy..." He drew in the deep

breath of a contented man. "It's good, Jess. Endlessly long, nothing I'd ever thought I'd be dealing with, but good. A year ago if anyone had told me that in the very near future I'd be a dad, *twice*..." He grinned. "It changes everything."

"And who would have ever thought that you'd actually end up settling here in Lilly Lake? Edie has done nice things for you, big brother. Real nice things, and you deserve the good life with her."

"Any chance that you and Julie...?"

Jess shook his head before Rafe had finished the question. "With Julie, I find more ways to screw up than most people could even think of. And not just little things."

"For what it's worth, I think you'd be good together."

"It's not worth anything. Julie and I have bad history. You know that. And I'm not doing anything to make it better. In fact, I think I made it worse." He chanced a glance at Julie, who had brought Ghazi around to the near side of the paddock. She was still on the Arabian's back, but she was leaning forward, almost lying across the horse's neck, stroking his muzzle and, if he knew Julie, probably whispering sweet nothings in his ear.

"How?"

"Kissing her."

Rafe grinned. "That's all? You're worried about a kiss? Usually, that's the start of something."

"After she heard me say I was glad to get away from her?"

"Well, there is that. So, did she slap you?"

Jess shook his head. "As a matter of fact, she was pretty blasé about the whole thing. Didn't seem to care one way or another."

"But you do?" Rafe arched skeptical eyebrows, staring at his brother. "Because aren't you the one who keeps telling me he doesn't want a commitment?"

"A kiss isn't a commitment."

"Could be the prelude to a commitment, though."

"It wouldn't work, couldn't work."

"I recall saying pretty much the same thing myself. Now I'll be the first to admit I was wrong."

"But we're not alike, Rafe. Never have been. You were the one who stood up to the old man and got hit for it, while I was the one who kept quiet and flew under his radar a lot of the time."

Rafe shook that off with a shrug. "Wasn't in your nature to fight back. Sure as hell was in mine, though. But it doesn't matter now, does it?"

"Well, maybe not as far as I'd hoped." Jess glanced out again at Julie. It was hard to keep his eyes off her, hard not thinking about her. "Did you know that only time he ever beat me was when he thought Julie was pregnant? He overheard Julie and me talking about it. Said bad things about Julie after that. Came after me with a shovel."

"Son of a…" Rafe snapped. "If you'd told me…"

"What would you have done? Come home, beat him. Or let him beat you again? You were already out of it, Rafe. I didn't want you coming back into it."

"But you didn't go to Aunt Grace, did you?"

Jess shook his head. "The old man was crazier than I'd ever seen him. I didn't want Aunt Grace, or Julie, involved because I was afraid he might hurt them, too."

"It always dumbfounded me how he could be such a good doctor, and such a miserable excuse for a human being."

"Some things can't be explained. Once I asked Aunt Grace why he was like he was and she told me it didn't matter. That there were some questions in life that didn't have answers."

Rafe nodded. "The old man was one of those questions, I guess."

"I guess," Jess said. "Anyway, he'd made some threats against Julie, said he'd have her sent away. Remember Judge Frayne? He used to play golf with the old man. Anyway, he said he'd go to the judge and see to it that Julie was removed from Aunt Grace's custody and sent to a juvenile home. He accused Julie of getting pregnant only so she could get her hands on Corbett money, and I think that was the first time I ever stood up to him, told him to leave her alone or I'd be the one taking the shovel to him"

"Bet that didn't go over well."

"He tried hitting me again."

"And…?"

"I got him first. He was old, drunk. I was young, angry. He came at me, and…" Jess shrugged. "That's when I knew I had to get away. I wanted to kill him, Rafe. All that anger in me, I was afraid I would."

"This was all before she'd discovered she *wasn't* pregnant?" Rafe asked.

"The sequence is all kind of a blur." He would never tell anybody, not even Rafe, that Julie already knew she wasn't pregnant, but had kept it a secret. She wasn't being deceitful or manipulative, even if that's what he'd accused her of. But that's how it would have seemed if he'd said she'd known for days and hadn't told him. "But I'm pretty sure I didn't know she wasn't pregnant at that time."

"So, what happened after that?"

The part of the story he'd never told. The part that was still so painful. But this was Rafe. It was time he knew. "First let me say I was confused. I loved Julie, but I had to get away, had to physically put myself in another place. I

was scared that I would kill the old man, that it would go beyond threats or feelings."

Rafe swallowed hard. Didn't say a word. Just put his arm around his brother's shoulders for support. "There were too many things for me to deal with. I didn't know what to do, couldn't think, couldn't function. So I went down to the stables one day, decided to take Storm out for a ride, just to get away for a while and clear my head. But the old man was standing there in the middle of the aisle, proud as punch, with a gun in his hand." He swallowed hard. "Standing next to Storm's body. He told me the horse wasn't mine, that nothing in this world was mine, that he could give and take anything from me he wanted to…my horse, my aunt, my pregnant girlfriend."

"I'm sorry, Jess. I never knew what happened to Storm. I figured the old man did something to him, but I didn't want to ask, probably because I didn't want to know how far he'd go."

"Like I said, I wanted to kill him, Rafe. I swear to God, I really wanted to kill him that day. And that shovel he'd taken to me…I took it to him. Knocked him to the ground with it, then stood over him. Had my foot on his chest, shovel ready to swing. And he looked up at me and laughed. Told me I didn't have the guts to go through with it. But for a moment, he was wrong. I did, because he'd killed my horse, and threatened my aunt, as well as the girl I loved. The girl I thought was carrying my baby. The only thing that stopped me from going through with it, though, was that he *was* right. I *didn't* have it in me. Didn't want to have it in me. It was actually the day I decided I wanted to help, not hurt."

"I'm sorry you had to go through it. Sorry you didn't let me help you"

"Help me get through what? Being just like the old man? Because that's who I turned into for a little while, Rafe. The old man. When I found out Julie wasn't pregnant, I accused her of trying to trap me. Said the same things to her the old man had said to me. Heard these ugly, hurtful words coming out of my mouth, and I couldn't stop them. That's who I was, who I'd turned myself into."

"I'm not going to let you sit here and criticize yourself, Jess. We both lived in the same hell. It was the old man who did this. Not us. Not me. Not you. He's the one who put you in that place, who made his demands, who killed Storm."

"And I'm the one who killed…well, so many dreams. Donna's, Julie's… But to Julie's credit, she's been good to me since she came back to Lilly Lake. Much better than she should be, considering what I put her through. Better than I deserve from her."

"And after that you two never connected at all over the years?"

Jess shook his head. "I thought about it, but I didn't know how. I did ask Aunt Grace about her several times, and all she would ever tell me was that Julie had a good life going, that she was doing well for herself, that she was happy. So why would I want to interfere in that?"

"Did Aunt Grace ever know what happened? About the pregnancy scare, or what the old man did?"

"If she did, she never said anything to me. But she wouldn't have, would she? Aunt Grace took care of things quietly and she may have had something to do with how I never heard from the old man again after I left Lilly Lake. Not one, single word." Jess sighed. "Anyway, I appreciate the hospitality. It's been nice staying here with you, Edie and Molly, but I need to go back to the cabin. Sitting here

watching Julie isn't doing me any good. But back at the cabin..."

"You'll be alone. Sitting there all by yourself, brooding."

"Actually, I've got more hospital expansion plans I'd like to work on and I hesitate to say this because when I do you'll probably try and hold me to something I don't want to commit to, but I'm enjoying it. In fact, I'm enjoying it so much I think I may knock out the whole west side wall and expand emergency services out about halfway across the staff parking lot. It'll double the emergency-room space, and maybe even give us enough space to build a full-service trauma surgery." He pushed himself to his feet. "And, no, I'm not going to be your trauma surgeon."

"So says you," Rafe said, chuckling.

"So says me, emphatically," Jess responded. "That's not my thing anymore."

"Like living in Lilly Lake wasn't my thing anymore?" Rafe challenged.

"Aunt Grace always said I was the stubborn one, and she was right. I am. So don't hold your breath waiting for me to take up the scalpel, because you'll just turn blue and pass out. Now, if you'll excuse me, I'm going to go and thank your lovely wife for the hospitality, pack my things and move out." Supporting his weight with his cane, Jess headed toward the front door.

"Do you have feelings for her, Jess?" Rafe called after him.

Jess smiled. "I've still got things to sort out in my mind about Donna. But Julie...maybe I do. Or maybe it's just something from the past creeping in, messing up my mind. I don't know. It's not going to make any difference one way

or another. Like they say, there's too much water under that bridge."

"So why not build a new bridge and see what happens?"

Why not? He could think of at least a dozen reasons, and each of them began with *Julie deserves better.* She did. She absolutely did.

It was probably the worst thing she could be doing under the circumstances, but Rafe had been called into the hospital for an emergency surgery, so there was no one else available to take Jess home to his cabin except Edie, and she was busy with Molly. So Julie had said yes. It was late, anyway. Time to put Ghazi back in his stall, then go home. So the detour didn't matter. But she was nervous in any case, because of what had happened between them. More than that, because of what she'd finally admitted to herself.

The thing was, if she truly wanted to live in Lilly Lake again, she was going to have to get used to running into Jess from time to time. He did come home occasionally. And he was part owner of the hospital in which she worked. So maybe they wouldn't exactly be tripping all over each other, but those occasional bumps wouldn't be avoided. This evening was going to be one of those bumps. It was a short ride, however. And perhaps she and Jess could get things back on track. Or, at least, find their spot in the middle. Friends, acquaintances, two ships passing in the night, whatever. "Your foot feeling better?" she asked, holding open the car door for him.

"Swelling's gone down, so next time I stick my foot in my mouth it shouldn't be so bad."

She laughed. "Can we just get past…well, whatever it is that's making us do stupid things?"

"Kissing you wasn't stupid," he said as she shut the car door.

Outside, Julie walked slowly to the driver's side, hoping the heat of the flush creeping into her cheeks wasn't turning her bright red. No, kissing him hadn't been stupid. It had been more than stupid. It had been a disaster. One huge catastrophic event that had caused her to lose sleep. "So, I'm assuming you have sufficient food back at your cabin to tide you over for a couple days, since you won't be driving."

"Shouldn't we talk about it?" he asked.

"Your food situation?" Dreadful evasion. Her mind wasn't racing fast enough to change the subject to anything that made sense. In fact, she was so nervous she was on the verge of babbling.

Jess didn't reply to her inane response to him. Rather, his body language went rigid, and he folded his arms across his chest. Folded them *severely,* Julie noted out of the corner of her eye. Well, maybe it was for the best. This whole state of affairs between them was going from marginally okay to bad, and she wasn't sure there was a way to make it better, or even fix it a little bit. And even if they could fix it in the present, the past couldn't be fixed so easily, if at all. So, there they were. Two people flirting with feelings that wouldn't be realized. Feelings best avoided.

She sighed heavily and resigned herself to a quiet ride out to Jess's cabin. Almost like a couple of strangers. And so it went for a few minutes, until they were sitting in front of the cabin. Then Jess finally spoke. "Would it be easier for you if I went back to the city? You're the one trying to make a life for yourself here, and I'm the one who's only passing through from time to time. I want to make this easier for you, Julie. Which means that if what it will take is me going back to the city right now, that's what I'll do."

"No, don't. We need to figure out how to make this work

between us. And right now I think it's good that you and Rafe are getting closer. I'd feel terrible if my being here was the reason you couldn't."

"But we're caught in a bad place, Julie. Can't go back, can't go forward."

"Maybe we don't have to go anywhere," she said, even though she knew that could never be the case between them. Not after that kiss.

"Or maybe we do," he said, almost as an afterthought as he climbed out of the car, shut the door and hobbled up to his cabin.

She thought about stopping him. Thought about getting out of the car and asking him what he meant by that, but she knew the answer. Their unfinished business was so thick that it was an entity unto itself. Thick, and curdled, she thought as she turned the car around in his driveway and headed back to her house. But she didn't get far. Just a few hundred feet down the road, she jammed on her brakes. This wasn't the way she wanted to live, always straddling the tentative edge. Teetering, yet never falling. Jess was the only one who'd ever made her feel so…unsure, and she had to put an end to it. Move on emotionally, once and for all. Or stay, and be honest with him about how she felt. So rather than taking the time to turn the car around again and risk losing the momentum of her new found conviction, Julie hopped out and ran the short distance back to Jess's front door. Once there, she paused to take a deep breath, and without thinking looked in his window before she knocked.

She saw him there, standing in front of his fireplace, holding a picture of…it had to be Donna. His shoulders were slumped, he had the look of a man dejected. Maybe a man in love who still grieved his loss. Transfixed, she continued watching for a moment, looking through the glass

as he sat the picture back up on the mantel, then backed away, stopped and looked at it again.

"This is crazy," she whispered. "He still loves her." Which was why he'd told Rafe he'd never do it again... never get involved in that way. In Jess's heart, there was only one woman. Julie knew that now. Had her answer even before she'd made her confession. So rather than knocking, Julie backed away from the window, then turned, ready to run down the three wooden steps and straight to her car. But before she'd touched foot on the first step, Jess opened the cabin door.

"Something wrong?" he asked, looking clearly puzzled over finding her there. "I thought you'd gone."

"I, um...I decided I should come back and see if I could fix you something to eat. With your foot and all, you need to get off it, prop it up, get some rest. So, um..." She shrugged. "Food. Can I do that for you?"

Jess chuckled. "You really do have a fixation, don't you?"

"Just the nurse in me."

He stepped back. "Well, never let it be said that I tried to quash the nurse in you. I don't have a lot in the way of groceries, but if you can find something that will assemble into a passable meal, you're welcome to have at it. As long as you stay and eat with me."

Hesitating a step before she entered, Julie squared her shoulders and braced herself. For what, she didn't know. Maybe just a pleasant couple of hours with Jess, maybe the most nerve-racking two hours she'd ever spent in her life. Either way, she hated being so indecisive. Wished she had Grace to talk to. Grace had always known what to do in any situation. While she'd never really told you what to do, she had always been a gentle guide, or a not-so-subtle push in the right direction, whichever method you needed.

Right now, she sure did need a push or a guide. "Look, Jess, I did…" She swallowed hard, caught herself staring at the photo on the mantel. Donna in full military uniform looking like the kind of woman Jess should have been with. "She was beautiful," she said. "Donna…I'm assuming that is Donna."

"She did turn a few heads," he said, on his way to an overstuffed easy chair in front of the window. "You don't mind if I sit down, do you?"

In answer, Julie scooted a foot stool underneath his leg once he was down. "Did you two meet in the military?" she asked, backing away from him.

"She was my superior officer, actually. I had the rank of captain, she was a major." He smiled fondly. "Her first order to me was to drop and give her twenty push-ups."

Julie laughed. "You were insubordinate?"

"A little bit. I saw her from behind. Let's just say that I admired the view, and made a comment to that effect. When she turned around… Pure fire in her eyes. I knew I was in trouble, especially when I saw that she outranked me." He chuckled. "And she was so cool, dishing out my punishment. She simply pointed to the floor and said 'Twenty.' There was no mistaking what she meant."

"But you challenged her, didn't you?"

"You know me that well?" he asked, settling back into his chair.

"Well enough. And I'll bet it didn't take Donna long to figure you out either."

"She said pretty much the same thing."

"So, what was your punishment after you challenged her?"

"Twenty push-ups, followed by bedpan duty. I got to clean them when I wasn't on duty in surgery." He grinned. "A nice little lesson in humiliation."

"Bedpans…" Julie laughed so hard her side ached. "I'd have loved seeing that. You cleaning all those…"

Laughing, too, he held up his hand to stop her. "Every day for three days. She called it teaching me my lesson."

"Any woman who can have her way with you like that…"

He cleared his throat, breaking the direction of the conversation. "I, um…I have some more ideas for the expansion, if you'd like to go over them now."

"The expansion?" Such an abrupt change in conversation caught her off guard. Told her something she needed to know. Told her that it was time to let go of everything concerning Jess. The past, the fantasy. The back and forth feelings she was having. Time to get rid of all of it. Jess was where he wanted to be, and she wasn't included. "Oh, you mean the hospital."

"I want to turn the emergency room into a whole trauma unit…trauma beds, trauma surgery. I know you were working on plans to expand existing services, but the hospital needs to go beyond that. We can turn ourselves into the major hospital in the region for all kinds of trauma with a little extra effort. So…" He stood, then wandered over to his desk, punched a few computer keys and turned the screen toward Julie. "Interested?"

Once her head spun back to the place it should be, she glanced at his work. "That's a lot more than I thought it was going to be. Makes my contributions seem pretty insignificant."

"Your contributions are what got me to this." He turned off the screen, then plopped down in the desk chair. "Lilly Lake needs more. Rafe and I can do that, and we've decided we want to."

"But you're not staying once you're all better, are you?"

"That's right. I'm not. But that doesn't stop me from

taking over this project. I want to do that, Julie. Want to see what I can do to make the expansion something that will benefit everyone."

Which mean she was phased out. "It's your hospital," she said, trying to hide her disappointment. "I think if you want to invest in an expansion like what I imagine you're considering, then go for it. It would be a welcomed improvement."

"So why the frown?"

Julie shrugged. "I think I'm a little overwhelmed." Total lie. She was hurt. Didn't like being pushed aside. Wasn't going to show him he still had the power to hurt her so badly. "Going from an improved emergency department to what would amount to a little hospital inside a hospital…it's not what I'd expected. That's all."

"Your duties would be different."

"My duties?"

"As head nurse in the region's major trauma unit." He grinned. "Sounds like Julie Clark kind of responsibilities to me."

"Except I'm just out of school. Not experienced enough to manage something so…comprehensive."

"Sure you are. You have more trauma experience than most. And your management skills… Wait. You don't think you're getting pushed aside, do you, Julie?"

She laughed nervously. "I don't know what I'm getting, Jess. With you, it's up and down, something different every minute."

"It's still all yours. A blank canvas to do with as you see fit. That hasn't changed."

"Hasn't it? Because it seems like everything has changed."

"In scope maybe. But not in intent. And you're part of the intent, Julie."

For sure, it was a lot to think about. She was flattered, though. And honored Jess had all that trust in her. More than anything else right now she was nervous, thinking about his expectations, because he was trusting her more than anybody else ever had. No sane hospital administrator or owner would ever hire someone as inexperienced in trauma as she was to run what she believed Jess was about to create. Sure, a small emergency room was one thing. But this whole expansion to a major trauma unit?

"Shall I get cooking?" she asked.

"Don't worry about that, I have frozen dinners. How about I pop them in the microwave while you sit here at the computer, look at my notes and add your initial thoughts to them?"

"Are we still doing this together, Jess? The expansion?"

"Can you stand me long enough to do it?"

Pushed aside, not pushed aside…she wasn't sure which one caused the largest upheaval in her vacillating emotions. "How about I scrounge up a proper meal in the kitchen while I think about it, and we'll brainstorm ideas afterward if I decide to do it?"

"I never mean to hurt you, Julie."

"I know that." She did, too. But why did it always turn out that way? That was the question she pondered, along with her food prep, for the thirty minutes it took her to put a decent meal on the table. Chicken, vegetables, rice… emotions out of control. A few hopes creeping in. Hopes clouded by so much guilt.

"I didn't know you could cook," Jess said after his first bite. "It's good."

"Just stir-fry. I'm not exactly a domestic goddess, and I think anybody could do this." She stirred through the food on her plate, but didn't lift a bite to her mouth. "Look, Jess.

I really need to get going. This was a bad idea...doing dinner."

"Doing it right now, or doing it ever?" He reached across the table and squeezed her hand. "We should have been smarter back then, Julie. Both of us. But we weren't, and that's making right now awkward."

"Well, we can't change the past, can we? And for what it's worth, you had a right to hate me. I hated myself for a long time afterward."

"Because you thought you were pregnant?" He shook his head. "You were honest. You told me you weren't. And the last time I counted, there were two of us involved in all that, Julie. So I didn't hate you, couldn't hate you. But my old man..."

"I saw what he did, Jess. Saw what he did to your horse because of me. I was there that day, and I felt so bad because I'd known for a couple weeks that my pregnancy was a false alarm. But I was still wrapped up in some stupid fantasy. Then after I saw him kill Storm, and watched you take the shovel to him, I realized that if I'd told you sooner he wouldn't have killed Storm and you wouldn't have come so close to killing..." She drew in a quivering breath. "I'm so sorry for that, Jess. I was so wrapped up in my own little world, it never occurred to me that something like that could happen. And maybe, in some small way, what you said was true. Maybe I was trying to think of a way I could trap you. Not that I would have, in the end. But I did wonder what would happen if I simply didn't tell you I wasn't pregnant. But then after your father..."

She swallowed back a lump in her throat. "I understood why you left, Jess. I deserved it, probably even caused it, and I deserved everything you said." She pulled her hand from his and pushed herself back from the table. "I had

nightmares for months. And I was so afraid that if Grace knew I was the reason you left she'd want me gone."

"We were kids. Kids do, and say, dumb things."

"But that's not an excuse. Look what happened because of me. You loved that horse, Jess. I saw your pain, pain that you had to go through because of me."

"Because of my old man, Julie. He's the one who killed Storm, not you."

She shook her head. "It was my fault he got to that place." She swiped away a tear sliding down her cheek. "And I'm so sorry. Can you ever forgive me?"

"There's nothing to forgive."

"How can you say that, Jess? You're a mess, I'm a mess. I'm walking on eggshells because I don't want to…"

"What, Julie? You don't want to what?"

"Make the same mistake twice. I like this new life. Love it. So I have to know that if we do work together on this project, this life I love isn't going to be taken away from me because of our…history. We're crazy right now. Both of us. And that kiss…it just opened too many old wounds. I can't do that. Won't do that."

He raised an eyebrow. "Well, I've got to give you credit for one thing. You're honest."

"I have to be, Jess. Look what we've done to each other in the past."

"In the *past*," he reminded her.

"But the past is going to repeat itself if we're not careful. *And you know that!* Look at the circles we're going in, you confused over Donna, me confused over you. That's how it started the first time, both of us confused over so many things in our lives. So you can't kiss me again, Jess. Can't do…anything. Or I'll leave Lilly Lake. That's my decision." Brave words. Truth was, close proximity to Jess

scared her to death, no matter how brave she sounded. This was where it had to truly end for them.

So, she did leave. Carried her plate to the kitchen and continued walking straight out the door, feeling sad for all the things that never had never been. Not angry. Not even hurt. Just very, very sad. But so was Jess. And there really was no going back for them. No going forward either, except as friends, colleagues and partners in hospital business. She and Jess, though...they would have made beautiful babies together. Unfortunately, life had moved on, and they'd both been swept away to other places.

Still, for a moment, she could almost see herself with a baby in her arms. Their baby. Almost...

CHAPTER EIGHT

LIKE the old saying went, the night wasn't fit for man or beast. Only tonight it had started in a deluge, one predicted as slight showers, then had gone horribly wrong after that. Jess stood at the front door, filling up the frame with his broad shoulders, watching her debate whether or not to make a run for it or simply tuck herself away on the porch swing and wait it out. "You're really not going out in that?" he asked, when it became apparent that was her decision.

"It's just water. I'll get wet, I'll dry." Truth was, she really didn't relish the idea of going out there. But given the choice between that storm and the storm she felt around Jess, the lightning and thunderstorm seemed the better option. "Not a big deal."

"If the road washes out, it will be," he warned, keeping his distance.

"Look, I'll be fine, Jess. Besides, I'm not going straight home anyway. I need to stop by the stables and see how the horses are doing before I leave. We've got a few in there who are going to spook pretty badly in the storm, and someone needs to make sure they're doing okay. You know, get them settled in, calmed down."

"Let Johnny take care of them."

"He's at his daughter's this evening. Over in Jasper. He just texted me to see if I could get by and look after the

horses, and I said I would." Actually, she'd texted him and volunteered. It was her quickest way out of the cabin, and away from Jess. Being anywhere near him confused her, and she needed to keep a clear head.

"Well, if you have to go to the horses, then I'm going with you."

She pointed to his foot. "With that? I don't think so."

He held up his cane. "With this."

"No! I can't let you do that, Jess. First off, Rafe would kill me. He ordered you off that foot for a few days, and even though you seem to be getting along fine, I'm not going against his orders. Second, I don't need your help out there. I'm just going to have a look at a few skittish horses and calm them down if they need it. And if the storm gets any worse than it already is, I'll spend the night in the stables. I'll be fine. You don't have to worry about me." She walked over to the edge of the steps, then looked back at him. "One thing I've learned over the years is how to take care of myself. Started doing it when I was young, and haven't stopped. And I'm good at it, Jess. Better than most. Even in the rain." *And through the tears she wanted to hide in the rain.* With that, she stepped off the porch and started to run to her car. But halfway there, she heard Jess shouting at her. So she looked back, only to find him making his way in her direction…limping, dodging ruts, using his cane as a feeler.

"Jess, stop it! Go back!" she shouted at him as a clap of nearby thunder literally shook the ground underneath her. "I told you I don't want you coming with me!"

But he wouldn't do it. Wouldn't turn around. Which was exactly what she expected from him…that stubborn, pig-headed… "Jess!" she shouted again, when she noticed he was picking up his pace. She could outrun him, get to her car, get in and drive to the stables. And leave him

standing there. But Jess was obstinate enough to walk that half-mile, which distressed her more than it frustrated her. Damn him, anyway. He knew he shouldn't be doing this! Yet here he was, the quintessential Jess Corbett, on the path to another huge risk. "Why can't you listen to anybody?" she shouted at him. "You do these stupid things, take all these risks... Jess, it's crazy."

His answer was to pause for a moment, then shrug. "Someone has to."

"No, they don't, Jess! That's just it. Putting yourself at risk unnecessarily doesn't help anybody. It makes them worry...makes *me* worry. And if people are worrying about you, how can you expect them to do the things they need to do? Like Rafe? He's in emergency surgery right now. What if he knew that you're out here, getting ready to do God only knows what? How's that going to affect him in surgery, if he has to worry about you?"

"But he doesn't *have* to worry about me."

"If that's what you think, then you're just being blind. Of course he has to worry about you. So does Edie, and Molly. So do I. It goes with the territory...you know, family and friends. That's what it's about, Jess, whether or not you want to admit it. You are part of this little Gracie circle of people, so that concern is going to come right at you! And because of that, you've got to take your actions into consideration and realize how they affect other people. I mean, what you're doing right now...it's stupid, considering your condition."

"Maybe it is, but those are my horses out there," he shouted back over the noise of the thunder rumbling in closer by the minute. "And there's nothing wrong with me. There wasn't when I was given a two-week *time-out* to rest, and there wasn't when Rafe taped up my foot. I'm

fine." He reared back and threw his cane as far as the eye could see, considering the weather conditions. "Just fine."

"Why are you doing this, Jess? Not just coming out in the storm this way, but everything? Why are you doing what you do? Is it because you feel guilty? Survivor's guilt, maybe? Donna died, you didn't? Because if that's the case..."

"You're right, I feel guilty about Donna, in ways nobody would ever understand. Or maybe they would if they know me. You know, Jess Corbett being true to his nature, not bending an inch. Not even for the woman he loves. Well, I don't need counseling because of it. And I sure don't need everybody who's supposed to care about me standing off on the sidelines, looking concerned and trying to get me to change the error of my ways. I do what I want to do, because..." He shrugged. "You know what, Julie? I don't know why. Okay? I honestly don't know why. Maybe it's just who I am, who I always was. Don't know, don't care. But what I do know is that instead of everybody trying to change me, they ought to just accept me for what I am and what I do. Life comes with risks and mine just seem... bigger. I'm not irresponsible, I don't have a death wish. I just...react. And I accept that in me." He swiped the rain off his face. "The one thing I'll do, though, is consider the people who care for me, and try to temper some of my re-actions to make them—*you*—feel easier."

She scrambled after his cane, then brought it back to him. Had Donna been at odds with him over his actions? Because what she sensed coming from Jess wasn't survi-vor's guilt so much as something much deeper. Something much more paralyzing. "I think that's all anybody has ever wanted, Jess. Not to change you but to make you realize that they—*we*—are part of who you are and what you do.

You don't do these things alone. We do them with you. Just recognize that."

His expression softened. "You know we're better than friends, don't you?"

"I don't know what we are, Jess."

"When you included yourself in that circle of concern for Jess Corbett, you knew."

She wouldn't dispute him on that. She'd always known who they were, and that was the problem. "Just think about the people who care. That's all I'm asking. That, and would you please just go back to the cabin and let me handle the horses?"

He chuckled. "You know, I really like the way you can take a simple conversation and turn it around without missing a beat. The thing is, you're quick to point out just how stubborn I am, but you've got a good case of it going yourself. And you do need help, Julie! Even though you won't admit it, even hate to admit it...you've always been like that, by the way... Anyway, you may be able to take care of *yourself* without any help, but you can't take care of those horses by yourself. Not in this storm!"

She hated that he knew her so well. At the same time, though, she liked it. It was to no avail, of course. Their time had come and gone, and it wasn't going to get a replay. Yet knowing that he could anticipate her like he did gave her back a little bit of the sixteen-year-old girl who'd loved falling head over heels in love with Jess. "There's nothing I can say to change your mind?"

"Like I said, you're not doing this alone. Not tonight, not under these conditions. I'm not walking away from you this time, Julie."

I'm not walking away from you this time... She wasn't exactly sure how to take his words, and for most of the short ride down to the stables she tried not thinking about

them, tried not to attach any particular significance or interpretation. But each time she allowed them to float through her thoughts, her skin prickled, and her stomach churned. Because she knew what she wanted him to mean, and it was the same thing she didn't want him to mean.

But it had been her choice to come back to Lilly Lake. The thing was, she'd known what could happen, and she'd come anyway. That's probably what confused her more than anything. She'd walked right into it, then fought it every step of the way. But what was she really fighting? At this point, she didn't know.

"I think the storm's getting worse," Jess commented as they rounded the last bend before Gracie Stables, then stopped.

"Look, Jess. I'm going over to the main stable. I need to see what condition the horses are in there, then I'll take a look at what's going on in the other stable. Since you're going to work no matter what anybody says, would you see what's going on in here?" She referred to the smallest of the three stables where the younger horses were generally kept. "You know, figure out which ones need the most help? We've got a couple of babies in there, and I haven't been around long enough to know how they're going to do in this storm."

Jess swung himself out of the car, and stood there for a moment, simply looking at her, looking like he wanted to say something. But he didn't. Instead, he nodded a loose acquiescence then walked away without a word.

But what was there to say? He still loved Donna. Maybe somewhere in all those conflicting emotions, they could salvage a friendship. Maybe they couldn't. And right now she just didn't have time to think about it.

"We didn't get them all in," one of the volunteers shouted from the far end of the stable. He was a young

boy, not quite twenty. Wiry, but slight. And bent on a career in equine medicine. Bobby Lee Bright. "Storm came out of nowhere, and we were trying to get them all stabled, but we got caught off guard."

Now her nerves were on edge. Having horses out in a storm like this, especially horses in the delicate condition so many of them were, wasn't good. "How many?"

"Fifteen. One I'm particularly worried about. We couldn't get her rounded up, and she's totally spooked... she's coal black, no name yet."

She knew exactly which one. Poor thing had come in with lesions on her hindquarters and maggot-infected open sores on her front legs. Malnourished. Wobbly on her feet. And so sweet and loving with just the smallest amount of attention. Thinking about that horse scared to death out in the storm... Nothing else mattered. She had to get that horse in. "Who else do we have here to help us get them back?"

Bobby Lee came running up to her, out of breath. "Just Summer Adair. She's over in the pasture right now, trying to get the horses into the corral there. I did call a couple other people who are on their way, but right now it's just the two of us...three, including you."

Four, including Jess, who wasn't going to be counted out of this even though, in her opinion, he should be. "Okay, I'm going over to the pasture to see what I can do. You stay here, make sure everything's locked down tight, see if you can get a couple more people out here to help, because we're going to need to brush these horses down. Oh, and if you think we've got any horses that need medical attention, call the vet." She thought about Jess, and having him at her side right now would have been nice. "I'm going to stop at the small stable on the way over to the pasture, so

radio Summer and tell her I'll be over there in a few minutes."

"You okay?" she called to Jess once she got to the smallest stable. He was making his way down the stable row, looking into each and every stall.

"I'm okay, but I've got a couple who are pretty badly spooked. I called Doc Halliday to come and sedate them or do whatever he thinks will get them through the storm the best way, so he'll be out here in a little while. How's everything else? All squared away?"

"No, it's not, Jess. We've got a problem...fifteen horses loose over on the pasture. Summer's trying to round up as many as she can and get them into the corral so we can bring them back across. One of the horses is critical, though, which worries me because she might bolt. So I'm on my way over there now. Got Bobby Lee in the large stable, taking care of things, and a couple people on their way in." She looked at the filly that was nuzzling Jess from behind. A spirited chestnut. "Do you have a horse of your own now?" she asked, as she started to gather up the equipment she needed...flashlight, rope, boots.

"Haven't had one of my own since Storm." Pulling a yellow rain slicker off a hook by the door, he shook his head. "I just ride whichever one Johnny tells me to take out."

The chestnut, a real looker with huge, soulful eyes and a very strong personality, nudged Jess forward so hard he stumbled right into Julie. Maybe it was time for Jess to change that, for him to make that particular break from his past. One step forward... "Well," she said, moving away from him enough to let him help her into the slicker, "I think you're being chosen."

He glanced back at the horse, then chuckled. "If that's

the case, I think you should know that the one doing the choosing is named Julie."

Was that a double entendre, or did he simply mean the horse? "Her name's Julie? Did you just make that up?"

"Her name is Julie. Swear, that's what Molly called her." He pointed to Julie's hair just before she pulled a rain hat down over it. "Red hair color, and all. Molly said the chestnut reminds her of you, hence the name." He shrugged, smiled. "So you think Julie's choosing me?"

"I think the horse is choosing you."

"Only the horse?"

Now she was flustered. Didn't know how to respond even if she could have gotten the words out of her mouth. "Look, when I have time, I'll stop by the house and thank Molly for naming the horse after me. In the meantime…"

"In the meantime, just relax, Julie. Okay? We've got some things to figure out, but later."

Things, like his feelings for Donna? Or how he'd said he didn't want to do that again? Too many things, as far as she was concerned. Too many big things that could otherwise be defined as obstacles. All that going against her feelings… And he thought she could relax? "The only thing we have to figure out is how to get those horses back over here as quickly as possible."

Jess handed her a radio as she brushed past him on her way out the door. "You don't need to be the one going out there by yourself to get those horses."

She shrugged it off. Actually felt pleased he was concerned for her. Felt anxious, too, just to get away from him. "It's not a big deal. And it's probably easier than what you're going to have to do to dry the horses once we get them back over here. I'm worried about pneumonia, since a few of those horses aren't in the best physical condition.

Until Doc Halliday gets here, you're the one who'll have to take care of that."

"And I'm worried about you," he said, grabbing her by the yellow lapels and pulling her over to him. "This would be the place where I'd kiss you...a nice, circumspect kiss on the forehead. But I won't. I want you to know that's what I'd be doing right about now, though."

"Isn't telling me you'd be kissing me pretty much the same thing as kissing me?" she asked, feeling even more flustered.

"Trust me, telling and doing are two different things altogether."

Hiding her confusion, she pushed him back. "Save it for the *other* Julie, okay?" Then, before he had a chance to respond, a chance to break down her barriers yet again, she turned and ran to the paddock across the road, never once slowing down, never once looking back. Even though she could feel him watching her.

"She's pulled up lame," Summer called from across the corral once Julie got over there. She was referring to a filly called Fancy, named for the number of pretty markings on her, all of them different. "Got spooked and jumped the corral. I think it might be a bowed tendon. She was already back at the knee to begin with, so it makes sense." Back at the knee referred to an equine condition where the horse's knee was offset so as to let the knee hyper-extend or bend backward.

Julie stopped, looked at the filly, who was standing off a way, looking at her. "Jess is in the front stable, and he's expecting the doc any time. See if you can take Fancy in there before she hurts herself any more."

"I'm not sure you should be over here by yourself. I mean, I know you're one of the foundation volunteers, but..."

Julie held up her hand to stop her. "I grew up here. Lived in Gracie House, know my way around a horse."

Summer laughed. "You're *that* Julie? Grace mentioned your name, but I never made the connection."

"I'm *that* Julie."

"Then I turn the literal reins over to you. And I'll send someone back to help you as soon as I have someone to send." With that, she spun away, and started to make her very slow way over to Fancy, who seemed to back away with every movement Summer made.

Julie watched for a moment, then turned into the wind and pushed through it to get to the other side of the corral where several of the horses were standing together in a clump. Every step of the way, advancing three steps forward and getting blown one step back, she thought about how Jess's physical strength would have been a huge help right now. Help she would have loved. But his moral support was what she needed most. The kind of strength that would brace her in more ways than physically. Important ways.

However, she could still envision the look in his eyes when he'd stared at Donna's photograph...a look that had betrayed his true heart. It wasn't anything she could compete against. Nothing she wanted to either.

"Doc's going to stay in the stable," Jess yelled, coming up behind her. Like Julie, he was dressed in a yellow rain slicker, with a rain hat pulled low over his face. Looking like he was ready to be out in the pasture, he wore mud boots and carried a flashlight in one hand, with a rope coiled around his shoulder.

"You can't be out here. Your foot..."

"This is what I do," he said, catching up to her. "I rescue. And my foot's fine enough."

"Jess, we've still got fourteen horses to lead out of the

pasture. Fourteen, after Summer gets hold of one we've got hurt. That's a lot of work…"

"Seven for you, seven for me," he said, actually going ahead of her by several steps. Then he stopped, turned back and held out his hand for her. "Are you with me?"

"I'm with you," she said, taking hold of his hand. "But, Jess Corbett, if you so much as grimace or wince, I'm going to tie that rope around you and drag you back to the stables myself. Understood?"

She was so cute when she was taking charge. "Understood." Somewhere close by, a bolt of lightning split the sky, followed by an almost immediate boom of thunder, which caused one of the horses to spook and sail over the pasture corral fence, then head straight down the road. The horse was running in blind fear, and the outcome wouldn't be good for it if they didn't get it back. Soon. He knew that, and from the expression he saw on Julie's face, she knew it, too. But they had other horses… "We'll get him later," he promised, coming up on the fence, still holding onto Julie's hand.

"Her. It's a filly. Came to us in bad shape…parasites, pronounced muscle weakness, eye infection. Hope you're right, that she'll come back. We haven't had her too long, 'though I think she oriented to the pasture pretty well. But in a storm like this…"

A storm like this was always the question, wasn't it? He hoped the filly would come back, but in reality he feared that was just wishful thinking. On a night like this, a spooked horse could run for hours. Exhaust itself. And a horse that wasn't in good shape to start with…well, he wasn't about to say or suggest anything negative to discourage Julie. She wore her heart on her sleeve for these animals, and he knew just how much that heart caused her to want to run down the road after that horse. So if think-

ing that the horse would come back on its own made her feel better, that's what he wanted her to think.

Another crash of the thunder sent three of the horses to charging the corral fence, but before they could injure themselves, Julie hopped over and literally waved them back into the center of the area. Arms flapping, she ran directly toward them, shouting at the tops of her lungs. "Back! Get back!" she yelled, running in a zig-zag pattern to make sure she was being seen by the horses. Jess, on the other hand, entered the corral through the gate and immediately lassoed the largest of the three panicked horses, then started to pull him back toward the gate.

"Good rope skills," Rick Navarro called from out of nowhere. "Rafe's still tied up in surgery, so I thought I might be of some use out here."

"Thanks," Jess said. "Don't get to use them much lately. Nice to know I can still hold my own, bad foot and all. Look, Rick…"

Rick held up his hand to stop him. "As far as I'm concerned, we're good. Okay? The past is the past, and we've all made our share of dumb mistakes."

"Some dumber than others."

Rick chuckled. "You're right about that."

"At least let me say the words. Maybe you don't need to hear them, but I need to say them. And I'm sorry. All the things I said, all the things I did… We bullied you and you didn't deserve that. No excuses. What we did was wrong. Rafe and I…we both have a lot of regrets but I want you to know that you're one hell of a hospital chief of staff, and I consider myself fortunate that you've decided to stay with us in spite of how Rafe and I treated you."

"We all grow up," Rick commented, extending a hand to Jess. "And learn from our mistakes."

"And learn from our mistakes," Jess repeated, taking

Rick's hand. "Some of us with more mistakes than others. So, how about we see what we can do to get some of these horses back across to the stable? Since I'm not so fast on my feet right now, Julie and I can round them up here and you can lead them back across."

"That I can do. But there's going to be a cost involved," Rick replied, as one particularly rambunctious stallion caught his eye. The horse was literally scoping out the fence, getting ready to charge and keeping an eye on Rick at the same time.

"Whatever you want. Name it."

"A horse for me…maybe that wild-eyed chestnut over there." He pointed to the horse that was watching him, challenging him. "And a gentle one for my son."

"Small price to pay. Glad to do it," Jess said, slowly stepping away from Rick. "So let's see if we can get that chestnut right now. Okay?"

"Okay by me," Rick said, keeping himself in full view of the horse while Jess edged his way behind it and roped it, one attempt all slick and tidy, like he was a rodeo cowboy. Then handed the rope over to Rick.

Over the next little while, volunteers wandered in and, amazingly, all the horses were brought to safety within half an hour. Little by little, they were being dried, then checked by Doc Halliday. It was a sight to behold, Jess thought to himself as he stood back and watched the people show up and simply throw themselves into the work. Some were Gracie Foundation volunteers who worked regularly with the horses. Others were merely people who had responded to the call for help that had gone out from the hospital. People he knew, people he'd yet to meet. Rick was squarely in charge of the group, too, a natural leader without even trying. Jess liked the man, was glad they'd put aside differences. Rafe was right about him. Rick did

need to be brought in as their third partner. That's the least he could do. That, and a couple of horses.

Also, he could see why Rafe had decided to stay in Lilly Lake. Get away from the malignant memories of the old man, and it really wasn't such a bad place. Rafe was happy here now. But that was Rafe.

Could *he* be happy here, too? Because part of him really wanted to be. And part of him was scared to death of what he'd do with that happiness if he ever let it in. Which part, though, would win out if it came down to a battle? Because every time he looked at Julie, he felt the battle brewing.

CHAPTER NINE

IF ANYTHING, the weather was getting worse. The brute force of the storm seemed to have doubled, and what should have been a fairly easy walk down the private road separating the two properties—the Gracie property and the land where Jess and Rafe's family home had once stood—was anything but. In fact, each step was more labored than the one before, and it was all Julie could do to keep herself upright. If not for the fact that the wind blowing back against her was so hard, she'd have probably toppled straight over face-first in the mud. Thankfully, as the wind fought against her, it was also helping her stay upright. With great effort, though, as the wind's intent was clearly to knock her over.

Had Jess discovered her missing yet? She hoped not. He didn't need to be out in this, and he would have been trudging along with her, shoulder to shoulder, if he knew where she was. More than that, she didn't need him anywhere near her right now, as the more they were together, the more she wanted to stay near him. Like an addiction. That addiction, topped by a whole boatload of confused feelings…even some solitary time in the thick of the storm was a welcome relief as she needed to do so some substantial sorting out. But how did anybody even begin to sort something like this?

Of course, there was the possibility that she was simply stalling or putting off the inevitable, that this whole situation with him would never work. Or maybe she was just plain scared to read ahead to the ending. Definitely too many confused feelings to make sense of right now. On top of that whole mess, Jess had his own set of problems going. He was larger than life, a man who laid down his own terms and didn't sway after that...always had been like that. That's why she'd been so drawn to him when they'd been kids. She'd felt safe with him. Why she was still so drawn to him. He walked his journey the way the man of her dreams would, which had made him a tough act to follow after he'd walked away from her. Or, in her case, impossible to follow, hence the lack of boyfriends, man friends, male relationships in her life...another part of her mess. Nobody lived up to Jess. Nobody came close.

Truth be told, she liked that quirk in him that pushed him to the edge, that made him do what others didn't dare. It's what made him real. And exciting. And so attractive. It's also what scared her the most because she understood it, and to expect him to change that part of himself was to, in essence, diminish him, to make him less than he was. So those were feelings she had to deal with, too, which was why she needed time away from him where his mere presence wasn't influencing her. Even if it was time spent in what was being called the worst storm Lilly Lake, New York, had experienced in more than a decade.

So she'd ducked out, hopefully unnoticed, as everybody hurried to dry off the wet horses. Jess included in that. Naturally, by now she was hoping she'd have found the filly, affectionately called Fugitive, and be on her way back to Gracie Stables before anybody missed her. She was scared to death for that horse, wouldn't rest until...well, optimally, Fugitive was brought back safe. Unfortunately,

the farther she trailed on in this mess, the more discouraged she was getting. There were no signs of a horse coming this way, no tracks in the mud, no nothing. Not that she was able to see much at all. In addition, the beam from her flashlight was beginning to flicker, meaning low batteries, meaning no light in a matter of minutes. So she kept it shut off and fought her way on down the road, her discouragement as thick as the mud in which her boots were sticking.

Twenty minutes into her search, Julie squelched off the road to catch her breath. Her lungs and legs burned, she had a headache, her jaw hurt from clenching it so tight. And now she was beginning to wonder if she should give up the search and try again in the morning, after the storm had passed through and daylight would definitely be on her side. It was a plausible idea, even a good one. But every time she thought about that sweet horse out in this, lost, scared… Somebody'd rescued *her* once, when she'd been out there lost and scared in a so-called storm of her own making, and that's the thought that carried Julie right back up to the road to continue on. Except this time, before she even pushed herself forward into the storm's wall, something caught her attention. A light in the distance? Someone coming up the road behind her? Or maybe just the reflection of some distant lightning?

Julie stopped, looked. Sure enough, it *was* a light, and she knew whose. He was in a truck, catching her in the headlights. Slowing down once her image was framed in the beam, thereupon coming to a complete stop just a few yards away from her. "You're driving?" she yelled at Jess over the din of storm sounds. "You know Rafe told you not to."

Jess opened the truck door, then stepped out, grinned

his notoriously engaging grin and put on an exaggerated shrug. "You thought I'd actually listen to him?"

Of course she didn't. If he had listened, he wouldn't be the Jess Corbett she...

"I thought you'd exercise some common sense," she replied before that thought took shape, approaching him.

"And *what* about bringing the horse trailer out to get a missing horse isn't common sense?"

She stepped directly into him, directly to a place where their faces were mere inches apart. "The part where you're driving." Then she spun away and headed to the driver's side door.

He followed, smiling a smile she couldn't see. A different smile from his usual grin. A smile of insight. "Been doing it since I was ten or eleven. Or, for the sake of being legal, sixteen. So you're right. I'm driving. And you wouldn't have it any other way, would you, Julie? Let me rephrase that. Reverse our situations, where you're the one with the bad foot and I'm the one wandering around out here, looking for the horse. Would you have driven out with the trailer, against doctor's orders, to help me?"

She turned to face him, at once blocking him from getting near the driver's door. Sure, it was a test of wills. She knew that. But she also knew that someone had to set Jess straight, here and now. He was injured, and the nurse in her would have done no less for any other patient. Of course, the nurse in her wouldn't be having the sexy thoughts she was having for Jess. Admittedly, the sparring between them always was sexy, even in the middle of a horrendous storm. "Your point being?"

"One point, one fact. We're alike."

Well, she hadn't expected that. Didn't exactly want it, since alikes didn't attract. "If we are, then it's a good thing *opposites* attract," she snapped back, disappointed that he

saw them being alike. Climbing up into the truck cab, she mulled over the reality. Opposite, alike... The thing was, they probably were alike. Grudgingly, she recognized it, wondered about it. Even worried that if opposites did attract, what could two alikes find for themselves, provided they ever got to the place they wanted to find something for themselves, long shot that it was? "So, are you getting in?" she yelled, more out of frustration than trying to be heard. "Or are you going to stand out here on the road and wait for me to come back for you later on?"

His grin reappeared. "You'd leave me here alone?"

"Yeah, I'd leave you here alone because I have a horse to find. My priority, Jess. My only priority." She slammed shut the truck door and rolled down the window. "You're slowing me up."

Jess chuckled. "Somehow, Julie, I don't think anything in life has ever slowed you up if you didn't want it to." Rather than going around to the passenger's side, though, he opened the driver's side door and swung himself up, effectively pushing Julie across the bench seat. "And before you say it, I'm fine to drive. Foot doesn't hurt...much."

"Doesn't hurt *much?*" she sputtered, wondering if she wanted to get out altogether or stay pressed up to him, where it felt so good. Pleasant memories were flooding back...the hard crush of his body to hers, the way her own body practically betrayed her every time Jess touched her. She was older now, but she felt that same sway of betrayal, even through several layers of soaking-wet clothes and two yellow rain slickers. Which made exiting the cab, *immediately,* the only sensible thing to do. Except nothing inside her was able to push her toward the passenger's door. Not one single scrap of willpower to be found in that truck .

"Didn't we already have this argument?" he asked. "You know. The one where you point out something that's for

my own good and as much as I appreciate it, I'm too stubborn to take your suggestion."

His head was turned so that she couldn't clearly see the grin on his face, but she could sure feel it burning a hole in her countenance. Feel it chipping away her defenses. "Apparently we didn't have it all the way to its logical end."

He laughed outright at that. "You mean not all the way to the end you want? And you call me stubborn?"

"I'm not stubborn so much as…"

"Inflexible?" he volunteered.

"Practical," she corrected. "You're injured, I want to drive because of that. That's being practical, Jess. So, is it that you don't trust my driving? Is that what this is about? Because I drove an ambulance in my early days as a medic. I can probably out-drive you on your best day, and the proof is in the lack of me having an injured foot and you having one because of a moment of bad driving." She sat back, crossed her arms over her chest in the self-satisfaction that she'd won this round, then tossed him a *bet-you-can't-top-that* grin. "Next argument?"

But he did top that, in a seriously provocative voice and an argument that couldn't be won. "What I don't trust, Julie, is me looking for the horse…not with something much nicer to watch sitting right next to me, distracting me. Which you will." Well, apparently, those were the words for which she didn't have a comeback. Words that were actually tingling all the way to her toes. Because Julie simply didn't respond. Couldn't respond.

"What? Nothing to say?" he teased. "Did I finally manage to say something for which you don't have a reply?"

"Oh, I have a reply," she lied, balling her trembling fists. Everything was trembling, arms, legs, lips…her heart. This was getting so dangerously close to being real, and she was surprised to find how unprepared she was for what

she wanted. "Which will have to wait because we need to be concentrating on the rescue,"

"I'm a patient man, Julie. Willing to wait as long as I have to." He glanced into his rear-view mirror in preparation to pull onto the road, and saw what appeared to be a large flashlight beam coming down the road. "I think that's probably Bobby Lee," he said after several seconds. "He's really worried about the horse. I told him to stay back, but he's stubborn, like the rest of us."

Julie leaned across and opened the passenger's side door for the boy, who was out of breath as he climbed in next to her.

"They spotted Fugitive about half an hour ago," he said, gasping. "She went right up to the front of Brassard's Pub, looked in the window like she wanted in."

Julie heaved a sigh of relief. "Then she's okay?"

"Yes and no. Several of the people ran outside to get her, and she spooked. Took off running in the direction of Sutter's Creek. Running fast, is what Will said. He chased her down on his motorcycle for a little way, but it was too muddy to go far, too dangerous. He'd heard we lost one, so he figured the filly was one of ours. Anyway, when he got to that big turn in the road, down by Trace Hollow, Fugitive took the path...the dirt path. Will decided not to go on because it's washing out in the storm. So he called."

"But it hasn't been that long," Julie said, trying to sound hopeful, even though she wasn't. "So we'll probably catch up with her, maybe where the path joins with the road again on the far side." A tediously long, dangerous trek.

"Or she'll head straight through the woods," Jess said. "Which means we won't be able to do much until morning."

"I'm not giving up," Julie said, her stubborn streak clearly showing.

"And I didn't say we would. But we have to be...what was the word you used a few minutes ago? Practical? We have to be *practical* about this." He reached over and squeezed her knee. "I want to get her back as much as you do, Julie. But I'm not going to let you risk hurting yourself to do it."

"So we give it another hour," she said.

"Then come back tomorrow if we don't get her," Jess added. "Come back *together*."

"But if we're going to give this another hour tonight, why don't you two drive back to the turn in the road?" Bobby Lee suggested. "Hopefully Fugitive hasn't strayed too far off that. In case she has, though, I'm going to take the shortcut on foot. She might double back to Brassard's, since she already knows that trail, and if she does, I can get her. So, one hour. If we haven't found her by then, we'll come back out at first light, with more people."

Julie looked out the truck windshield at what seemed to be yet another storm front brewing. "It's getting worse again. I think you should skip the shortcut and ride with us, Bobby Lee."

He shook his head. "That's wasting time. And I'll be fine. I've taken that shortcut hundreds of times. No big deal." He clicked the handle of the truck door to open it. "See you at the turn."

In a way, he reminded her of Jess. Brave, stubborn... Nice catch for some girl someday. "Before you go, tell me why didn't you call us, instead of running down the road after us?" She held up her cell phone.

Bobby Lee grinned sheepishly. "Had to make a choice... new textbook or cell phone bill." Then he shrugged. "Grace was sort of helping me with the school expenses...she wanted me to come back to Lilly Lake as a vet and take care of her horses when I graduate. But after she died..."

Julie pressed her phone into his hand. "Take it. You can't be out there in this storm without being able to call in case…in case you find the horse before we do."

Bobby Lee tucked the phone into his pocket. "See you in a while."

After Bobby Lee was gone, and she and Jess were on the road for Sutter's Creek, Julie still sitting pressed to Jess's side, she asked, "Does anybody even know how many people Grace helped over the years, or was helping when she died?"

"Not sure. I suppose if anybody knows, it would be Henry Danforth."

"He was her lawyer, wasn't he?"

"And confidant."

"Do you think he'd tell us?"

"Does it matter?" Jess asked. "Aunt Grace wasn't after any recognition, which is why she didn't want people knowing what she did. She was always afraid the city might erect some kind of statue in her honor…" He laughed. "She called it a pigeon roost. Said she didn't want to see herself immortalized with pigeons pooping all over her head."

Julie conjured up that image, and laughed at it. Yes, that was definitely what Grace Corbett would have said. "You're a lot like her, Jess. Did anybody ever tell you that?"

He shook his head. "No, I'm not. Not even close."

"Sure, you are. When Grace saw the need, she helped. The way you do. For her, it wasn't for the glory. It's just who she was, something she had to do. And it's who you are, too. Grace rushed in, you rush in. And you both save lives. Sure, in different ways. But it's the same thing. In fact, right now you're thinking about helping Bobby Lee, thinking about picking up where your aunt left off in getting him through veterinary school. Aren't you?"

"He's a good kid. He deserves a break…and a cell phone. And, yes, I'd like to see him be able to come back here and look after the horses. So why not help him? Aunt Grace thought he deserved it, and she was the best judge of character I ever knew. Maybe a little financial aid to make things easier for him and, when the time comes, some mentoring on the finer points of running Gracie Foundation. He'd be a natural for the job."

"And you'd be a natural helping Bobby Lee." Impulsively, she twisted in Jess's direction and kissed him on the cheek.

"What was that? A kiss?"

"An *exception* kiss."

"So those are allowed? I must have missed that part in the rule book."

"You can make light of it if you want, but she'd be proud of you, Jess. You're going to do a very nice thing for Bobby Lee."

"But she wasn't proud of me," he said, tapping on the high beams as the truck moved forward. "Not since I came home from Afghanistan and decided not to be a doctor. I think that broke her heart."

"You know that for sure?"

"She kept telling me I was wasting my talent, not taking advantage of the things I had in life. That I had more to give. That I was underestimating myself, or maybe she meant underplaying myself. I don't know which, and I never asked because I was just so…" He gripped the steering-wheel tighter.

"Angry?" she asked.

"That, and a whole lot of other things."

"You loved Donna. Losing her the way you did…"

He shook his head. "That wasn't what caused the changes in me. I couldn't save her. With all my medical

training, in the end there wasn't anything I could do except hold her. She'd been shot...sniper fire." Slowing the truck, he pulled off to the side of the road, and sat there, listening to the squeak of the windshield wipers, watching the drops on the windshield be wiped away, yet trying to look through them before they were.

"It was never enough for me, Julie," he finally said. "No matter what I did, it was never enough. I always had this feeling inside me that there had to be more. And I don't mean it had anything to do with the guilt my old man heaped on me year after year. You don't get impervious to it, but you do get used to it. Then there was Aunt Grace who always...*always* told me he was wrong. The hell of it is, Rafe and I both went on to be doctors. I'm sure the psychiatric community as a whole would have something interesting to say about that, considering that's what the old man was, and I sure don't know how Rafe accounts for his choice...we never talked about it. But for me, I figured going into medicine was my way of showing myself that I was better than my old man, that I could do better than he did. I still had this...this emptiness, though. Couldn't shake it, didn't know how.

"The thing is, when I was in Afghanistan, that's when I started to feel like I was...suffocating. That I wasn't doing enough. Then I met Donna and we clicked. It was fast, and pretty intense. Good chemistry, I suppose you could say. Then one day I woke up engaged to be married and everything changed. I was getting a new life. I was getting...everything. Truth was, I was happy for a couple of months. Donna was making plans...plans for things I honestly didn't know could ever happen in married life or a family situation. Aunt Grace was the closest thing I had to a mother, and she wasn't exactly the type to put on

an apron and make brownies. But that's what Donna was turning into before my eyes."

"And it scared you?"

Jess shook his head. "It didn't scare me so much as it... crowded me. Somehow, I'd pictured an entirely different kind of life. One that wasn't so...involved. Or maybe just involved in a different way."

"How would that have worked, Jess?"

"Beats the hell out of me. But the more I thought about it, the more I came to understand something in myself. I couldn't be in a marriage, couldn't survive in a marriage with Donna. I loved her, but not the way she needed to be loved, and there wasn't a damn thing I could do to change that."

"So maybe you could have avoided the marriage certificate and just gone with the committed relationship. It works for a lot of people."

"Maybe, but the thing is, it was the commitment part I didn't want. All I could think of was coming home every day at five o'clock, settling in to a nice little dinner and an evening of television with Donna. That was her vision, but it couldn't be mine. It wasn't enough."

"Not even if you had children."

"Not even with children. And it's my lack, Julie. Wasn't Donna's. She knew who she was, knew what she wanted. I didn't."

"How did Donna react to all that when you told her?"

"She didn't react, because I never got around to telling her how I was feeling."

"You mean she died..." Julie bit off her words. "Oh, Jess. I'm so sorry you didn't get it resolved with her."

"That's it. I did, but not the way I should have." He shut his eyes, drew in a deep breath and leaned his head back against the truck seat. "I started pulling away from her

weeks before she died. Nothing drastic. The first thing she noticed was that I stopped helping with wedding plans. Then I quit talking about our future. Didn't get involved in the house plans she was sketching. And every time she asked what was wrong, I told her it was just battlefield fatigue, that I was stressed out. See, I wanted to run, but this was the one instance in my life where there was nowhere to run. So I suppose I was hoping for some kind of miracle to drop down on me and make everything all better. But it didn't. I kept pulling further and further away, and it just got worse. Coward that I am, I was thinking that she'd get tired of our relationship, and of me, and break it off."

"You're not a coward, Jess. I think you just didn't want to hurt her."

"That's true. I didn't. The thing is, Donna really did make my life better. I could see it, Julie! I could feel it. But it wasn't…wasn't enough for me. Or maybe I wasn't enough for it. I don't know."

"Maybe you were just being too hard on yourself."

"The way the old man was always hard on me?" He shook his head. "I don't think so. Because I kept feeling this…this huge void inside me, even when Donna was making me feel better."

"But you lived a tough life with him, Jess. Nothing was ever normal for you, and maybe that's what scared you about Donna—she was offering you a normal life for the first time in your life."

"I'm not sure I ever believed I was worthy of it, or even wanted to be worthy of it." He turned to face Julie. "After she died, I overcompensated for that. I know it. In fact, I *know* that every time I do something someone else considers too risky. That's me, trying to prove to myself that…"

"That you're worthy, that what you're doing is enough?"

Julie said gently. "Trying to fill up that emptiness you've always felt?"

"Something like that. And I know it doesn't make sense…"

"It does, Jess. You were playing it safe up until you met Donna because that's the only way you knew how to survive. It got you through all those years with your dad, and it was the starting point for you and Donna."

"It should have been the starting point for us. *Should have been.* But I never got to that place. There was Donna, making all these plans, so excited by the prospect of our new life together. And there was me, pulling away, and trying to fake it when I couldn't get far enough away fast enough. Donna brought everything and I brought… nothing. And she couldn't fill me up, Julie. I know that sounds bad, but she couldn't fill me up."

"Did you ever try to end it with her?"

He sighed heavily. "I'd started to end it. Told her I had serious misgivings about how we were going to make the relationship work, that I didn't think I had it in me to be all the things she wanted me to be. I told her that when we got back to the States I wanted to take a break, go off somewhere by myself and think for a little while. Told her I wasn't ending it, just postponing it. She started to cry, of course, and asked me what she'd done to cause it. I told her it was me, all me. That I felt…dead inside. That nothing in my life fit.

"Naturally, that hurt her. It wasn't what I'd meant to do, but that's what I did anyway. Taken this very strong woman and made her…weak. All she wanted was confirmation that I'd get over it, that her life would be normal again, that everything we'd planned would still work out. But I couldn't give it to her. None of it. Not one single ounce of hope except that we'd talk later." His voice cracked. "If I

live to be a hundred, I'll never forget how hurt she looked. It reminded me of you that day, Julie, when I walked away from you. History repeating itself."

She laid a sympathetic hand on his arm. "But you made it right with Donna after that, didn't you? Or even a little better after you talked? Please, tell me you did!"

Jess shook his head. "She was killed an hour later."

"Oh, my God! I'm so sorry, Jess. I...I don't know what to say."

"Do you know what it's like, going to sleep every night knowing that what you said might have been the reason she...?" He choked. "I distracted her, broke her heart then sent her straight into the battlefield."

"It was a war zone, Jess. You can't make what happened to Donna your fault. She was a medic who went out to bring back the wounded...under fire. What happened was a tragedy. It's a tragedy every day when someone dies in combat. But you weren't the one who killed her."

"Wasn't I?"

Drawing in a ragged breath, Julie scooted over in the seat and put her arm around Jess. But he shrugged it off.

"I don't need your sympathy!" he snapped.

"Well, you sure need something," she replied. "So tell me what it is."

"To be left alone. To live my life the way I want to and not have people watching me, worrying about me, getting involved with me."

"Too late for that. You're being watched already. And worried about. And from what I've seen, there are a whole lot of people already involved with you in one way or an-other."

Turning to look at her, "Why the hell do you even care, Julie? I push you away, you push me away. So why are *you* the one coming to my rescue?"

"You know, I've asked myself the same question more than once lately. Truth is, I don't have a good answer. Not one you'd believe. I mean, I could say something like that's just who I am, or I'm only doing what I was trained to do. But that's not it. So how about I say that it's because I loved you so much back then, and leave it at that?"

"You were too good for me back then," he said.

"Of course I was! One of my many flaws."

He pulled off her rain hat to stare at her rosy-cheeked, beautiful face. Then sighed heavily. "Why are you such an optimist? Here I've just told you what a bad person I am, and you're still coming to my rescue. I don't deserve that, Julie."

"Everybody has confidence in you, Jess. Including me. You're not a bad person just because you were having doubts about your relationship with Donna. It happens to everybody at one time or another. Unfortunately for you, the timing turned an uncomfortable situation into a tragedy. But that doesn't make you bad, and I have an idea you were very kind and gentle trying to let Donna down. You just don't want to see it because you're afraid of letting someone else down. You lived with the letdowns when you were a kid…your dad let you down, life in general let you down."

"I let myself down."

"No, you didn't. In fact, look how far you've gone to get yourself away from the things that let you down…you're a doctor, Army surgeon, firefighter. What I think, Jess, is that you're afraid you're too much like your father. You project his characteristics into yourself, probably because you're afraid that's how you really are. Kind of like me when I was a kid, pushing people away first, before they pushed me. Maybe that's why you were pushing Donna. I

don't know. But what I do know is that it's a self-defense mechanism. Strike first, before you are struck.

"Sometimes I think it's easier to defeat yourself than let someone, or something, defeat you. That's all you're doing now. Striking first. Defeating yourself. Probably all you did with Donna. The thing is, I knew your father, Jess. Saw the awful things he did to you, and you're not at all like him. In fact, there's nothing in you that's like anything he was. When you walked away from me, we were dealing with childhood issues. It hurt me, it hurt you, we hurt each other, because you had your goals and I had my fantasies. But we were both wounded kids, Jess, reacting the way wounded kids would react. Then we scarred over and grew up."

"Some scars bigger than others," he said.

"Maybe so. It's just that you've never let anybody get close enough to help you with that scarring-over process."

"You mean someone like you?"

"Or Donna. Did you ever tell her about your childhood? She might have been a great support to you."

He shook his head. "There were a lot of things I intended to tell her, but never got around to. It's hard to live your life on a battlefield. And I suppose I lived under the delusion that most of us do, thinking there's always more time."

"But there's not. We only get this moment. Then, if we're lucky, we get the next one."

She scooted back to her side of the seat. "And like I keep telling you, you're being too hard on yourself…in every moment. Especially when the person you need most to talk you out of it isn't here anymore."

She was so wrong about that. The person he needed most was here, right now. And she was the only one who'd ever filled that void in him. *The only one.* So, how did he

deal with that? Or did he even deal with it at all? One more thing to add to their heap of mistakes—that Julie had filled him in a way Donna never could. "Look, I think we'd better get on down to Sutter's Creek after that horse." Shifting the truck into forward, he pulled back onto the road, mad at himself for pretty much everything in his life. At his age, something should have resolved by now. Instead, it was more complicated than it had ever been before. This time, though, he was wiser. Julie was all that counted, and she was better off without him. He'd just have to make sure that was the outcome…Julie, *without* Jess.

CHAPTER TEN

"Over there," Julie whispered, almost too apprehensive to breathe. "I think the headlight caught her…" She pointed to a thicket just at the turn of the road. "And unless the truck spooks her, we might be able to just walk up to her. By now, she's probably pretty tired, so I'm hoping she's not so inclined to run away again." Julie glanced around, didn't see any signs of Bobby Lee yet. "I'm surprised he's not already here. Anyway, you go back and get the trailer ready for me. I'm going to try and approach her, and hopefully she'll respond to me."

"You know she will," Jess said, switching off the headlights. "They always do. Man and beast alike." He opened his truck door and slid gingerly into the mud, sucking in a sharp breath as the slight jolt sent a bolt of excruciating pain up his leg. "I think you're going to have to take the lead on this one."

"Your foot?" she whispered, opening her own door and slipping outside. At the same time, she reached underneath her rain slicker to her jacket pocket and grabbed hold of several sugar cubes. Always be prepared was what Grace Corbett had taught her. Tonight, Julie was praying that a handful of sugar was all it would take with the horse. What it would take with Jess, though…

"What is it they say about doctors making the worst

patients?" Out of the truck, Jess walked around to Julie's side, using the truck as his support.

"They say that some doctors who don't follow orders need to be tied up for their own good." She watched him make his way slowly around the truck. "Getting worse?" she asked.

"And if I were to admit that I re-twisted my foot a while ago?"

"Then I shrug..." She shrugged. "Say, too bad. And figure you know enough to quit when you have to because I know if I say anything else, we'll just be wasting time we don't have. Even if my personal preference would be to have you go sit in the truck and take care of yourself."

Jess laughed. "You always have to get in the last word, don't you?"

"Only if my last word is the word you need to hear." She grabbed a coil of rope and slung it over her shoulder.

"And who would be the one to determine that?" he asked.

"Me," she said, smiling.

"Okay, while you're getting in your last word, I'm going to call for backup. If the filly runs off again, I'd like to have enough people close by that we don't have to spend tomorrow doing this all over again. Personally, I'm in the mood to go back, get out of these wet clothes, put my feet up and have myself a nice, hot cup of coffee."

An image of the two of them getting out of their wet clothes together flashed through her mind. Thankfully, it was a quick flash, come and gone in an instant. "Call Bobby Lee, too. If he's anywhere near here, he might be our best bet to chase her down if she runs."

"Grace did a good thing with you," Jess said before he went all the way back to the trailer.

"What do you mean?"

"Training you to the horses. You love them the way she did and you honor her in taking care of them like you do."

"Thank you," she said, quite touched. "I think that's the nicest thing anybody has ever said to me." She turned away when he did, trying her best to focus on the filly hiding in a clump of bushes, maybe a hundred yards ahead of her. The thing about Jess, though, was that he was never out of her mind. Which made it doubly important that she focus now. She *had* to get this horse. Thank God the rain had reduced itself to a drizzle for the moment. She was crossing her fingers that it would stay that way, no thunder, no lightning, until Fugitive was safe in the trailer or back in the stable.

"Okay, sweetheart," she whispered, as she approached the bushes. "I know you're in there. I saw you hiding, and I don't think you've gone anywhere yet."

She listened for a rustle, heard nothing.

"I have something for you." Stretching out her hand in front of her, she opened it to let the horse smell the sugar. "Here it is, come get it."

Listening again, she heard a snort and quickened her pace, but not so much as to spook the filly.

"There's more where this came from, sweetheart," she said. "I have a whole pocketful." Ten more steps, then she paused. "And you can have it all. Promise." Ten more steps, then she stopped again. "But I'm going to need for you to meet me halfway." Because if she went into the thicket, the horse might panic, then run again and injure herself. Or, as much as Julie didn't want to think about this, *she* could get injured. "So, come on out now. Let me see you."

Wiggling her hand, she felt the sugar cubes starting to melt in the drizzle. It wasn't good, as she had only another handful left. Consequently, she had to make this count. One way or another, it was time to make *everything* count.

"We're getting down to the real deal here," she said to the filly. "Time to quit playing the game and do what you need to do." The same could be said of her life, couldn't it? Time for her to quit playing the game, time for her to do what she needed to do. And if Jess wasn't at that same place, and she was pretty sure he was not, well…she wasn't sure what would happen then. Wasn't sure what Jess would or would not do. But life was too short to waste wondering when you could be trying. With Jess, she wanted to try, even though she was pretty sure he'd do some pushing for a while. This time, though, she wasn't a kid. Her total involvement with Jess wasn't a fantasy world. If anything, the roots of realty were so deep they weren't going to be easily pulled out or tossed away. In other words, she'd wait, if that's what she had to do. Wait, and let those roots hold her where she wanted to be held while Jess was trying to push. "So, either you're coming out, or I'm coming in." And taking the big risk if she did.

As it turned out, she went in. It seemed the only expedient thing to do when a low rumble of distant thunder threatened the approach of yet another storm front. Thankfully, it hadn't startled the horse, but Julie wasn't about to get this close only to have the beast run when the next clap of thunder got a little closer. So she plowed straight into the thicket of bushes, kept her head down, batted away avenging branches trying to scratch her face, stepped on more squishy things than she could even imagine and didn't stop until she was standing almost face to face with the horse, who instantly became more interested in the sugar than anything else. "I trust you're going to make this easy on me," she said, when Fugitive gently licked what was left of the sugar in her hand. "At least easier than Jess will. Too bad a couple of sugar cubes won't do the trick with him."

In response the horse turned up her lips and whinnied.

"Okay, so maybe a couple more cubes. Is that what you want?" She pulled them from her pocket and held them up. After Fugitive had licked them from Julie's hand, she gave the horse a hug, then slipped a rope around her neck at the same time and tightened it. Then, like she was loading a horse on an everyday walk around the paddock, she led Fugitive straight to the trailer, no fuss, no muss, where Jess took over and got the filly inside. "Good girl," she said, once the horse was safe and comfy.

"I'm impressed," Jess said a few minutes later, once the trailer gate was safely latched.

"And I'm exhausted. All I want to do is go back to the stable, find a quiet corner and go to sleep."

"How about a nice, soft bed in a moderately comfortable cabin in the woods? Might not have all the same charm as a bale of straw in a stable, but it's closer than your house, meaning you'll be asleep a full fifteen minutes earlier there than if you go all the way home."

"Don't tempt me," she said, leaning back against the side of the truck, wondering if she had enough energy to make it to the passenger's door.

"You know you shouldn't have come out here by yourself," he said, stepping closer to her, putting his arms around her, pulling her into his chest.

She savored his support, his strength. Needed it for a moment. Needed someone to hold her up physically and emotionally. "*You* know you shouldn't have been driving that truck, not with your foot getting worse the way it is."

"We do what we have to do," he said, settling into the embrace.

"Because that's who we are," she said, on a contented sigh.

"Because that's who we are," he repeated.

"What are we going to do, Jess? We make all these resolutions to stay out of each other's lives, to walk away, to stay detached, then look at us. First chance we get and here we are, doing everything we know she shouldn't be doing. So tell me. What are we going to do?"

"Hell if I know."

Her sentiments exactly. Right now, maybe in the long run. She didn't know, didn't particularly care. At the moment she was in Jess's arms. That's all that mattered. One moment. "Well, since neither of us knows, how about for starters we hurry and get this horse back to the stables? Then get out of our wet clothes."

"And by getting out of our wet clothes, you would mean...?"

She laughed. "One step at a time, Jess. Moment to moment. That's the *only* thing I can mean right now. No promises, no plans. That's the deal." It sounded calculating, but that was the only way she could do this. Because if Jess knew that her proposed deal was wrapped so tightly around her heart it hurt, everything would change. She wasn't sure how, but she was pretty sure she didn't want to know yet. Especially since there was so much to work out between them, so many complications and doubts. So much to confront, or avoid. The proverbial elephant in the room. And their elephant seemed bigger than most.

An elephant she was perfectly willing to avoid for a while. Moment to moment...not perfect, but good enough.

"Should we shake on it?" he asked, grabbing hold of Julie and pulling her back into his arms.

"I think this is way better, deal or no deal," she murmured, unable to resist reaching up to press her lips to his. Familiar, firm... The kiss started with passion, no building up to it, nothing tentative. It was the kiss she knew from him, the one that turned her knees to jelly and sucked away

every last ounce of self-control she wanted to pretend she had. The remembered taste of him…she'd dreamed about it, yearned over it through the years. Never been able to get past a first kiss with anyone else because the first kiss with Jess had been everything. And now, as tongues touched, and probed, and she felt his hard erection pressed to her pelvis, this was the dream playing out in reality, the only thing she'd ever wanted, ever needed… "Jess," she murmured, ready to give herself over right there. "Do you think we should…?"

At that moment, his cell phone jingled, and his immediate reaction was to pull it from his pocket to silence it. But she stopped him… "It might be someone wondering where we are. I think we need to let them know we've got Fugitive and we'll be back in a few minutes."

"Not the way I wanted this moment to end." He stepped back, cleared his throat and looked at the number calling him. "It's Bobby Lee," he said, clicking on. "Hey, I tried calling you a few minutes ago to let you know—"

Jess stopped in mid-sentence, listened, then gasped, "Where, exactly?"

"What is it?" Julie whispered.

Jess's reaction was a frown. "Look, don't move. I'm on my way. Do you understand me, Bobby Lee? *Do not move.* You're going to be fine, and we're going to get you out of there, but be very careful." He handed the phone to Julie. "He's injured. We've got to go find him. He's not sure where he is. Thinks he took a wrong turn on the shortcut. Don't have any more details because he was fighting just to be coherent. I think he's probably slipping in and out of consciousness. Also, I don't have any medical supplies with me, so call Rafe or Rick and get help. Tell them where we are right now, have them call Will to get a search and

rescue started, and the police department as well. We need everybody on this we can find, as fast as possible."

Without missing a beat, Julie made the necessary phone calls while Jess gathered up the few items they had available to them, items taken from the back of the truck—rope, flashlight, blanket, shovel and extra rain slickers. His cane, a reminder to both of them how difficult this was going to be. And this time no arguments. She wasn't going to let Jess put himself at risk. She needed him too much... "Bobby Lee's not answering now," Julie said, grabbing the rope, blanket and shovel from him.

"I'm not surprised. I think he's pretty critical." He pointed to the path about two hundred feet off from where the truck was parked. "And I think that's where we have to start our search since that's where the shortcut comes out."

"You can't do the hike, Jess. I'm serious. Driving is one thing. But this is dangerous, and...and you're going to hold me back. I can't wait for you."

"Who's the one taking the risk?" he asked her as he headed off to cross that span between the truck and where the search would officially start. "Because going out there, alone, isn't smart. Goes against all the rules."

She laughed. "Well, then, I've just changed the rules. Also, I suppose that officially makes us quite the pair, doesn't it, since you change the rules all the time, too?" She gave Jess a quick kiss on the cheek and he slipped her the flashlight. "Stay on the path. I don't want to have to come looking for you, too."

"Be careful," he said, as she turned and ran off into the woods.

"You, too," she called back. She didn't like leaving him behind that way. Probably didn't like it as much as he didn't like being left behind, but there wasn't anything else she

could do here. Bobby Lee needed help, and someone had to respond. Tonight she was that someone.

Just like Jess, she said to herself as she headed down the path. Maybe that's when she understood...truly understand the nature of the man she loved.

The admission of what she'd known in her heart all along stopped her in her tracks. She did love him. Had never stopped loving him. She smiled to herself, and kept moving forward. "Just like Jess." This time, being alike didn't scare her. In fact, it was all she wanted to be.

"Where is she?" Rafe asked, running up to his brother's side.

"About ten minutes ahead of me. Couldn't stop her." Actually, he was proud of Julie. Sure, he didn't like the idea of her being out there alone, but she was...Julie Clark. And that said it all.

"Well, Rick is taking the trail from the other way in, and he's got Will with him. Will's got the call out for as many volunteers as we can find, Edie's gone down to the stable to coordinate the effort, so we'll be at full strength in about twenty minutes."

"Edie?"

"She may be ready to deliver any minute now, but there's no way anybody's going to keep her out of the action. You know how she is...strong. Like Julie. Something we have in common, loving strong women." As the brothers walked the trail, shoulder to shoulder, Rafe flashed his light back and forth, illuminating everything in a wide swath in front of them.

"Like I keep telling you, you got lucky, big brother."

"Don't I know that. So, tell me. When are you going to get that lucky? Or let me rephrase that. When are you

going to quit being so stubborn and see you and Julie for what you are?"

"It's complicated." Jess paused for a moment, leaned on his cane to take the weight off his foot.

"You know you and your doctor are going to have a serious discussion about your lack of good judgment when it comes to following doctor's orders, don't you?"

"Get in line. I think Julie's got you beat on that one."

"Like I said, when are you going to get as lucky as I got? And don't go telling me it's complicated again, because that's just putting off the inevitable. You love her. That's all there is. The rest of it doesn't matter. I know they always tell you not to put the cart before the horse, but I think you should. Grab hold of Julie and hang on tight before you figure out the rest of the mess, instead of waiting until the mess is figured out before you grab hold of her. It's easier when you have two figuring it out together, and it's a whole lot more fun. Life's too short to wait. So, don't."

"Easy for you to say," Jess snapped, taking up the march again.

"I was there, Jess. Same old man, same conflicts. The thing is, if you mess this up with Julie, if you walk away from her again for *any* reason, he wins. The issues don't go away. Mine haven't. But having Edie there to help me... What I'm trying to tell you, little brother, is that if you wait for everything to be perfect before you make your move, if you wait for everything to uncomplicate itself, you're going to spend the rest of your life alone. Julie loves you now, and you love her now. That's *all* you need."

"Right. Blink my eyes and life gets better. That's not me, Rafe."

"Not me either. But guess what? It did get better. The old man didn't win in my life. I did."

He wanted to believe it could be that easy. Wanted to believe. To win. "Look, Rafe, don't let me hold you back. You can cover more distance without me, and I think we're in real trouble with Bobby Lee. You need to go on ahead." Pushing people away wasn't all that difficult, especially when you had the right motivation. With Rafe right now, it was for the good of the patient. With Julie, it was going to be for her own good. Had to be for her own good. And had to be soon. Because the two of them together...that was the one factor in all this he couldn't control. When the two of them got together there was no control. "I'll be fine hanging back."

Rafe patted his brother on the shoulder. "Okay, I'll let you get away with putting it off. *For now*. But think about what I said. I resisted the whole thing with Edie because I thought I was too much like the old man to marry and have a good life. He damaged us, Jess. Nobody should ever have to go through what we did, but we survived it. And the thing is, Edie makes it better for me. There was no way I ever thought it could happen, thought that someone could help me put the past behind me and give me so much to look forward to in my future. But Edie does it for me, every day, every minute, little brother. Julie will do the same for you, when you finally decide to let her." With that, he went ahead of Jess, which was fine, because as Jess was bringing up the rear in this search, thinking about a future with Julie was all he had on his mind. Last time he'd given it as serious a consideration as he'd been able to, he'd been a kid, and he'd come to the same conclusion then, too. Life with Julie was better in every aspect. Back then, though, the complications hadn't seemed so... difficult. But back then, in spite of everything his old man had put him through, his view on life with Julie had been idealistic. Marry her, be happy.

Now he had to concentrate on getting that stupid idealism out of his head. Or try figuring out what to do with it if he couldn't.

"I'm dialing my cell phone every minute or so," Julie told Rafe, who'd caught up to her. "So, how's Jess? I didn't like leaving him behind, but…"

"Limping along. Wrenching the hell out of his foot with every step. Headed for a couple weeks of bed rest at the least. Surgery at the most. But okay, otherwise."

She chuckled. "It's hard to keep him down, isn't it? But that's Jess. We can't expect him to be, or do, otherwise."

"Which is what always gets him in trouble." Rafe flashed the light ahead of him, and let his beam come to rest on Rick, who was approaching from the opposite direction.

"Darn," Julie muttered under her breath. They'd covered the whole shortcut now, and nobody had found Bobby Lee. "So, it looks like we go off trail," she said, doing a mental assessment of just how spread out this search was about to become.

"Well, I'm going back out to the trail head and lay out a search grid," Will said. "I've got at least thirty people who've checked in with Edie, and she's holding them, waiting for me to clear them to come out and start looking. I didn't want to do that if there was any chance we'd find him on the path."

"So I think the three of us should split up and cover as much of the area as possible before everybody else gets here, because that's when it's going to get crazy. Lots of people, lots of noise…" It was necessary, she knew that. The more people looking for Bobby Lee, the better his chances of being found and helped. But people obliterated tracks, drowned out subtle moans. In other words,

the bad with the good. She wanted these next ten minutes to herself and, without another word to Rafe and Rick she headed back in the direction from which she'd come.

"Do you know how much she's like your brother?" Rick asked Rafe after they'd noticed that she'd left them behind.

"Having one of Jess in the family can be pretty exasperating at times. Not sure what I'm going to do with two of them."

"You think that's what's going to happen?" Rick asked.

Rafe nodded. "I'm pretty sure. As soon as Jess comes to his senses."

"Bobby Lee!" Jess shouted. His pace had slowed even more. He was off trail now, since there was no point in following the same trail both Julie and Rafe had taken before him. "Can you hear me, Bobby Lee?"

He wanted to hear something, but the only thing that responded to him was the distant thundering echo of yet another storm front moving in. Which could sign Bobby Lee's death warrant if they didn't get to him first. "Come on, Bobby! Answer me!"

He paused, listened. Heard…nothing at all damn it! Not one damned thing. And so it went for another few minutes, calling, not being answered. Worrying about the storm, about Bobby Lee's condition, about his own condition as far as Julie was concerned. It was all a frustrating jumble, complicated by the fact that his foot was giving out. Even if he were to find Bobby Lee now, there was no way he was going to make it out of these woods on his own. In fact, he was about done. It was time to admit that if he went any farther, he was going to cause himself permanent damage.

And if he didn't go any further with Julie, that would be the worst damage of all. Fight her off as he might, Rafe

was right about one thing. It was time to win. Otherwise he'd spend the rest of his life going around in the same circles he'd gone in up until now, never finding what he was looking for. But how the hell could he do it and not make a mess of it? That was the question that plagued him over and over.

And the guilt over Donna... "Damn," he muttered as the rain started to pick up again. He'd loved her, but not enough. He'd wanted to love her more, tried to love her more. But it wouldn't have ever been enough because she'd expected things from him that he couldn't be. And all the love in the world couldn't have forced the changes in him that he'd have needed to be with her. Bottom line...they'd been wrong for each other, and nothing about that could have been overcome. She'd wanted him in a way he could never be, and he'd wanted her in a way that she could never be.

But that look on her face... He could still see it, even now, when he shut his eyes and slid to the muddy ground underneath a pine tree to wait out the rescue. It was still there. That look. But only for a moment. Then all he could see was Julie. And instead of feeling his usual nothing, he felt...everything.

CHAPTER ELEVEN

JESS snapped his eyes open as words from an old tune jolted him out of his momentary slump. "Bobby Lee?" he called, pushing himself to his feet. He was around here. That had to be Julie's phone ringing. Somebody was calling Bobby Lee!

"Where are you?" he called out, turning on his flashlight.

"Jess?"

"Julie?"

"I heard your phone ring." He hobbled away from the tree, now barely able to put weight down on his foot. "It's close." The tune played again, and Jess couldn't help but smile. Rafe was right. Life with Julie was better. Even in the little jingle of an inconsequential song.

"Are you okay?" Julie asked, running up to his side.

"Trying to be." More than that, wanting to be.

She immediately put a steadying arm around his waist as she hit redial, and listened for her ring tone. "Over there," she said, pointing to an area just off to the right.

Which was exactly where they found Bobby Lee. On the ground, in the mud. Unconscious. A tree had crashed down on him and he was crushed underneath it, his slight body barely visible in the damage. Finding him anywhere

in the storm was an amazing feat. Finding him there was a miracle.

"Pulse weak," Julie said, taking her first assessment. She looked up at Jess. "But it's not good. Thready, irregular. Maybe indicating internal hemorrhage."

"We've got him," Jess said on his phone. "Look, Rafe. I'm guessing crushed pelvis. Legs, too. Probably some internal injuries, maybe bleeding, considering the size of the tree that's got him down. Have the O.R. on standby, because he's not going to be stable enough to transfer someplace else when we get him in." If ever there had been a time they needed a full-out trauma unit, this was it. "Remind me to work faster on those trauma plans when we get back," he told Julie, sliding down to the ground next to Julie. "And kick me if you don't think I'm making it my top priority."

"Does that mean you're going to be hanging around Lilly Lake for a while?" she asked, wiggling down to her stomach to get a better look at Bobby Lee's situation.

"Maybe. I've been giving it some thought."

She glanced up briefly, water dripping off her rain hat in a steady stream. "Really? How hard can I kick you?"

"As hard as you want." Jess scooted in the direction of Bobby Lee's head. "Toss me your flashlight, will you?"

She did. "And how often can I kick you? Not that I intend to, but just in case…"

He flashed the light into Bobby Lee's eyes, letting out a sigh of relief when he saw exactly what he wanted to see. "Equal and reactive." A very good sign, meaning that if they were lucky, he didn't have substantial neurological damage. "Oh, and kick me as often as I need it. For the rest of my life, if you have to."

She looked over at him for a moment, studied his face, but didn't comment. "Bobby Lee, it's Julie. You're going

to be fine," she said after a long pause. She was trying to position herself now to press a hand underneath the log in order to see what kind of bleeding she might be missing in the rain, in the mud, in the dark. "Jess and I are going to get you out of here in a couple of minutes, so just stay with us, okay? Listen to my voice…concentrate on it." Her hand pulled back slippery, and a quick sniff revealed the distinct coppery smell. Somewhere under there was an open wound. "Um, Jess…I think we should try and dig in around him, but only enough for better access since I think he could be crushed." They needed to get an IV in him as soon as someone brought it down the trail. Needed to get a pressure bandage on the open wound. Needed a better way to access and evaluate for more injuries. "Also, we're dealing with what I think could be a substantial open wound. I'm feeling a lot of bleeding." She pulled back, flashed the light under there again, couldn't see it.

Jess raised up. "Where?"

"Mid-abdomen I think. Didn't feel a puncture, but…"

No more words were spoken between them. Jess shot to his feet, then stepped over the tree. Within a second he was digging with his hands, trying to free as much of Bobby as possible, without causing more damage. Julie was doing the same on her side, frantically scooping away the mud, fighting off the increasing wind, the increasing rain.

"We may have to get him out, risks and all," Jess shouted at her, as a bolt of lightning split the sky. "See what we can get immobilized. Hope he's not bleeding internally. Because with the way it's coming down now…" He glanced up as a loud crack somewhere overhead forewarned what he feared most. "Julie!" he screamed, shoving himself forward to cover as much of Bobby Lee's face as he could.

But too late. The top of a tall pine tree came crash-

ing down on them, trunk, branches, needles, and he felt
the thunk of it on his back, his legs. Felt the prick of the
needles instantly shooting into skin like tiny darts. Felt...
woozy. "Julie," he murmured. "Can you hear me? Julie..."

No answer. And the thoughts that went through his
head... *Not again!* She couldn't be...she wasn't... No!
"Come on, Julie," he choked, trying to get through the
impossible clump of vegetation that fought to keep him
pinned down in the mud. "Stay with me. Just...stay with
me."

Blindly, frantically, he reached out as far as he could,
tried to feel her. "Come on, sweetheart. Just grab my hand
and hang on." Yet nothing...except the rain and the wind.
And the racking pain shooting up his leg that threatened
to drag him down into the slumbering abyss with Bobby
Lee and Julie.

They were not visible now. None of the three of them.
Totally covered. No one would hear them. No one would
find them tonight. No one...

Jess's eyes began to droop. He recognized the signs of
exhaustion mixed with pain. Felt the arms of Morpheus
wrapping around him, lulling him to give in, promising
him a place where the pain would subside for a while.
But... "Julie," he mumbled, as she drifted into his thoughts,
"Julie..." His salvation...the only thought on his mind as
his eyes closed all the way.

Julie. Beautiful Julie...a nice face to drift off with.
The only face he'd ever wanted to drift off with. Julie...
Suddenly, his eyes shot back open. Where was she? He had
to find her. That was the single thought that propelled the
rescuer in him to take over, to fight off the pain threatening to drag him under. It's what he did, who he was. Who
Julie needed. So with no clear way to accomplish anything, he struggled to roll over onto his side, hoping that

somehow the shift in position would enable him to get to either Julie or move away from Bobby Lee enough to be able to help him. Turning slowly, trying not to put any pressure on his foot, he felt the stings of the cuts and scrapes from the tree on his face, his hands. Felt the burn of what he knew would require surgery and God only knew how much rehab slithering up his leg. But he found Bobby Lee's pulse, didn't note any appreciable change in it, thank God. "Julie," he yelled again, trying to push himself just a little farther in the direction where he knew she had to be. Still nothing from her, though, and he was frantic.

So now it was decision time. He could do whatever he could to take care of Bobby Lee or keep trying to find Julie. His heart wanted Julie. But he couldn't leave Bobby Lee alone.

Then it struck him. He had one chance…the only chance he'd have until help arrived. One that might, and probably would, end his risk-taking days. But it didn't matter. Nothing did, except Julie. So, gritting his teeth to what he knew would be coming, Jess rolled all the way over on his back and kicked up at the branches covering him, hoping he'd have enough strength left in his legs to do this. Adrenalin strength, as it turned out. Screaming at the top of his lungs to summon it up, he kicked the treetop up just enough to give him time to squirm up out of the mud and push it off to the side. It wasn't much of a kick even with the adrenalin, wasn't much of a push either, thanks to what was now a broken foot, but it gave him room…just enough room to crawl out from under the copious branches and needles then turn around and pull at the treetop, move it enough to get it all the way off Bobby Lee. And that's when he found her… Julie. Unconscious. Her face half submerged in the mud. But breathing. And with a strong pulse. "You'll keep," he whispered, brushing a twig from

her hair after he'd done a fast assessment. "Bobby won't, though. But I'm not leaving you, Julie. I promise, I'm not leaving you."

In that moment, his doubts seemed trivial. His fears seemed unimportant. Whatever concern had been rattling around in him all this time vanished because Julie was all that mattered. The rest of it…he didn't give a damn anymore. Just simply didn't give a damn. He loved Julie Clark, always had, always would. Now it was time to make everything they'd done wrong right. How would Julie feel about that? Well, he wasn't sure. But she'd been the one to kiss him first last time they'd kissed. That counted for something. Hopefully, it counted for everything because Julie *had* kissed him.

"He's fine," Rafe said, dropping down into the chair across the room from his brother. "Bobby Lee is stable. His injuries are significant, some broken bones, that gash in his belly, a moderate concussion, no internal damages, though. So we got lucky there, and he's probably going to be ready to transfer to a rehab center in a couple of days. And Sleeping Beauty here…" He nodded at Jess. "Not too bad, considering how it could have turned out."

"I'm awake," Jess said, still too groggy from the anesthesia to open his eyes. "So, how *did* it turn out?"

"For you it was a torn ligament, ruptured tendon, cracked talus, a couple of broken metatarsals, specifically the second and third. Oh, and a dislocation of distal phalanx of your big toe. All repaired. So the good news is you had a brilliant surgeon on the job," Julie said from the bed next to Jess, where she'd been resting since she'd been admitted with a moderate concussion. No other injuries. "The bad news is you've got at least three months ahead of you where you're going to be off your foot, come hell

or high water. With a pretty stern nurse who isn't going to put up with your bad behavior. And there's going to be physical therapy with that."

Jess groaned. "I don't need physical therapy, unless…" He attempted his usual, albeit lopsided-for-the-moment grin. "How do you define physical therapy?"

"You can't even open your eyes yet, and listen to you, already giving me trouble."

Rafe chuckled. "If I weren't so tired, I'd leave you two in private. But there's nothing in me that's going to get me out of this chair for the next hour. So, Julie, do what you have to with Jess. You have my permission to tie him down to the bed, if that's what…" His voice drifted off, and Rafe was dead to the world.

"You heard what your brother said," Julie said, pushing herself out of bed. She was washed clean of all mud now, and comfortable in a set of surgical scrubs. Her head ached, her muscles were sore, but she was comfortable because Jess was there. "He gave me permission to tie you to the bed. But would it be okay if I just crawled in next to you and held you down instead?"

"How long has that been your ring tone?" Jess asked, his question totally unexpected.

"I'm not sure what you mean," she lied.

He opened one eye to look at her. "Sure you do. Something about Jessie's girl? You know, from that old 1980s song." He hummed a bit of the tune in a very ragged way, then opened one droopy eye and looked at her. "Tell me, Julie."

"Okay, I've had it as long as I've had the phone. A couple of years. Had it on the phone before this, and the one before that."

"And…?"

"And in my mind I changed the lyrics a little to *being*

Jess's girl. Now you know all my deep, dark secrets. Are you happy?"

Jess finally opened both his eyes. "Very happy. Would it be okay if you crawled in next to me *every night* for the rest of your life? I made the offer before…letting you kick me for the rest of your life."

"That was an offer?" she asked.

"Thought it was a pretty good offer."

"Well, as offers go, I guess it was, considering that it was an offer à la Jess. But we still have some things to work out," she warned him. She knew he wasn't over Donna yet, wasn't over the pain he felt because of her death, or the guilt of pushing her away. But he wouldn't be working it out alone now, because Jess wasn't alone. Intellectually, he was coming to terms with what that meant. More than that, he was feeling it emotionally. And in those moments when he didn't…she did have permission to kick him. But a gentle, loving kick, and only from her heart to his.

"Old news. I love you, you said yourself that you want to be Jess's girl… Oh, and out there in the woods, when I thought I'd lost you…" The deep breath he drew in was ragged. "I never felt that emptiness with you, Julie. The only time in my life when I didn't feel empty was when you were making me feel…alive."

"We let too much get in the way of what's important," she said, crawling in next to him, lying on her side to snuggle. "When we were kids, it couldn't be helped. Everything was going against us and we weren't smart enough to figure it out. But we're not kids anymore, Jess. We get a second chance, and it's got to be the one that counts. *If you want it to count.*"

"Do you?"

"I've always loved you, if that means anything. I think that's why I always wanted to come back to Lilly Lake.

Even if I couldn't have you, you were here in so many ways. I was willing to let that be enough. But it's not, Jess. I do want to be Jess's girl. More than that, I want Jess to be the man he is. No changes necessary. If you decide you want to give up medicine and firefighting and raise alpacas, I'm with you. Or if you want to spend your days doing watercolor landscapes, I'll be the one holding your palette. Our life, Jess, isn't going to come with some preconceived plans. We'll find our way as we need to find it, and the rest of it we'll work on when we have to."

"In other words, keeping it simple?"

"In other words, keeping it *us*. We lost that chance once, but there's no one there to stop us now."

"No one," Rafe mumbled from his chair. "So kiss her, will you, Jess? So I can get some sleep."

"Brother knows best," Jess said, pulling Julie into his arms.

"So, that's the deal. I'll run the trauma department as a physician. But I'm also going to work with the fire department in the capacity of the new director of paramedic training services," Jess said. "And I'll be going out on runs, because I still like being there to make the first assessment. Best of both worlds. Although my firefighting days may be limited for a while." He held up his cane.

"Best of *neither* world yet," Julie reminded him. "One more month, *or longer*, on the cane, not negotiable." She put down the horse brush and walked over to Jess, who was sitting in front of the stall where the newest love of his life, a horse named Julie, was nuzzling him from behind. "You have such a way with the ladies," she said, bending down to kiss him.

"I have such a way with the Julies," he corrected.

"Strong redheads," she said.

He smiled. "Well you've got to give me credit for one thing…I've had plenty of time to finish the plans for the trauma department expansion these past few weeks. I turned them over to the architect a few days ago, and started working on something else. More expansion, actually." He held out a sketch pad. "Take a look, add your notes, make suggestions."

Julie frowned skeptically. "We can't knock out another wall, Jess. The rest of the space is promised to Pediatrics. Rick's got some ideas, and you know he's trying to get Summer Adair to come on full time as head nurse in the unit."

"Well, Pediatrics could be included."

She took the pad, opened it, looked at the first page, and a smile spread over her face. "Really?"

"The big old oak tree won't be touched either. It will be the centerpiece of our front yard and I expect to sit underneath it with the prettiest girl in the world for the rest of our lives."

Their place. Their house.

"It's permanent, Jess. Are you sure that's really what you want? Permanent roots in Lilly Lake? I know we said we'd stay here for now, but…will this be enough for you?"

"It will be everything because it's what we've always wanted." The dream that had begun when they had been teenagers, and was finally coming true. "It's time, Julie. Seventeen years is a long time to wait, so it's time to start again, and get it right."

Julie sat down on the bench next to Jess, and settled in perfectly when he pulled her into his arms. "My thoughts exactly, because I want to marry you, Jess Corbett, and have lots of babies with you."

"And lots of horses."

"Absolutely. For the next seventy or eighty years," she said, sighing the sigh of a very happy woman.

"What about the risk-taking thing?"

"I'm okay with it. Got myself used to the idea, as long as you promise not to be too casual about it. And to listen to the people who love you when we tell you we're worried."

Jess chuckled. "I'm not talking about the risks I take. I'm talking about the risks you take. Not sure I want the woman I love to be out there in the way of harm the way you seem to like being."

"Oh, so when the shoe is on the other foot, the fit isn't quite so good."

"I have a right to worry."

"So do I," she quipped. "And maybe, now that you know how it feels to be on the other end, you won't be quite so…well, I don't want to call it careless, because you're not careless. Maybe the word I want here is unmindful… unmindful of how much you're loved. And by some loved more than anybody else in the world."

"Believe me, I have a lot to be mindful of," he whispered, nuzzling her ear.

"So do I," Julie said, looking down the stall row at all the horses, and all the volunteers scurrying to take care of them. "Do you think Grace would have expected this… expected *us*?"

"I think it was always part of Aunt Grace's plan. She had this uncanny way of knowing when nobody else did. So I have this hunch that she knew you were the one for me the first time she ever laid eyes on you. Like I did, the first time I ever laid eyes on you. I think that's what she meant when she told me I wasn't taking advantage of the things I had in life. That I had more to give. That I was under-

estimating myself. She meant that about you, Julie. She knew we'd find each other again."

"And we did."

"Julie!" Summer shouted from the opposite end of the stable. "Got a horse on the loose, halfway over to Jasper. Probably a runaway. It's pretty beat up, malnourished, dehydrated. Still up on its feet, but the sheriff over there said we need to come get it right away because it's got a bad gash on its shoulder that needs treatment. Can you go take care of it?"

"On my way," she shouted back, then scooted off the bench and extended a hand to Jess. "Going with me?" she asked.

"For the rest of my life," he said, taking her hand. "Want me to drive?"

"Oh, yeah. Like I'm going to fall for that again. Last time you went against doctor's orders, this is what happened to you." She pointed to the cast on his foot. "This time, I may not be the doctor, but I have my own set of orders, and the answer to your question is..."

He hobbled up to Julie and pulled her into his arms, then kissed her hard. "And that's the answer to *my* question."

"Well, I think I like your answer better," Julie said, a contented smile sliding to her lips.

"Good, my love, because it's the same answer you'll be getting again, and again, and again..."

* * * * *

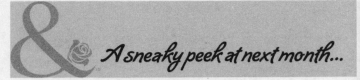

A sneaky peek at next month...

Medical Romance™

CAPTIVATING MEDICAL DRAMA—WITH HEART

My wish list for next month's titles...

In stores from 2nd December 2011:

❑ New Doc in Town & Orphan Under the Christmas Tree — Meredith Webber

❑ The Night Before Christmas — Alison Roberts & Once a Good Girl... — Wendy S. Marcus

❑ Surgeon in a Wedding Dress — Sue MacKay

❑ The Boy Who Made Them Love Again — Scarlet Wilson

Available at WHSmith, Tesco, Asda, Eason, Amazon and Apple

Just can't wait?

Visit us Online

You can buy our books online a month before they hit the shops! **www.millsandboon.co.uk**

1111/03

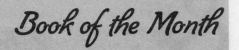